The National Latino & American Indian Scholarship Directory

Special Introduction by Edward James Olmos

EmpoweringStudents.com
The best source for what Latino & American Indian students need to know about college

WPR BOOKS: Latino Insights
Carlsbad, CA

Dedication

This book is dedicated to my parents who instilled in me at an early age the value of higher education. We lost my father, Don Whisler, on September 11, 2007, but we still have my mother, Biddy Louise Whisler, who still pushes for all to go to college.

This book is also dedicated to all of those early champions of college for Latinos that I've had the joy of working with over the years like Rudy Acuña, Juan Andrade, Manuel Baca, Roberto Cantú, Jésus Chavarriá, Roberto Cruz, Leo Estrada, Arturo Franco, Ernesto Galarza, Juan Gómez Quiñones, Myriam Grajales Hall, Alma Martinez, Ambassador Julian Nava, Armando Navarro, Jesus Nieto, Edward James Olmos, Ed Peña, Jeff Penichet, Maria Quezada, Tomas Rivera, Octavio Romano, Julian Samora, John Valdez, Lea Ybarra, and many others.

Credits

The book was conceived and created by WPR Books under the leadership of Kirk Whisler, Publisher.

Publisher & Executive Editor:	**Kirk Whisler**
Co-publisher & Director of Marketing:	**Andres Tobar**
Scholarship Researchers:	**Annie Perez, Ana Patiño, Jim Sullivan, Zeke Whisler, Harrison Langford, Alice Perez, Abraham Larrondo, Jesus Menera,** and **Kirk Whisler**
Articles:	**Katharine Ann Díaz, Kirk Whisler, Andres Tobar, Enrique G. Murillo, Jr., Patricia A. Aguilera**, and **Annie Perez**
Sales:	**Jim Sullivan**
Website & Technical work:	**Tony Díaz**
Layout of the book:	**Jim Sullivan**

Kirk also wants to thank his wife, Magdalena, for her patience in this effort.

ISBN 978-1889379-40-1. Latino Literacy Now is a key participant in producing this publication.

No database is ever perfect and within hours of 'being updated' at least one of the records will have become outdated. We spent several thousand hours updating these records, but we want you to be aware that some of these records will have become outdated and some of these scholarships will no longer be available. We apologize in advance for any problems this might cause. While every precaution has been taken in the preparation of this book, the author and publisher assume no responsibility for errors or omissions, or for damages resulting from the use of the information contained herein. For updates as they happen please go to www.EmpoweringStudents.com

WPR BOOKS: Latino Insights

3445 Catalina Dr., Carlsbad, CA 92010-2856

www.WPRbooks.com *760-434-1223* kirk@whisler.com

Table of Contents

The National Empowering Students Advisory Board

Robert Alanez
Senior Partner
Milagro Communications Group

Dr. Juan Andrade, Jr.
President
United States Hispanic Leadership Institute

Manuel Baca, PhD
Vice President
California Community Colleges Board of Governors

Nora de Hoyos Comstock, Ph.D.
President
Las Comadres para las Americas

Maria Contreras-Sweet
Board Chair
ProAmerica Bank

Jorge Corralejo
CEO
Latino Business Chamber of Greater Los Angeles

Dr. Antonio Flores
Executive Director
Hispanic Association of Colleges & Universities

Delia Garcia
Sr Liaison, Office of Minority Community Outreach, National Education Association

Dr. Maggie George
President
Diné College, *Navajo*

Frank D. Gomez
Public Affairs Executive
Educational Testing Service

Ignacio Gomez
Award winning Artist

José Gonzalez
Site Mngr. DC-MD-VA, Thomas Shortman Training Fund, SEIU Local 32BJ Training Fund

Myriam Grajales Hall
Manager for the University of California for News & Information Outreach in Spanish

Jorge Haynes
Director of External Relations
California State University System

Kahseuss Jackson MBA
Economic Development Coordinator
Confederated Tribes of the Warm Springs Reservation of Oregon

Roy Jasso
Senior Vice President
Wells Fargo Bank

Consuelo Castillo Kickbusch
Founder
Educational Achievement Services

Hank Lacayo
State President
Congress of California Seniors

Dr. David P. López
President
National Hispanic University

7 Ways To Use This Book

The book lists over lists 1,900+ sources of funding a college education which collectively offer over 220,000 individual scholarships totaling over $840 million. There's also helpful text on preparing to go to college, a college timeline, and how to find a career you'll love. Much of the resources within the book are focused on the two most underrepresented groups in college: Latinos and American Indians. That is why the book includes over 70 Insights from community leaders on the value of going to college. This book is a great resource for students in high school who are thinking about college – or are already in college and need more money.

1. Learn from the many insights from leaders that we offer throughout the book starting with a great Introduction from actor/activist Edward James Olmos. Use the Insights from our various professionals to provide advice on questions you might have, and share them with friends to motivate them about going to college.

2. Use the College Timeframe in the book to plan your future while you are in High School.

3. Use the Resource Center listings throughout the book as a jumping point to links to websites; to carefully selected research; key organizations; and helpful books. These lead you to thousands of pages of additional information.

4. Use the Current College Trends article that starts on page 30 to better understand the variety of directions college is going in. We also have comprehensive data articles within the Latino and American Indian sections.

5. Use the DOL website profiled on page 50 early and often to help decide on the right career for you. And please do not forget to do internships (see page 54).

6. Use Section 4 and 5, on Latinos and American Indians, to get a better understanding of key organizations, resources, etc. these communities have.

7. Most of all, spend time searching within our detailed list of scholarships. Please remember that data is always changing, so if you reach a dead end on one agency there's likely a positive one around the corner. Keep looking. Use Section 6, Major Scholarships, to get a feel for the various fields of information provided. Finally, use the CD in the back of this book to make it easier to search and find the scholarships best suited to you.

Kirk Whisler

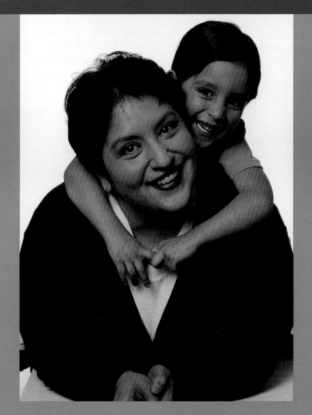

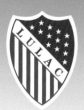

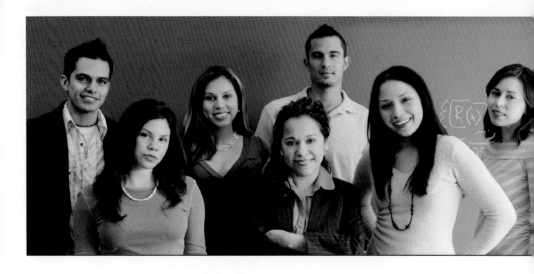

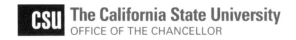

SECTION ONE
COLLEGE IS THE GATEWAY

INSIGHTS
"Somebody Made an Investment in Us"

"The degree you earn. . . is going to be the BEST tool you've got to achieve the American promise–by far. I'm only here today, and Michele is where she is today, because scholarships and student loans gave us a shot at a great education. It wasn't just that we worked hard, it was also that somebody made an investment in us. That's what America did for us. This country always made a commitment that a good education has to be within the reach of everybody. Everyone that's willing to work for it, we've said 'You've got a shot.' That's what has made us special. That's the commitment we've got to reaffirm today.

We've got to make college more affordable for you. We can not price the middle class out of a college education when most new jobs in America require more than a high school diploma. Helping more of our young people afford college should be at the forefront of America's agenda. It shouldn't be a Democratic or Republican issue."

President Barack Obama*, April 24, 2012 at the University of Colorado, Boulder.*

Why College Will Change Your Life

By Edward James Olmos

I want every one of you to get everything out of life that you can. I want you to find a career that is both financially rewarding and, just as importantly, one that you enjoy. I want you, if you want, to get married and have a family. I want each of you to find a way to give back to your community. Going to college is a great step towards accomplishing all of these desires.

College opened my eyes to so many things. If I'd never gone to East Los Angeles Community College, and then on to Cal State University Los Angeles, I'm confident that I never would have become the actor/director/activist that I am today.

Here are four more reasons to go to college:

- To be a role model to your

Edward James Olmos reading to students

siblings and neighbors.

- To make your mother and father proud.
- To earn a better living.
- To provide a better life for your family in the future.

I know how much effort has gone into this Directory – and how much it offers to each of you. I hope you'll make good use of the Directory in achieving your college goals.

Over the years I've spoken at over 400 college campuses and I'm always amazed at the excitement that college students have. This excitement is not merely about college, but also an interest in living and discovering new things and thoughts.

I look forward to seeing you at one of my visits to a college soon,

Edward James Olmos

INSIGHTS

"My Degree Is a Priceless Thing That I've Done for Myself"

"College changed my life in several regards. From the time I was a freshman in high school going to college was a goal. While both my parents have masters degrees and PhDs, a lot of my family members had never realized their ambition to graduate from college. Some of my cousins that were my age were struggling to get through high school. This motivated me to set my goals higher and to work harder. Going to college made me want to look at giving back to my community and be a role model. Since graduating it has helped me tremendously. It has taught me more understanding of my culture and how to take it into my life. I live in two worlds: I live in my native culture and I live in modern society with everybody else. My degree is a priceless thing that I've done for myself."

Melonie Mathews
Miss Indian World Coordinator,
Gathering of Nations Pow Wow,
Pueblo of Santa Clara Tribe

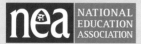

College Timeline: The Key Dates To Keep You On Track

Below is a general guideline of steps you should follow while preparing for college. For a more complete guide to planning for college, please go to http://studentaid.ed.gov/prepare-for-college/checklists.

1. Prepare for college early.

Preparing early for your college education will help you position yourself to get into the college you want. We recommend that you start as early as the eighth grade. Even if you are in your junior or senior year, however, you can still choose, apply, and get accepted to the college best for you, if you plan carefully.

Regardless of the grade you are in now, there are some general notes to remember and rules to follow:

⇨ Pay attention to deadlines and dates.

⇨ Your grades are important but the difficulty of your coursework can also be a significant factor in a college's decision to admit you. In general, most colleges prefer students with average grades in tougher courses than students who opt for an easy A.

You should also note that most high schools grade Advanced Placement courses on a 5-point scale rather than the 4-point scale used for other classes, essentially giving students a bonus point for tackling the extra difficulty (e.g., a B in an AP course is worth as much as an A in a non-AP course).

⇨ College admission officers will pay the closest attention to your GPA, class rank, college credit, AP courses, and standardized test scores.

⇨ Participation in extracurricular activities is also a good idea in high school. Activities that require time and effort outside the classroom (such as speech and debate, band, communications, and drama) indicate a willingness to cooperate with others and put forth the effort needed to succeed.

⇨ Computer science courses or courses that require students to use computers in research and project preparation can also help aid your future college performance.

2. Plan a career.

Choosing a career and a

INSIGHTS
"College Woke Me Up"

"College woke me up to a whole new world, if you really work hard and are persistent you can accomplish anything you set your mind to."

Denice Garcia,
Director of Boards & Commissions, City of San Diego

corresponding major will help you decide which colleges are right for you.

3. Find the college that's right for you.

Get information online about the school of your choice. Some schools have online admission applications for you to complete.

High School Seniors should complete the Free Application for Student Aid (FAFSASM) on or after January 1st. To learn about ways to Get Money for college go to the Funding Your Education area.

4. Take the necessary assessment tests.

Most colleges in the U.S. require that students submit scores from standardized tests as part of their application packages. The most commonly accepted tests are the ACT Tests, SAT Reasoning, and SAT Subject Tests. For information about which you should take, talk to your high school counselor or to the admissions office(s) at the college(s) to which you will apply.

The ACT Tests For detailed information about the ACT Tests, registering for these tests, how to prepare for the tests, what to take with you on test day, and understanding your scores, visit www.act.org.

The SAT Tests For information on and registering for any of the tests described below, visit www.collegeboard.org.

SAT Reasoning (formerly SAT I). The SAT Reasoning Test is a three-hour test that measures a student's ability rather than knowledge. It contains three sections: writing, critical reading, and math. Most of the questions are multiple-choice.

SAT Subject Tests (formerly SAT II). The SAT Subject Tests measure knowledge in specific subjects within five general categories: English, mathematics, history, science, and languages. The specific subjects range from English literature to biology to Modern Hebrew. SAT Subject Tests are primarily multiple-choice, and each lasts one hour.

Both the SAT Reasoning and SAT Subject Tests are offered several times a year at locations across the country.

Other common tests

For information and registration for any of the tests described below, visit www.collegeboard.org.

The Preliminary SAT/National Merit Scholarship Qualifying Test, commonly known as the PSAT, is usually taken in the student's junior year. It's a good way to practice for the SAT tests, and it serves as a qualifying exam for the National Merit Scholarship Corporation's scholarship programs. The PSAT measures skills in verbal reasoning, critical reading, mathematics problem solving, and writing.

The two- to three-hour **Advanced Placement (AP) Program** exams are usually taken after the student completes an AP course in the relevant subject. (Speak to your high school counselor about taking AP classes.) A good grade on an AP exam can qualify the student for college credit and/or "advanced placement" in that subject in college. For example, if a student scores well on the AP English Literature exam, he or she might not have to take the college's required freshman-level English course. Most AP tests are at least partly made up of essay questions; some include multiple-choice questions. The tests are offered each spring; each test is offered once, with a makeup day a few weeks later.

The College-Level Examination Program® (CLEP) offers students the opportunity to gain college credit by taking an exam. Usually, a student takes the tests at the college where he or she is already enrolled. Not all colleges offer credit based on CLEP tests, and different colleges offer different amounts of credit for the same test, so do your research before committing to an exam. Your best source of information is your college.

5. Once you have narrowed your selection, arrange to visit the campuses in person. This is an important step in the decision process, so whenever possible, plan a visit to the schools.

6. Discover your payment options. You should look into scholarships, student loans, and other financial aid options before you apply to a particular college or university. The Federal government has $80 billion available for funding education beyond high school.

Apply online. If you currently are a high school senior, you should complete the FAFSA as early as you can, but no earlier than January 1.

Grade 8

In addition to your research here, you should ask counselors, teachers, parents, and friends any other questions you have about college.

- Talk to your guidance counselor (or teachers, if you don't have access to a guidance counselor) about the following:
  - ⇨ The importance colleges and universities place on grades, and what year in school grades will start to be considered in the admissions process
  - ⇨ College preparatory classes you should be taking in high school (grades 9 through 12)
  - ⇨ Academic enrichment programs (including summer and weekend programs) available through your school or local colleges

Think about pursuing extracurricular activities (such as sports, performing arts, volunteer work, or other activities that interest you).

Grade 9/Freshman Year

- Talk to your guidance counselor (or teachers) about the following:
  - ⇨ Attending a four-year college or university

INSIGHTS

"My Major Was Math and Math Is Used Everywhere"

"Going to college helped me improve my job with the company I was working for. Every job since then being a college graduate has come into play. My major was Math, and math is used everywhere."

Mike Ceplina, *Tribal Council Member, Little River Band of Ottawa Indians, Michigan*

Insights

"College Gave Me the Chance to Improve"

"College gave me the chance to improve myself and be a better citizen. I'm happy I did it."
Frank Andrade, *Publisher of La Oferta.*

⇨ Establishing your college preparatory classes; your schedule should consist of at least 4 college preparatory classes per year, including:
- 4 years of English
- 3 years of math (through Algebra II or trigonometry)
- 2 years of foreign language
- 2 years of natural science
- 2 years of history/social studies
- 1 year of art
- 1 year of electives from the above list

⇨ Using the U.S. Department of Education's Student Planner to keep track of your courses and grades
⇨ Enrolling in algebra or geometry classes and a foreign language for both semesters (most colleges have math and foreign language requirements)
Remember, you will have more options if you start planning now for college and keep your grades up.
- Create a file of the following documents and notes:
  ⇨ Copies of report cards
  ⇨ List of awards and honors
  ⇨ List of school and community activities in which you are involved, including both paid and volunteer work, and descriptions of what you do

Grade 10/Sophomore Year

- Talk to your guidance counselor about the following:
⇨ Reviewing the high school curriculum needed to satisfy the requirements of the colleges you are interested in attending
⇨ Finding out about Advanced Placement courses.
- Continue extracurricular activities
- Take the PSAT in October. The scores will not count for National Merit Scholar consideration in your sophomore year, but it is valuable practice for when you take the PSAT again in your junior year. You will receive your PSAT results in December.
- Register, in April, for the SAT II for any subjects you will be completing before June.
- Take the SAT II in June.

Grade 11/Junior Year

Fall Semester
- Maintaining your grades during your junior year is especially important. You should be doing at least 2 hours of homework each night and participating in study groups. Using a computer can be a great tool for organizing your activities and achieving the grades you want.
- Talk to your guidance counselor (or teachers, if you don't have access to a guidance counselor) about the following:
⇨ Availability of and enrollment in Advanced Placement classes
⇨ Schedules for the PSAT, SAT Reasoning Test and SAT Subject Test, ACT, and AP exams
⇨ Discuss why you should take these exams and how they could benefit you.
⇨ Determine which exams to take. (You can always change your mind.)

⇨ Sign up and prepare for the exams you've decided to take.
⇨ Ask for a preview of your academic record and profile, determine what gaps or weaknesses there are, and get suggestions on how to strengthen your candidacy for the schools in which you are interested.
⇨ Determine what it takes to gain admission to the college(s) of your choice, in addition to GPA and test score requirements.

August:
⇨ Obtain schedules and forms for the SAT Reasoning Test, SAT Subject Test, ACT, and AP exams.

September:
⇨ Register for the PSAT exam offered in October. Remember that when you take the PSAT in your junior year, the scores will count towards the National Achievement Program (and it is good practice for the SAT Reasoning Test).

October:
⇨ Take the PSAT. Narrow your list of colleges to include a few colleges with requirements at your current GPA, a few with requirements above your current GPA, and at least one with requirements below your GPA Your list should contain approximately 8-12 schools you are seriously considering. Start researching your financial aid options as well.
⇨ Begin scheduling interviews with admissions counselors. If possible, schedule tours of the school grounds on the same days. You and your parent(s) may want to visit the colleges and universities during spring break and summer vacation, so that you do not have to miss school. Some high schools consider a campus visit an excused absence, however, so if need be, you may be able to schedule interviews and visits during the school year, without incurring any penalties.

INSIGHTS
How To Increase Native to Native Procurement

"If your leadership understands Native buying and the power that it brings and the opportunity it has to create jobs on the reservations and Indian communities THAT IS POWERFUL. Then it goes down to your procurement. The national center has done a great job with their website portals for Indian businesses. We want the procurement people to talk to the businesses on how they can streamline. Native to Native means bringing Indian Country to work."

Margo Gray-Proctor,
Chair, The National Center for American Indian Enterprise Development, Osage Nation

November:
⇨ Review your PSAT results with your counselor.

December:
⇨ You will receive your scores from the October PSAT. Depending on the results, you may want to consider signing up for an SAT preparatory course. Many high schools offer short-term preparatory classes or seminars on the various exams, which tell the students what to expect and can actually help to boost their scores

January:
⇨ Take Campus Tours online or in person to further narrow your list of colleges to match your personality, GPA, and test scores.

February:
⇨ Register for the March SAT and/

or the April ACT tests. Find out from each college the deadlines for applying for admission and which tests to take. Make sure your test dates give colleges ample time to receive test scores. It is a good idea to take the SAT and/or ACT in the spring to allow you time to review your results and retake the exams in the fall of your senior year, if necessary.

March:

⇨ Take the March SAT Reasoning Test.

⇨ If you are interested in taking any AP exam(s), you should sign up for the exam(s) at this time. If your school does not offer the AP exams, check with your guidance counselor to determine schools in the area that do administer the exam(s), as well as the dates and times that the exam(s) you are taking will be offered. Scoring well on the AP exam can sometimes earn you college credit.

April:

⇨ Take the April ACT test.

⇨ Talk to teachers about writing letters of recommendation for you. Think about what you would like included in these letters (how you would like to be presented) and politely ask your teachers if they can accommodate you.

May:

⇨ Take SAT Reasoning Test, SAT Subject Test and AP exams.

June:

⇨ Add any new report cards, test scores, honors, or awards to your file. Visit colleges. Call ahead for appointments with the financial aid, admissions, and academic advisors at the college(s) in which you are most interested. During your visits, talk to professors, sit in on classes, spend a night in the dorms, and speak to students about the college(s). Doing these things will allow you to gather the most information about the college and the atmosphere in which you would be living, should you choose to attend. Some colleges have preview programs that allow you to do all of these; find out which of the schools that you will be visiting offer these programs and take advantage of them.

⇨ Take the SAT Reasoning Test, SAT Subject Test and the ACT tests.

⇨ If you go on interviews or visits, don't forget to send thank you notes.

Summer Between Junior and Senior Years

- Practice writing online applications, filling out rough drafts of each application, without submitting them. Focus on the essay portions of these applications, deciding how you would like to present yourself. Don't forget to mention your activities outside of school.
- Review your applications, especially the essays. Ask family, friends, and teachers to review your essays for grammar, punctuation, readability, and content.
- Decide if you are going to apply under a particular college's early

INSIGHTS
"It Opens Your Eyes"

"College made me more responsible and aware of what was going on both within my community and statewide. It opens your eyes to a lot of different avenues of work. It makes you more aware of the world."

Joseph Moose,
Paiute-Shoshone Indians of the Bishop Community

decision or early action programs. This requires you to submit your applications early, typically between October and December of your senior year, but offers the benefit of receiving the college's decision concerning your admission early, usually before January 1. If you choose to apply early, you should do so for the college/university that is your first choice in schools to attend. Many early decision programs are legally binding, requiring you to attend the college you are applying to, should they accept you.

• Read your college mail and send reply cards to your schools of interest.

Grade 12/Senior Year

Fall Semester, September:

⇨ Check your transcripts to make sure you have all the credits you need to get into your college(s) of choice. Find out from the colleges to which you are applying whether or not they need official copies of your transcripts (transcripts sent directly from your high school) sent at the time of application.

⇨ Register for October/November SAT Reasoning Test, SAT Subject Test, and ACT tests.

⇨ Take another look at your list of colleges, and make sure that they still satisfy your requirements. Add and/or remove colleges as necessary.

⇨ Make sure you meet the requirements (including any transcript requirements) for all the colleges to which you want to apply. Double-check the deadlines, and Apply.

⇨ Give any recommendation forms to the appropriate teachers or counselors with stamped, college-addressed, envelopes making certain that your portion of the forms are filled out completely and accurately.

⇨ Most early decision and early action applications are due between October 1 and November 1. Keep this in mind if you intend to take advantage of these options and remember to request that your high school send your official transcripts to the college to which you are applying.

October:

⇨ Make a final list of schools that interest you and keep a file of deadlines and required admission items for each school.

⇨ Take SAT and/or ACT tests. Have the official scores sent by the testing agency to the colleges/universities that have made your final list of schools. Register for December or January SAT Reasoning Test and/or SAT Subject Test, if necessary.

⇨ Continue thinking about and beginning writing (if you have not already started) any essays to be included with your applications.

November:

⇨ Submit your college admission applications.

December:

⇨ Early decision replies usually arrive between December 1st and December 31st.

⇨ Schedule any remaining required interviews.

~~January:~~ October

⇨ Submit the Free Application for Federal Student Aid (FAFSASM) on or after January 1st. Contact the Financial Aid Office to see if you need to complete additional financial aid forms and check into other financial aid options. In order to be considered for financial aid, you'll need to submit these forms even if you haven't yet been notified of your acceptance to the college(s) to which you applied.

⇨ Go to the FAFSA on the WebSM now to complete the form. Or complete a paper FAFSA.

⇨ Request that your high school send your official transcripts to the colleges to which you are applying.

⇨ Make sure your parents have completed their income tax forms in anticipation of the financial aid applications. If they haven't completed their taxes, providing estimated figures is acceptable.

⇨ Contact the admissions office of the college(s) to which you have applied to make sure that your information has been received, and that they have everything they need from you.

February:

⇨ If you completed the FAFSA, you should receive your Student Aid Report (SAR) within 2-3 weeks if you applied via paper. If you applied on-line, you can receive results via e-mail by the next business day after electronic submission. If corrections are needed, correct and return it to the FAFSA processor promptly.

⇨ Complete your scholarship applications.

⇨ Contact the financial aid office of the college(s) to which you have applied to make sure that your information has been received, and that they have everything they need from you.

March/April:

⇨ If you haven't received an acceptance letter from the college(s) to which you applied, contact the admissions office.

⇨ Compare your acceptance letters, financial aid and scholarship offers.

⇨ When you choose a college you have been accepted to, you may be required to pay a nonrefundable deposit for freshman tuition (this should ensure your place in the entering freshman class).

May:

⇨ Take Advanced Placement (AP) exams for any AP subjects you studied in high school.

⇨ You should make a decision by May 1st as to which college you will be attending and notify the school by mailing your commitment deposit check. Many schools require that your notification letter be postmarked by this date.

⇨ If you were placed on a waiting list for a particular college, and have decided to wait for an opening, contact that college and let them know you are still very interested.

June:

⇨ Have your school send your final transcripts to the college which you will be attending.

⇨ Contact your college to determine when fees for tuition, room and board are due and how much they will be.

Summer After Senior Year

• Participate in any summer orientation programs for incoming freshmen.

• Now that you know you will be attending college in the fall, it is a good idea to evaluate whether to get student health insurance in case of any unforeseen emergencies or whether your family's insurance coverage is sufficient.

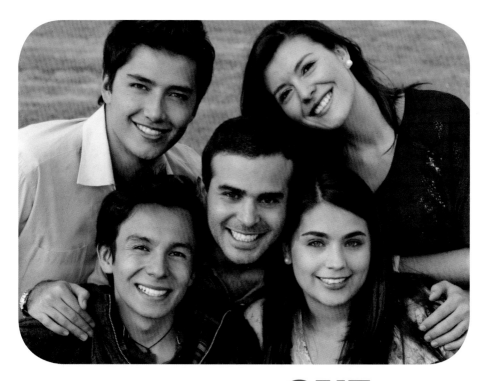

Preparing To Go To College
By Andres Tobar

Should I go to College?

Why is a college education so important? For the student who is turned off by the idea of continuing school after graduation, it is important to consider what such a decision has on the rest of his or her life. Consider the following facts provided by the ACT (American Collect Testing), Inc. (http://www.actstudent.org/college/index.html):

• Every bit of education you get after high school increases the chances you'll earn good pay. Most college graduates earn more money during their working years than people who stop their education at high school earn.

• The more education you get the more likely it is you will always have a job. According to one estimate, by the year 2028 there will be 19 million more jobs for educated workers than there are qualified people to fill them.

• Continuing education after high school is much more important for

Insights

"Half of the People I Knew in Business School Are Working For Their Tribe"

"I went to Haskell Indian Nations University – the only four year university in the country that is all Native American. There's about a thousand Native American students. Half of the people I knew in Business School are now working for their tribes. 5-10% of the people we do business deals with are Haskell alumni. It's great networking since anywhere you go in Indian Country everyone knows Haskell. You're like family when you go there – it's opened a lot of doors. It's federally supplemented and tuition is very low so there no reason that anybody can't go to school there."

Burton W. Warrington,
CEO,
Prairie Band LLC,
Menominee, Potawtomi, & Ho-Chunk Nations

your generation than it was for your parents' generation. Today most good jobs require more than a high school diploma. Businesses want to hire people who know how to think and solve problems.

• Education beyond high school gives you a lot of other benefits, including meeting new people, taking part in new opportunities to explore your interests, and experiencing success.

For most high school students, attending college is an important graduation goal. The question each student needs to answer is "Am I doing all that I need to do in my education to apply and attend college?" It is equally important to look inside oneself and build personal motivation and desire to achieve this goal. The next step is putting in place a personal plan that will lead to successful college admission and financing. Many tools are available in this Directory for locating sources of college financial aid. Other important steps of a student's plan to make college a reality follow here.

What classes should I take in high school to meet college admission standards?

In order to prepare for a college education, high school students should select classes that are as challenging and rigorous as available. Successful completion of higher-level courses in math, science, foreign language, history, and language arts are expected. Some college programs or highly selective schools may expect their incoming freshmen to have achieved very advance math and science courses. This is particularly true for programs that accept freshmen to study engineering or pre-medical studies. A good way to determine what courses should be taken is to review the types of diplomas given to graduates. Often school systems will offer "advanced diplomas" for students who have completed a rigorous course of study. Ask your guidance counselor what classes you need for college and do research on the standards of various colleges you have heard of or might want to attend.

For many students, planning for college may begin as early as middle school. In order to take the classes necessary to apply to college, students must complete certain course prerequisites. It is not too early for students to discuss college and pathways to higher levels of math, science, and foreign languages with their middle school guidance counselor or homeroom advisors. It may be hard to think about college this early, especially for students who are uncertain they will attend college, but it is wiser to select the classes usually taken by a college-bound student. Either way, the student receives a stronger education and will have more choices at graduation.

If a student decides he or she wants attend college but may not have taken the required courses, there are still ways to prepare for college admission. For students who have not graduated, courses can be taken in summer school. If already graduated from high school, preparatory programs are available through community colleges or junior colleges. These institutions also offer two-year (associate) degrees that provide a pathway to admission into a 4-year college. Students who earn an associate degree and maintain a good GPA can often enter as a junior or third-year college student. Students need to remember, however, that unlike high school, education after high school is not free. In order to save money it is better to take your college preparatory classes while still in high school.

For students who are pursuing a college preparatory program in high school, strong consideration should be given to enrolling in high school classes that are identified as Advanced Placement (AP), if available. Not only do students who score well on AP exams earn college credits from taking the AP course, but also having AP courses on the student's grade transcript demonstrates to college admission officers that the student is motivation to excel and taking a rigorous course of study. AP courses also give an extra point in the student's grade point average (GPA). For example, a final grade of "B" or 3.0 in an AP class will be computed as a 4.0 (equivalent to an "A") on the student's transcript. If AP classes are not available, students should ask about taking honors classes. Working to keep one's grades up is an important goal. Students should aim for making the honor roll and other academic recognitions, if available.

College-bound students should remember that college admissions officers pay particular attention to the three basic indicators of college success when admitting students: The student's (1) GPA; (2) class rank; and (3) SAT or ACT score. To be eligible to apply to the broadest choices of colleges and scholarships, students should pay attention to these important numbers during their high school years. Any student who hits an academic rough patch or is struggling in school should not stand by and hope it gets better! Take action and ask for help from your family, and your teacher or your guidance counselor. They want you to succeed. In the end, your hard work and dedication will pay off!

What about standardized tests for college admission? How should I prepare?

Most college admissions require students to take a college entrance exam, either the Standard Aptitude Test (SAT) or the American College Test (ACT). The score on this test will help admissions officers know about your readiness for college. It

INSIGHTS

"My Children Have Everything They Need, Because I went to College"

"I think going to college has helped my children a lot because they have a better life than I did growing up. They are the beneficiaries of all the suffering I went through and all the things I had to pass up on when I was studying at night for college and thinking everyone else was out having a good time. Now my kids go to a great school. They have health insurance. They have everything they need because I went to college."

Heather Levi,
Association of American Indian Physicians, Southern Cheyenne and Kiowa Tribes of Oklahoma

is also a useful tool to help decide what colleges and universities are best suited to the student. The higher his or her score on the SAT, the more competitive the student becomes. Most high school students take the SAT during their junior year. Students can take the test more than once and only the highest score will be reported to colleges. A "practice" test of the SAT called the "PSAT" or "Preliminary SAT" is available for students to take in their sophomore year. There are many ways to prepare for taking this test, including practice tests online. Ask your guidance counselor if there are preparatory SAT or ACT classes available in your community. Many experts believe that one of the keys to doing well on these tests is to practice taking the test many times in advance of the actual exam. The more one takes the exam, the more comfortable one becomes with the format of the test, allowing the student to focus energy on the exam questions. Since SAT or ACT exam is usually taken during the student's junior year, this is also a good time to begin identifying the eligibility criteria and deadlines for scholarships that would needed to pay for college.

Another important way to prepare and improve SAT or ACT scores should start as soon as possible – develop a habit of reading for pleasure. Find books or magazines in the library that interest you and develop the habit of reading for fun. Studies have shown that students who read for pleasure often do better on standardized tests. Reading is a way to built your vocabulary and learn words used within the content of their meaning. Reading for pleasure also helps increase the speed that one reads, an important skill for college. Another important skill for college is learning to write in a way that is grammatically correct. Most students who speak English as a second languages find they are working to catch up academically with their classmates. Students who face such challenges should know that with the right classes and by seeking out help – whether from a mentor, tutoring, or being part of a special programs for non-native speakers – they can be competitive in school.

To build these important skills, students should seek out activities that push them to use their reading and writing abilities – whether working on the school newspaper or yearbook, joining a creative writing club or book club, participating

INSIGHTS

"California Community Colleges Provided Open Access"

"I am very fortunate that the California community colleges provided open access for me to be able to enter higher education. My college education earned in the community college and California state university systems, as well as at the University of Southern California have provided me opportunities and rewards that have filled my life."

Manuel Baca, *Political Science Professor at Rio Hondo College and Vice President of the California Community Colleges Board of Governors*

in the Model UN, or volunteering for a school play or concert – such activities will not only improve reading and writing skills, but also provide extracurricular activities to include on college applications.

When should I write my college essay?

Nearly all colleges require their applicants to include a personal essay. Most college-bound students begin to outline and draft their college essay in their junior year with the goal to complete the essay before the beginning of their senior year. It is wise to seek other caring adults from your family or school for feedback. Consult with your guidance counselor and your English teacher as you develop your essay. Be open minded and welcome their comments and suggestions.

How can an undocumented immigrant student go to college?

Students who are undocumented immigrants will encounter obstacles in obtaining a college education in the United States. These students are not eligible for most state and federal financial aid, and in many states are required to pay out-of-state or international student tuition. The DREAM Act, a proposed law that has been introduced at both the state and federal legislatures, would make it easier for undocumented high school graduates to attend college. Unfortunately only a few states have passed this type of legislation into law at this time. It is important to discuss this matter with your guidance counselor to get the latest information about ways to obtain more education after high school. (for more on the DREAM Act, read "The Dream Act" in Section Four of this book)

What is the most affordable college path to take?

For most students, attending a public college or university close to home will be their best option. This will ensure that the cost of tuition and living expenses are the most economical. For the high school student who has excelled academically in grades and test scores, however, it is possible that colleges and universities will offer generous packages to attend their institution and such offers should be seriously considered.

Is it ever too late to apply for college?

It's never too late to apply or attend college. Some students only decide they want to attend college during their last years of high school and don't have time to take the necessary college preparatory course work. Others have already graduated from high school before making this decision. Some students enter military service and finish their tour ready to go back to school. One way to address this is to enroll in adult education classes or a local community college and take the recommended courses that will help you get into college. Many adult education programs offer classes focused on improving basic college skills such as writing or refresher math courses. Take advantage of these programs as they will sharpen the critical skills needed for college success.

RESOURCE CENTER
HELPFUL RESEARCH ON GOING TO COLLEGE

Please remember that some websites may be more helpful to you than others. No single site will have all the answers, or even always correct answers, but visiting a variety of sites can lead you to the right decision. Please go to www.EmpoweringStudents.com for more helpful websites.

College Calendar:
http://studentaid.ed.gov/prepare-for-college/checklists
http://studentaid.ed.gov/sites/default/files/college-prep-checklist.pdf

Finding the Right Colleges For You, U.S. Department of Education:
http://studentaid.ed.gov/prepare-for-college/choosing-schools

College Affordability and Transparency Center: For objecting information on colleges, their cost and majors:
http://collegecost.ed.gov/

Educational Testing Service:
www.ets.org

Complete College America:
http://www.completecollege.org/completion_shortfall/

Information for International Students:
http://studentaid.ed.gov/PORTALSWebApp/students/english/intl.jsp

Studies: These studies are available on the enclosed CD and on www.EmpoweringStudents.com; plus more studies are available on ES+. Here's 727 additional pages of information:

- *The Condition of Education 2012*, NCES
- *The Internet & the Future of Higher Education Study*, PEW
- *With their whole lives ahead of them study*, The Bill & Melinda Gates Foundation
- 1970 vs 2010 education data, U.S. Census Bureau
- *America's Youth – Transition to Adulthood*, NCES
- *College Students Prefer Tablets for Reading*, Pearson Foundation

Resource Center
3 Great Books On College

Although we've worked hard to make this directory as comprehensive as possible, no one book has all the answers, so we felt you'd find these books helpful.

Campus Visits & College Interviews by Zola Dincin Schneider, a college advisor with over 20 years experience. This book explains everything college-bound students and their parents need to know about planning campus visits and preparing for college interviews. Among subjects the book covers are weighing options, mapping visits, making arrangements, how to read a college catalog, and what questions to ask the Interviewer.
The book includes 14 handy checklists to help students track their progress.

IN! College Admissions and Beyond by Lillian Luterman & Jennifer Bloom, mother and daughter team of college admissions consultants, is another must-read for students and their parents. In it the authors present a step-by-step strategy for completing winning admissions applications and getting you in to the college of your choice. "It is often the well-rounded student, an ideal many applicants strive for, who gets rejected." They suggest students create distinction by identifying a passion and "layering it," showcasing their interests and talents. Among the subjects the book covers are campus visits, letters of recommendation and college interviews. The book is further enhanced by fill-in charts, New Yorker cartoons, case studies, and sidebars for parents.

Latinos in College: your guide to success by Mariela Dabbah, award winning author of Help Your Children Succeed in High School and Go to College. From start to finish this book is packed full of vital information for college-bound students and their parents on everything from taking the mystery out of choosing and financing college and living away from home to managing your time and money and preparing for life after college. I found chapter 15, *Taking Advantage of What Your College Has to Offer*, particularly helpful. It suggests developing leadership skills by volunteering, joining or working for student organizations and associations. Another chapter that I found particularly helpful is chapter 16, which discusses being your own BFF (Best Friends Forever)by taking care of yourself while in college. Aside from studying make time for sleep, exercise, socializing, and eating well. At the back of the book you will find helpful resources including a list of Top Colleges for Latino Students. The book was published by Consultare in 2009.

by Annie Perez

SECTION TWO
FINANCING COLLEGE

INSIGHTS
"GI Bill Helped Open the Door"

"Going to college credited a number of possibilities that I couldn't even imagine. Because I'd served in the Navy during World War II, I realized I could do anything that anybody could do IF I applied myself to it. No one in my family had ever gone to college. My dad loved to read so we had many books in the house. The GI Bill helped open the door at community college and at Pomona College. When I went on to Harvard graduate school I had to borrow money, which I later paid back to the Dr. Francisco Bravo Scholarship Fund. He was a very successful surgeon and clinic owner who lent money to Mexican American medical students. I also earned money during the summer by repairing dented cars at Mercury Plant in Los Angeles. Harvard itself never gave me a scholarship."

Julian Nava, Ph.D.

In the 1950's, Julian became the first Mexican American to attend graduate school at Harvard; in the 1960's he became the first Latino on the Los Angeles Unified School District Board; and in the 1970's he became the first Mexican American to serve as the U.S. Ambassador to Mexico.

Current College Trends

We reviewed over 200 publications and websites to come up with what we feel are some of the most meaningful trends in college today. Let us know at kirk@whisler.com if there are other trends we should cover.

Who Is Going To College?

Percentage of youth 18 to 24 who are enrolled in college:

	1989	2011
Asian Americans	46.1%	60.1%
Whites (non-Hispanic)	34.2%	44.7%
African American	23.4%	37.1%
Hispanics	16.1%	34.8%
American Indians/Alaska Natives	15.7%	23.5%

Source: U.S. Department of Education

Applying To College

Students are on a trend of applying to more colleges. Prestigious colleges saw applications rise 7% last for incoming freshman classes according to the Nat'l Assn. for College Admission Counseling.

Full time vs Part Time

Figure 36-1. Percentage distribution of fall undergraduate enrollment in degree-granting institutions, by student attendance status and control and level of institution: Fall 2010

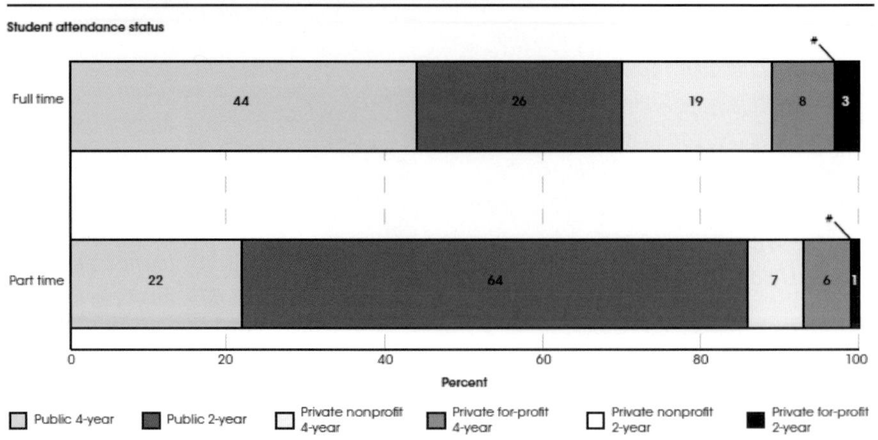

Source: **The Condition of Education 2012**, U.S. Department of Education

THE COST OF COLLEGE

Figure 40-1. Total cost of attending an undergraduate institution for first-time, full-time students, by level and control of institution and living arrangement: Academic year 2010–11

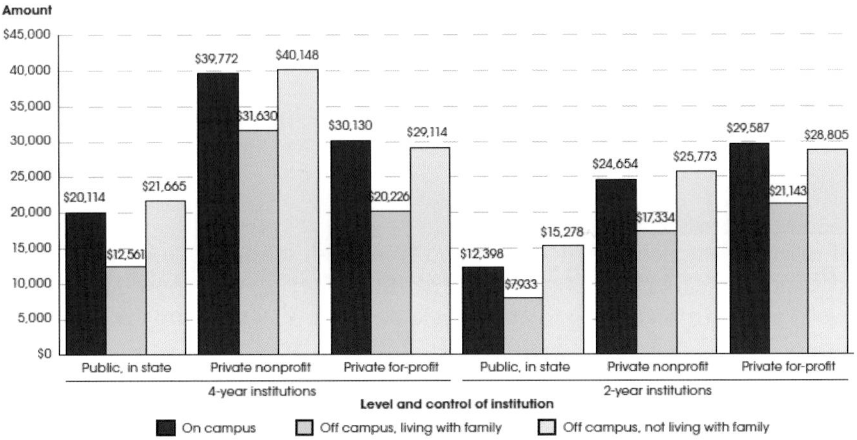

Source: **The Condition of Education 2012**, U.S. Department of Education

SUPPORT FOR GOING TO COLLEGE

Figure 41-2. Average amount of aid received by full-time, first-time, degree-seeking undergraduate students in financial aid programs, by institution level, control, and type of aid: Academic year 2009–10

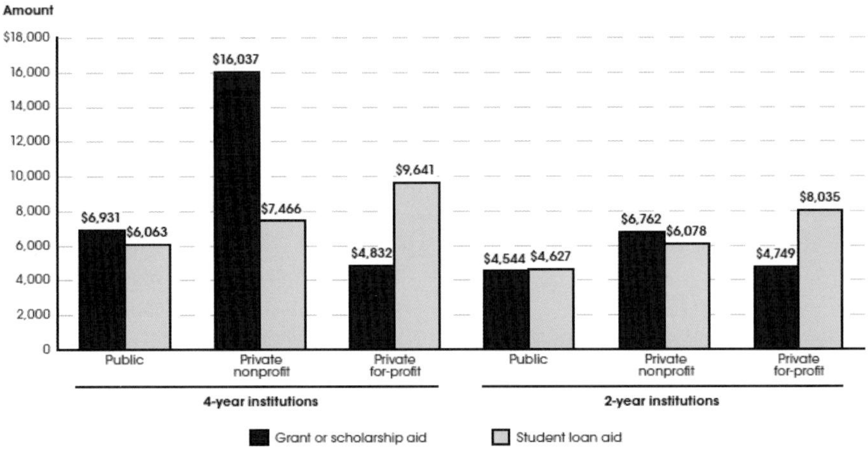

Source: **The Condition of Education 2012**, U.S. Department of Education

WORK & SCHOOL

39.8% of full time college students also have a job and 73.4% of part time students have a job. For full time students who work, 37.4% work less than 20 hours a week and 43.2% work 20-34 hours a week. For part time students, 44.7% work 35+ hours a week and 38.6% work 20-34 hours a week.

SCHOLARSHIPS TO TARGET

Don't overlook the SMALLER scholarships. While thousands of people go after the large scholarship funds, often very few, or no one, go after smaller ones. I spoke recently at a MEChA meeting at Palomar College. One student mentioned that he had spent around 20 minutes filling in a scholarship application to a local scholarship fund that got him a $1,000 scholarship – in large part because not enough people had applied for that scholarship. I'll devote 20 minutes to fill out a form every day for $1,000!

LOANS

For many young people who graduated from high school during the recession, the American dream of life getting better for each new generation feels like a myth according to an Associated Press-Viacom Study released in April of 2012. Yet despite the downturn in the economy, youth today remain optimistic about the future. If you need a little more money for college than grants & scholarships can offer, consider getting a study loan. As of April 2012, 986,494 Latinos had government backed student loans. In 1989, 9% of the households in the USA owed on a student loan. By 2010 that had grown to 19%. **In 2011, graduates who took out loans left college owing an average of $25,497.**

GENDER TRENDS

In 1967 33% of males aged 18 to 24 were attending a degree granting college or university, while only 19% of females were going. 44 years later females represent 57% of the students in college. For Hispanics it's 58% and American Indians 59%! The bottom line is that while decades ago many colleges catered to males primarily, today they serve an increasing majority of female students.

INSIGHTS

"We Are Losing a Generation of Male Latinos"

"Unfortunately we are loosing a generation of male Latinos who are not going on to college. It's attacking our family system and family values. We need to pay more attention to the education of our young males. It happened in the African American community and it could be worse in our community. Latinas can't find eligible Latinos to marry. By that I mean, people who can bring a paycheck home, be responsible parents, and have an education. That's something that we have got to deal with. You can't have the family relationships with that structure in place. Kids need positive male role models. Without positive role models they are having rough times. We have to make this a national movement. What frustrates me is that not enough people are talking about it. I don't hear anything at all about this being an issue. It used to be the opposite – there were barriers for Latinas to get into college, they were not allowed to leave the home. We fought those barriers. We dealt with those issues for women. Now we MUST pay equal attention to our Latino males."

U.S. Ambassador to the Dominican Republic
Raul Yzaguirre

Who Is Finishing College?

Figure 45-2. Percentage of students seeking a bachelor's degree at 4-year institutions who completed a bachelor's degree within 6 years, by control of institution and race/ethnicity: Starting cohort year 2004

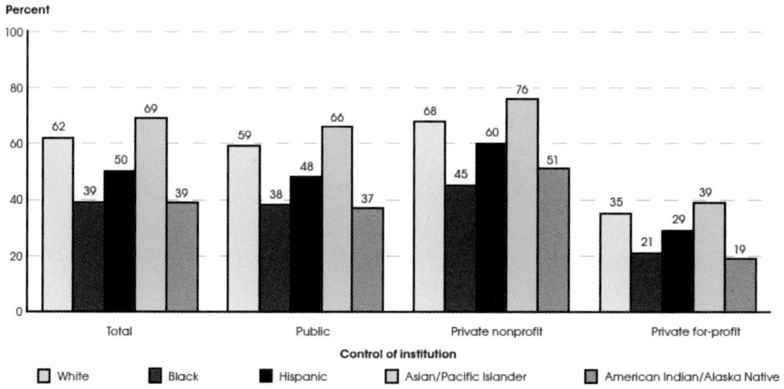

Source: **The Condition of Education 2012**, U.S. Department of Education

Educational Attainment of the Population Ages 25 and Older, 1971-2012

% completing

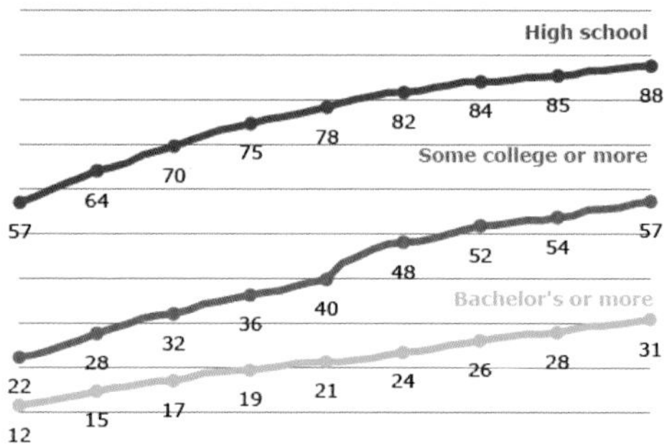

Source: PEW's Record Shares of Young Adults Have Finished Both High School and College, 2012

Earning Ability

Figure 49-2. Median annual earnings of full-time, full-year wage and salary workers ages 25–34, by educational attainment and sex: 2010

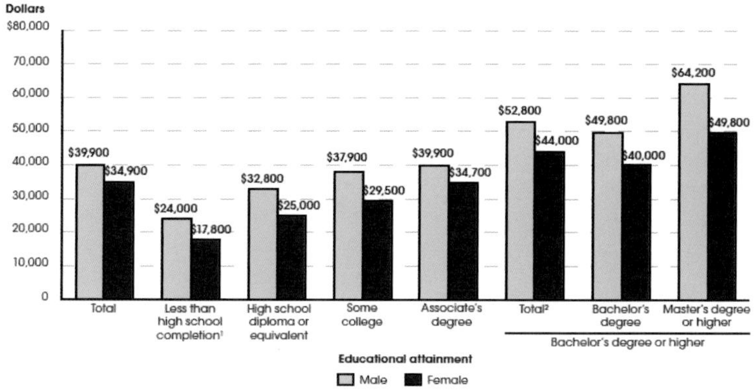

Source: **The Condition of Education 2012**, U.S. Department of Education

FINANCING COLLEGE

How Are You Going to Pay for College?

By Enrique G. Murillo, Jr, Ph.D. & Patricia A. Aguilera

Congratulations if you're reading this! It's important to dream big and have a plan on what you're going to do with your life after high school. Taking the appropriate steps and action to achieve your educational and career goals will be most beneficial to you as you pursue your college education. Everyone can go to college - but you have to be persistent and persevere in your journey across higher education and onto your career plans.

It's normal if you don't know exactly everything when you first start out, but you do know that you have to go to class and get good grades to establish your GPA goal and take the necessary college preparatory classes for college admission. Attend your school's college-planning night. You should also get involved in your school and community by joining clubs, sports, and volunteer organizations. You have to study and prepare in advance for college entrance exams by taking the SAT or ACT and any other placement exams in order to achieve high scores. High test scores will open many opportunities for you when applying to various colleges and universities, and when you eventually enroll. There are usually deadlines associated with the various tests. Check with your high school counselor or testing agency for these important dates as well as other important deadlines.

While your first priority is getting accepted and enrolling in a college or university of your choice, financial planning and paying for college are very important steps to take into consideration to avoid student loan debt. It is just as important and requires the same serious effort in planning. There's some work and steps involved, and the sooner you start, the more resources you will have to potentially save on college costs. Something to keep in mind is that tuition costs and college/university fees will almost undoubtedly continue to increase over the next few years.

For starters, begin by creating an expenses budget, determining what personal and family resources you have to pay for college, attending a financial aid workshop, and keeping a calendar of important deadlines. Look for ways to start saving costs in your daily life and have a clear understanding of your finances. There are additional costs that include: tuition/fees, housing, books, supplies, and transportation to consider in your budget. So figure out what college will really cost you and all the expenses that are included. Next, complete a FAFSA, which stands for the Free Application for Federal Student Aid. By completing the FAFSA it allows the U.S. Department of Education to properly determine the Expected Family Contribution (EFC) amount you and your family are able to contribute to your educational expenses. It allows higher education institutions to determine how much financial aid you may qualify for and the amounts they can award you. The principal source of funding for college/university is the federal government, and the FAFSA should be considered your first step to securing grants, scholarships, work-study, and student loans. The priority deadline for submitting a FAFSA is March 2nd. To apply on-line or for additional information visit http://www.fafsa.ed.gov. Depending on the state you live in, there may be additional state financial aid. Contact your high school counselor or financial aid office for more information on state aid.

Many of the goals you set for yourself while attending high school, like getting good grades, will also pay off when you're applying for grants and scholarships. You could also jump ahead and obtain some college credits while still attending high school. Make the most of your summer as well, both in high school and for the years you're in college. You can seek employment through a part-time summer job or paid internship. You can also save that gift money you received at graduation. Most importantly, compare college expenses and financial aid award letters before you decide where to enroll and attend. You may want to consider starting college at a community college, or live at or close to home and attend your local institution at first to save money and also avoid out-of-state tuition costs. Also, once you've started college it

INSIGHTS

"College Changed My Life"

"College changed my life immensely. Throughout the years I always dealt with the racism issue and in high school I was told I would not make it through college. I've worked with groups like Upward Bound to share my experiences with younger students. I'm the first generation in my family to go to college. My parents instilled in me to go and get an education since they did not have one. My father was a boarding school student and only went through the sixth grade. My mother later got her GED in the 1980s. I wanted to do something for my future and I was always told education was where it's at. The degree I choose was not easy: Management Information Systems and I have a degree in Spanish. With these degrees I can work anywhere. My goal is helping preserve our culture through our museum. Without my education I wouldn't be doing half the things I'm doing. I now serve on several nation boards. I funded my education by working two jobs. I did get some scholarships since I'm partially Hispanic and was an officer in Mecha."

Raphaella Stump,
Eastern Shoshone Tribe of the Wind River Reservation, Wyoming

is necessary to renew your FAFSA by March 2nd for the following academic year.

Apply for national, local, and any private scholarships you learn of, and for which you are eligible. Most colleges and universities also offer both merit and need-based scholarships. Check with your institution. Colleges and universities may have scholarship information and/or on-line applications on their website. If you're an undocumented student, find out if the particular state you reside in can offer you in-state tuition rates, and you may also qualify for institutional or privately-funded scholarships. You should always exhaust all grant opportunities and scholarships, because these funds are free and do not have to be repaid, before borrowing money with student loans. Apply for the federal work-study program to offset a portion of your educational expenses with part-time employment rather than accepting student loans that you may have been offered. Student loans should be your last option in financing your education and it's important to keep loan balances as low as possible, and be careful with credit cards.
If student loans are your only option to finance your education, there are low interest loans. Repayment on subsidized loans begin six months after a student graduates or stops attending school at least half-time. Unsubsidized loans are low interest loans that you pay as you go. For additional information on federal student loans, visit www.studentloans.gov. Regularly visit your institution's financial aid office as well as campus websites, bulletin boards and e-newsletters, as scholarships, grants and fellowship offers are often routinely posted.

Overall it's important to be practical, knowledgeable, and resourceful. For example, it's encouraged to find out if your bookstore carries used textbooks, and don't forget to always use your student discounts. Be sure to present yourself with honesty and professionalism in all your communications, encounters and applications, and talk to your academic advisors and financial aid counselors about any questions you don't understand, and by all means stick to your budget!

About the Authors:

Dr. Enrique Murillo *is Executive Director of the Latino Education & Advocacy Days (LEAD) Organization and Professor in the College of Education at California State University, San Bernardino. He served four years as Commissioner of the California Student Aid Commission (CSAC), the principal state agency responsible for administering financial aid programs for students attending public and private universities, colleges, and vocational schools in California.*

Patricia Aguilera *is Financial Aid Advisor and Student Employment Coordinator in the Financial Aid Office at California State University, San Bernardino. She is a member of the National Student Employment Association (NSEA) where she is a national trainer for student employment. Patricia also serves on the executive board of LEAD, the CSAC Strategic Planning team for California Cash for College, and the CSU Segmental Committee for the California Association of Student Financial Aid Administers (CASFAA).*

Resource Center
Financing College Websites

Our massive directory lists thousands of sources for financing your college education, but there's still thousands more. Please remember that some websites may be more helpful to you than others. No single site will have all the answers, or even always correct answers, but visiting a variety of sites can lead you to the right decision.

Please go to www.EmpoweringStudents.com for more helpful websites.

Here are some:

Federal Student Aid (English)
http://studentaid.ed.gov/

Federal Student Aid (Español)
http://studentaid.ed.gov/es

5 Reasons You Should Complete the Free Application For Federal Student Aid (FAFSA)
http://www.ed.gov/blog/2013/01/5-reasons-you-should-complete-the-free-application-for-federal-student-aid-fafsa/

Get Federal Help Paying for College
http://www.fafsa.ed.gov/

Financial Aid Overview
http://www2.ed.gov/finaid/landing.jhtml

Your Federal Student Loans: Learn the basics and manage your debt
http://studentaid.ed.gov/students/attachments/siteresources/11-12YFSL.pdf

SallieMae (materials in both English and Spanish)
http://www.thesalliemaefund.org/smfnew/sections/download.html

National Science Foundation: Gateway to 100s of scholarships
www.nsf.gov

Cal Grants
http://www.calgrants.org/

American Indian Scholarships & Grants, Bureau of Indian Affairs
http://www.bie.edu/ParentsStudents/Grants/index.htm

Resource Center
4 Financing College Books

View these books as an investment: spend a little on them now for a huge return later.

Financial Aid Handbook: Getting the Education you want for the Price You Can Afford by Carol Stack and Ruth Vedvik, Career Press, is a one-step guide to college selection and college financing, essential in today's economy. This book covers such topics as the seven biggest myths about paying for college, federal, state, and student loans, and completing the FAFSA and Profile. Its unique approach, aimed at college-bound young people, emphasizes basing the college search on what they can afford and "who will fund you to attend their institution." Special features include charts on calculating costs, financial aid timelines, and profiles of selected schools which offer the best merit aid. Together, authors Stack and Vedvik, have more than 70 years experience in college admissions and financial aid.

Financing College: How to Use Savings, Financial Aid, Scholarships, and Loans to Afford the School of Your Choice, a Kiplinger book by Kristin Davis is a must-read for the family of any college-bound student.
In it the author describes the best ways to develop a sound investment and savings plan for your child's college education, and how to get the most from financial aid, grants, scholarships, and loans.

The book is enhanced by worksheets, charts, and cartoons. Kristin Davis is a senior associate editor of Kiplinger's Personal Finance Magazine.

The Ultimate Scholarship Book: Billions of Dollars in Scholarships by Gen and Kelly Tanabe, is a comprehensive guide to more than 1.5 million in scholarship awards and grants. This well-organized, reader-friendly book covers such topics as where to find the best scholarships, writing a winning scholarship essay, getting great recommendations, and acing the scholarship interview. This husband and wife team, Harvard grades Gen and Kelly Tanabe, are the recipients of over $100,000 in merit-based scholarships and the authors of twelve books including Get Free Cash for College and 1001 Ways to Pay for College.

Scholarship Handbook, published by CollegeBoard is a comprehensive guide to over 1.7 million in scholarship awards. Special features include: eligibility indexes that match you to scholarships based on residency, religion, ethnicity, and field of study; number of applicants for each award; separate sections for internships; current information based on annual survey of scholarship sponsors; Scholarship Application Planners so students can keep track of applications and deadlines; and more.
This handbook also provides insider information on avoiding scholarship scams.

by Annie Perez

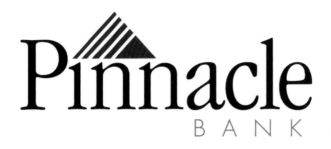

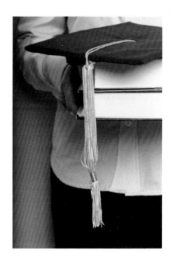

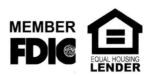

10 Ways To Use Scholarship Info

if you have decent grades, and well rounded activities and letters of support, odds are that you will find a scholarship or another form of financial aid from one source or another. The key is finding that source. We have worked hard to find as many appropriate sources as possible.

We have been doing scholarship directories since 1997 and have heard hundreds of success stories from our users. The typical user spends 10 to 30 hours researching and applying for scholarships or other financial aid, and in return they get, on average, several scholarships.

The average individual scholarship in this book is $3,800. So if you spend 20 hours researching and applying, and end up getting $7,600 in funding, that comes down to $380 per hour spent on the pursuit. I'd say that is a good return. We'd like to hear your success stories.

Here's some key parts of the Directory (see corresponding numbers on the "sample listing" on the next page):

1. *Type of Organization.* We've divided organizations into 7 categories: Businesses, College, Foundations, Government, Nonprofits, Tribes, and Other. Each has different types of programs. For instance, colleges normally only give to students at their college.

2. *Types of Programs.* This is key to understand the differences. While 75% of the programs in this Directory are Scholarships, we also have 99 Awards (often competitions); 120 Fellowships (often for graduate work); 44 Grants; 44 Internships (see a helpful article on internships in Section 3); and 167 Programs (some are for before college and others are for during college).

3. *Websites.* Probably 90% of all scholarship information and interactions are conducted via the internet today, so having the right website is

Insights

"I Worked on Campus as a Tutor"

"I funded my college education on my own. I come from a very large family–I had 12 siblings. My mom and dad were immigrants–as I was. When it came time to go to college I talked with my dad and he was very excited that I'd chosen to go to college, but he shared that while he'd love to help me he couldn't because he couldn't help all my brothers & sisters. I searched everywhere for financial aid and I was fortunate to find some loans and the work study program so I could attend UCLA. I worked on campus as a tutor and in the cafeteria."

Victor Franco,
NBC Universal/ Telemundo

These 132 scholarship offer on average over $500,000 a year in scholarships.
For these & 1,770+ more searchable scholarships see the enclosed CD.

HISPANIC SCHOLARSHIP FUND

ORGANIZATION | NON-PROFIT ① | SCHOLARSHIP ②

Organization **Hispanic Scholarship Fund (HSF)**
Department
Address 1411 W. 190th Street, Suite 325
Gardena State CA Zip code 90248

③ **WEBSITES** Where to apply: Online
Organization www.hsf.net
Scholarship

④ **ANNUAL OPPORTUNITIES (ESTIMATED)**
Scholarships Offered Annually: Over 1,000
Average per Scholarship: $4,000

⑤ **FIELD OF STUDY** All Fields of Study
GENERAL

⑥ **TARGET AUDIENCES**

Aimed At	[ ] Am. Indian	[X] Latino	[ ] African Am	[ ] Asian Am	[ ] Women	[ ] Tribe	[ ] Overall Diverse / Open to all
⑦ **College Level**	[ ] Pre College	[X] 1st Yr.	[X] 2nd Yr.	[X] 3rd Yr.	[X] 4th Yr.	[X] Graduate Studies	

⑧ Area Served: National
⑨ Citizenship requirements: Must be permanent resident or citizen

⑩ **BASIS FOR AWARD**

[X] Financial Need	[X] Grades	[ ] Interviews	[X] Extracurricular Activities
[ ] Essays	3.0 Minimum G.P.A.	[X] SAT ACT	[ ] Community Involvement
			[X] Letters of Recommendation

A typical listing found in this Directory (listings start on page 98).

key. Inevitably web domains addresses change. Recently all the federal government financial aid addresses change – often with no forwarding from the old domain. If the domain we list is invalid, please keep searching. We will also updating domains on www.EmpoweringStudents.com as they change.

4. *Annual Opportunities.* While this is a good way to see the major opportunities, don't overlook smaller scholarships that often don't get enough applicants.

5. *Field of Study.* Helpful field for helping you find opportunities in your field of study.

6. *Target Audiences, Aimed At.* Very important field for targeting appropriate ones to go after. Don't overlook the Women field for you women and the Overall Diverse field for all people of color (428 listings and $218 million in opportunities).

7. *College Level.* Another key field for targeting opportunities.

8. *Area Served.* This is always key: you need to make sure the scholarship is available to you and where you live and/or where you want to go to college. This is a key starting point.

9. *Citizenship Field.* If you were born in another country you will find this field very useful in finding appropriate opportunities.

10. *Basis for Award.* We all have strengths and weaknesses and this is a good way to find opportunities that fit our strengths.

by Kirk Whisler

RESOURCE CENTER
HELPFUL RESEARCH ON FINANCING COLLEGE

These studies are available on the enclosed CD and on the www.EmpoweringStudents.com; plus more studies are available on ES+.

Here's 229 additional pages of information:

- Do you need money for college? 2012-13
- Federal Student Aid for Adult Students
- Federal Student Aid Grant Programs
- How America Pays for College, Sallie Mae
- Funding Your Education, 2012-13 Guide to Federal Student Aid
- Top 10 Tips for Paying for College
- Mission Possible, The Toolkit that helps you Save, Plan & Pay for College, Sallie Mae
- Your Federal Student Loans- Learn the basics and manage your debt

En español

- ¿Necesita dinero para la universidad?, 2012-13
- Oficina ayuda federal para estudiantes, Programes federales de becas
- Misión ¡Possible!, El kit de herramientas que le ayuda a ahorrar, planificar y pagar la universidad, Sallie Mae
- Funding Your Education en español, 2012-13 Guide to Federal Student Aid
- Los 10 mejores consejos sobre cómo planificar y pagar la Universidad

INSIGHTS
"ALL ADDED TO MY GROWTH AND DEVELOPMENT"

"College made an immense impact on my life. First of all it allowed me to think on a broader scale and look for opportunities that I wouldn't have had if I didn't have a profes- sional degree from college. The atmosphere, the learning process, the ability to make new friends that are with you throughout your life because they become success as well, all added to my growth and development."

Gilbert Vasquez, *Vasquez & Company CPAs*

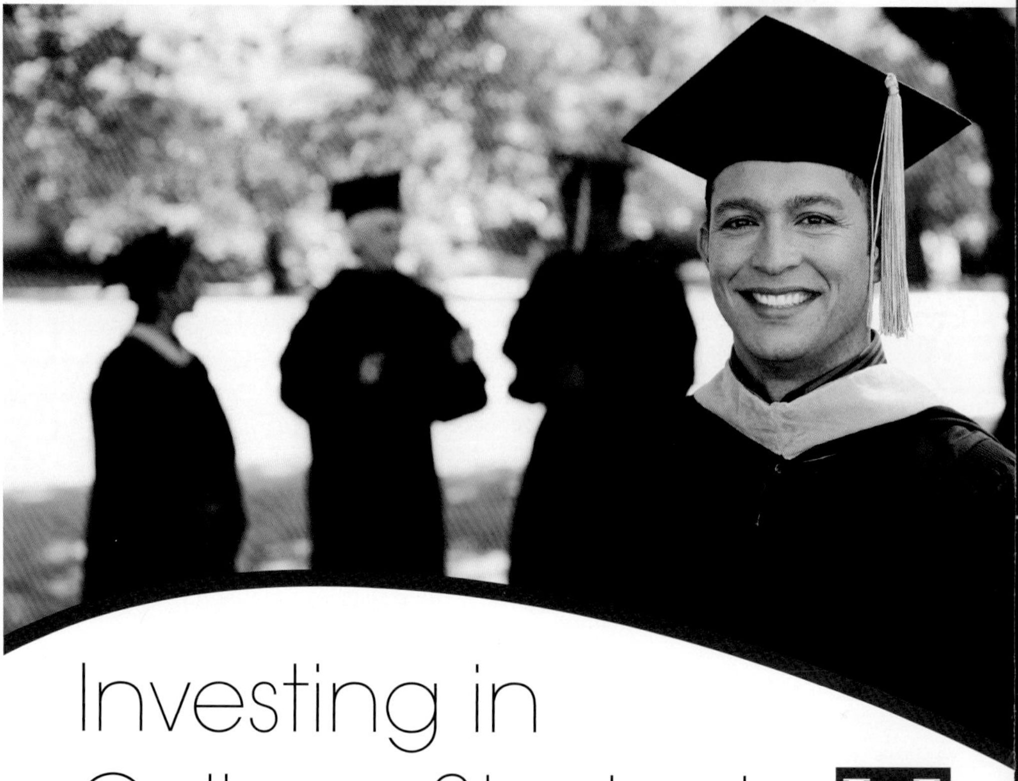

Section Three
Careers Not Majors

Insights
"It's Never Been More Impoprtant"

"I believe that college is not merely the best investment you can make in your future, it's the best investment you can make in your country's future. It's never been more important.

"In today's economy there's no greater predictor of individual success than a good education. That's at the top."

"A higher education is the single clearest path the middle class."

"Higher education, whether at a four year college or a two year program, can't be a luxury – it's an economic imperative for every family in America. Every family in America should afford it as long as those young people are willing to put in the work and study hard."

President Barack Obama
April 25, 2012 at the University of Iowa.

Choose a Career, Not a Major

By Kirk Whisler

When anyone starts college they are often asked 'What is your major?' by friends, family and people at the college. While you ultimately need a major that you will graduate in, it's important to realize that many people never work in the field of their major. A more appropriate question might be: 'What field would you like to have a career in?' or 'What occupation do you like?'

When I was a senior at Pacific High School in San Bernardino, and preparing to head off for my freshman year at U.C. Santa Barbara, my cousin Donna, who was all of a year older than me, gave me some very profound advice. She shared, "College is 25% what you learn in a classroom and 75% what you'll learn outside that classroom. You're finally making all, or most, decisions on your own. Financial decisions, foods, hobbies, movies, etc., will often be different than before."

When you head off to college you are learning to live independent of your family – and most likely evolving with new sets of friends. Often your likes and dislikes will change more in a few years than they did in the previous decade. I entered college as

Insights

"It was Important for Me to Understand the Theoritical View of Things"

"College changed my life in so many ways. It was important for me to understand the theoretical view of things. I was a public administration/public policy major and it was great to learn the theory and history behind issues. The second thing college taught me was how to research things. Not just how to use facts and figures, but rather the process of learning. When I came to the USA, not speaking a word of English, what I learned was that I wasn't dumb, I just had not learned the language. What college taught me was how to learn the languages of government and banking."

Maria Contreras Sweet,
Promerica Bank

a chemistry major and within four months knew that wasn't the career field for me.

Certain Professions Are Tied to Majors – But Most Are Not

If you want to be a lawyer, you have to go to law school; a teacher must have earned a teaching credential, a doctor goes to med school, and so on. This comparison is especially true for graduate degrees. Probably 40% of all college trained professionals MUST be trained in their profession and have obtained a degree that entitles them to be treated as a professional in that field.

In reality it means that roughly 60% of all college trained professionals may or MAY NOT end up working in the field they got their degree in. Look at all the professions that have no real major in college. Around 10% of all the people in the USA work in sales, and yet only a few colleges in the USA offer a Bachelors or Masters in some type of sales. An English major in college may well end up as a salesperson. The Occupational Outlook Handbook, described later in this section, includes 10 major sales categories, some paying amongst the highest salaries of any career.

I graduated with a major in History and a minor in Political Science. Even though I love reading history, especially Latin American history, I've never really worked in the field. But the thought process I learned about analyzing historical issues I've used in a variety of other ways.

Don't Believe Everything That You Hear About A Major

Over the years I've taught media, journalism and history classes at several different colleges. At one college the professors in the Journalism School were giving brief presentations to all the journalism students. I was appalled when the Dean of the J School described how this was a GREAT time to be going into the journalism field and about all the job opportunities. In reality a study had just come out that found only 12% of journalism students ended up with a full time job in the journalism field within two years of graduating. Pretty tough odds. When I confronted the Department Chair on this after the session he shared that he told students whatever was necessary to keep them with a major in his department so his department would keep getting funded. I'm not going to say that your professors will lie to you – just please do the appropriate research.

Think Back to When You Were Young

No little kid ever says 'I want to be an Agriculture Major', they say, 'I want to be a farmer'. A more important comparison is that once you graduate that you get a job that you find enjoyable to do and financially rewarding. Think of the classes that you take in college as steps towards this long term goals – and your major as a major step, or group of steps. Remember that often the learning processes that you experience are often more important than the facts.

We have more information within this section on how to tie this thought process together – and how to get experience in different fields so you can see if you like that profession.

Resource Center
Helpful Research on Careers

Please remember that some websites may be more helpful to you than others. No single site will have all the answers, or even always correct answers, but visiting a variety of sites can lead you to the right decision. Please go to www.EmpoweringStudents.com for more helpful websites.

Here are some:
U.S. Department of Labor's Occupational Outlook Handbook. The best site for almost any type of career information.
http://www.bls.gov/ooh/

National Center for Education Statistics: Most Popular Majors
Insightful data about trends in types of college majors
http://nces.ed.gov/fastfacts/display.asp?id=37

National Center for Education Statistics: Employment Experiences of College Graduates. Detailed information about graduation and careers for Latinos, African Americans, Asian Americans, and others.
http://nces.ed.gov/fastfacts/display.asp?id=561

Work Study information
http://studentaid.ed.gov/types/work-study

The Congressional Hispanic Caucus Institute's Internship Directory
A well organized site with dozens of meaningful internships.
http://www.chci.org/education_center/page/6th-edition-national-directory-of-scholarships-internships-and-fellowships-for-latino-youth

Internships sources & information. Database of thousand of internships
http://www.internships.com/

Career Studies
These studies are available on the enclosed CD and on the www.EmpoweringStudents.com; plus more studies are available on ES+, where you can find 336 additional pages of information:

- Fields of Bachelor Degrees in the USA, Census Bureau
- Help wanted study, Georgetown University
- K-12 Teaching Experiences of 2007-08 Bachelor's Degree Recipients, NCES
- The Condition of College and Career Readiness 2011, ACT
- The Top 25 Colleges for Latinos in the STEM Fields, 2010
- What a College Education is Worth, Census Bureau

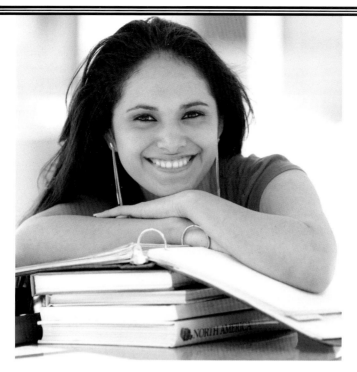

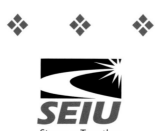

THE PERFECT WEBSITE FOR ALL CAREERS

The U.S. Department of Labor for years produced a wonderful book that almost no one knew about. The biggest drawback with the book was it's massive size of over a thousand pages in a large format. After more than a decade of transitioning and vastly expanding the information to a website they have created a totally amazing site that should be widely used from high school on up. We strongly recommend *The Occupational Outlook Handbook* to anyone who wants to finds the career that's the best fit for them. From the home page, www.bls.gov/ooh/, it all starts with 25 Occupational Groups:

- Architecture and Engineering
- Arts and Design
- Building and Grounds Cleaning
- Community and Social Service
- Computer & Information Technology
- Construction and Extraction
- Education, Training, and Library
- Entertainment and Sports
- Farming, Fishing, and Forestry
- Food Preparation and Serving
- Healthcare
- Installation, Maintenance, & Repair
- Legal
- Life, Physical, and Social Science
- Management
- Math
- Media and Communication
- Military
- Office and Administrative Support
- Personal Care and Service
- Production
- Protective Service
- Sales
- Transportation & Material Moving

Under these headings are hundreds of very detailed profiles of individuals professions. For instance under *healthcare* alone there's 44 career categories. For each of these careers there's highly professional data by:

- **Summary**: a great overview of this career (see sample, page 53).
- **What They Do**: Duties that are carried out by these professionals
- **Work Environment**: Work setting, work schedules, full time vs. part time, staff vs contract positions.
- **How to Become One**: What's needed: Education, Licenses, Certifications and more. Great insights in a readable format and links to more info.
- **Pay**: Not merely the average salary, but ranges by different qualifications and experience.
- **Job Outlook**: This is key since no one wants to spend years training for a job in a career with few openings. Shares employment trends over a ten year period.
- **Similar Occupations**: Helpful chart plotting similar occupations. This is GREAT for seeing other jobs that might be the one for you in the long run.
- **Contacts for More Info**: This is the jumping point for lots more information and organizations you should know about.

Additionally, you will find a list that looks to include a thousand or more occupations, as well as where to get more information about them, at www.bls.gov/ooh/a-z-index.htm#A.

I've chosen to highlight the summary page from the handbook for Kindergarten and Elementary School Teachers because I strongly feel there is a HUGE need for more Latinos to enter this profession. I come from a family where EVERYONE was a teacher, principal, professor, etc. My wife, Magdalena, teaches first grade at a school where over 70% of the students are Latino and yet only about 15% of the teachers are. Nationwide 23% of all children in K-12 schools are Latino – and yet only 7% of the teachers are. These kids need to have Latino role models – and their parents, who often prefer to speak in Spanish, need teachers they can talk with. Over the next ten years 281,500 new teachers will be hired. Think about this career, you might find it rewarding.

Some additional reasons that this is a great site:
• Numerous resources for additional information about careers in that field.
• The information is so detailed it doesn't merely have nursing as a profession, which ones need just an AA degree to those that needs a bachelors degree to nursing careers that needs an advanced degree.
• Another plus is that the site has hundreds if not thousands of pages of information in Spanish.
• In total there's tens of thousands of pages of information about hundreds of careers.

To illustrate the power of this site, there are at least half a dozen career oriented books where the majority of their information came from this site. Save money – and get more timely information – by using this excellent web site.

Now that everything is online, keep checking back as they continue to add exciting new features. And accessing the website is much easier than carrying around that heavy old book.

By Kirk Whisler

UNITED STATES DEPARTMENT OF LABOR

A to Z Index | FAQs | About BLS | Contact Us | Subscribe to E-mail Updates GO

Follow Us | What's New | Release Calendar | Site Map

BUREAU OF LABOR STATISTICS

Search BLS.gov

Home ▾ Subject Areas ▾ Databases & Tools ▾ Publications ▾ Economic Releases ▾ Beta ▾

OOH HOME | OCCUPATION FINDER | OOH FAQ | OOH GLOSSARY | A-Z INDEX | OOH SITE MAP | EN ESPAÑOL

OCCUPATIONAL OUTLOOK HANDBOOK

Search Handbook Go

Education, Training, and Library >

Kindergarten and Elementary School Teachers

FONT SIZE: ⊟ ⊞ PRINTER-FRIENDLY

Summary | What They Do | Work Environment | How to Become One | Pay | Job Outlook | Similar Occupations | Contacts for More Info

Summary

Quick Facts: Kindergarten and Elementary School Teachers	
2010 Median Pay	$51,380 per year
Entry-Level Education	Bachelor's degree
Work Experience in a Related Occupation	None
On-the-job Training	Internship/residency
Number of Jobs, 2010	1,655,800
Job Outlook, 2010-20	17% (About as fast as average)
Employment Change, 2010-20	281,500

Kindergarten and elementary school teachers teach basic subjects, such as math and reading.

What Kindergarten and Elementary School Teachers Do

Kindergarten and elementary school teachers prepare younger students for future schooling by teaching them the basics of subjects such as math and reading.

Work Environment

Kindergarten and elementary school teachers work in public and private schools. They generally work school hours when students are present, and use nights and weekends to prepare lessons and grade papers. Most kindergarten and elementary school teachers do not work during the summer.

How to Become a Kindergarten or Elementary School Teacher

Kindergarten and elementary school teachers must have at least a bachelor's degree. In addition, public school teachers must have a state-issued certification or license.

Pay

In May 2010, the median annual wage of kindergarten teachers was $48,800 and the median annual wage of elementary school teachers was $51,660.

Job Outlook

Employment of kindergarten and elementary school teachers is expected to grow by 17 percent from 2010 to 2020, about as fast as the average for all occupations. Growth is expected because of both declines in student–teacher ratios and increases in enrollment. However, employment growth will vary by region.

Resource Center
A Book That Makes a Difference

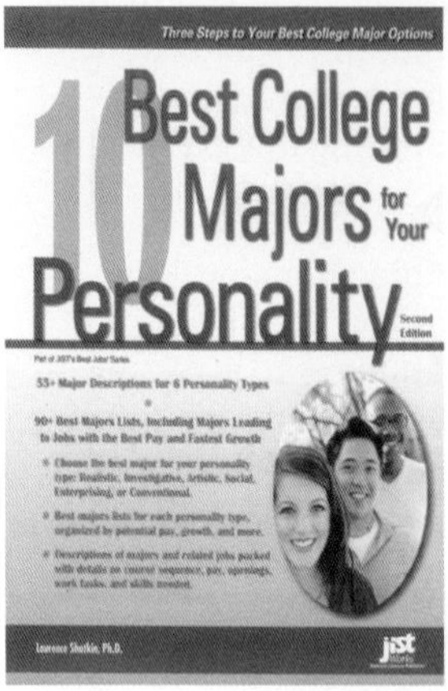

10 Best College Majors for Your Personality, by Laurence Shatkin, Ph.D., takes a unique approach to choosing a major. Dr. Shatkin has 30 years experience in the career information field and has a uthored many career and education books, including *50 Best Jobs for Your Personality* and *Panicked Student's Guide to Choosing a College Major*.

Insights
"Become a Teacher"

"If you want a guarantee that you'll make a difference every day – become a teacher."

President Barack Obama,
April, 2012 at the White House.

In Part I, you'll learn about personality types and how they relate to college majors.

In Part II, you'll take a short easy-to-complete assessment designed to help you discover your personality type: Realistic, Investigative, Artistic, Social, Enterprising or Conventional.

In Part III, you'll browse over 90 Best Major Lists to find the major best suited for your personality.

The major lists are arranged into groups beginning with the 10 best majors for each personality type. Other lists rank majors by earning and job-growth potential. More specialized lists rank majors related to jobs by education level, worker demographics, and jobs requiring verbal and math skills, among other things.
Finally, in Part IV, the author provides over 55 major descriptions giving insight into what courses to expect, specializations to choose from, potential job openings and pay. This unique approach takes the guess work out of choosing a major and turns it into a science.

by Annie Perez

Six Ways Internships Provide Insights

I'm a huge believer in internships and feel they should be widely offered at all levels from Junior year in High School on up. Over the years I've had over a hundred interns work for people within my staff or myself. We've hired many into full time or part time jobs. These interns learned a lot about publishing and at the same time we got a good look at their skills and interests.

While I was publisher of Nevada Magazine from 1986 to 1992 we had a number of interns from both the University of Nevada and from a local high school. All but one of these was a very positive story. A young lady was working in our Editorial Department and after she'd been there about two months I could tell she was not happy. I brought her into my office and asked what was wrong. She shared that all of her life she'd wanted to be a journalist and she was graduating this semester with a degree in journalism. This was the FIRST TIME she'd ever worked as a journalist and she could tell it was much different than the movies (*All the President's Men* was big at that time) and she didn't know what to tell her parents who had funded her education. While I couldn't solve this young lady's problem, this situation forever opened my eyes up more to the need to do internships EARLY and OFTEN.

Ways internships provide insights:

1. **To get hired into a career**. Today rarely is anyone hired into a meaningful career without meaningful experience in that field. What's the best way to get that experience? Through internships.
2. **Learn from fellow workers**. You learn from your fellow workers what they think about their career choice – and you hear both the positives and negatives.
3. **To gain current knowledge**. Your college professor may have worked in a particular field 10 or 20 years ago, but the business that you will have your internship at is in that field TODAY working with current technology and needs.
4. **To do better in your classes**. Often what you learn from internships will make coursework easier in your various classes. Once I started doing internships I could not believe how much easier all my college classes seemed to be.
5. **Unpaid internships lead to PAID internships**. The best way to get a paid internship is to do one or two unpaid internships first.
6. **MOST IMPORTANTLY: Finding the right Career**. In most cases a variety of internships will help you decide on what career you'll enjoy far better than any course you'll ever take.

Three phases of internships:

High School. Try doing one or two relatively brief internships in industries that you think you might want to eventually work in. Do not worry that they might be unpaid. You will most likely be working in a support position such as helping with mailings, copy work, basic data entry, etc. Keep your eyes open and be listening. What you learn here will help you decide if you like this profession – and how offices operate. One of my first internships was with a political campaign. I was silk screening posters, something my father had taught me when I ran for office in junior high. Where the silk screening was being done was right outside the office where the candidate had all his meetings. I got to hear everything that was going on while I did my work. I listened intently and went on from a very minor roll in that election to serve as staff or manage 24 different campaigns.

Your first two years of college. I know you will be busy with many other things your first few years of college, but please try to find time for at least one internship. Once again, don't worry if it isn't paid – all of this will pay off in the long run. As you get older and more experienced, you will start having employers in professions you might want to go into asking if you want a paid internship, a part time job, or a full time job for the summer. In most cases today you have to do unpaid internships before you are going to get paid ones.

The rest of college. If you have followed the two steps above you should now be able to get most of the internships that you really want. Look at it though the employers eyes: you now have a variety of office experiences at increasingly professional skill levels. This is what an employer wants for those meaningful paid internships and summer programs where you are working with trained professionals. You are now becoming a person that will get the internships you want – and in the future, the jobs you want.

Good luck with your internships.

by Kirk Whisler

Insights

"I Have A Family Background That Expected Me To Go To College"

"College changed my life by opening doors I never thought possible. I have a family background that expected me to go to college. While I was growing up on the reservation I never thought about going to college until I got there and started meeting new people that I'm still in contact today. Every child growing up on a reservation needs to see an off reservation university and what it can do for them, not only personally but professionally."

Clay Colombe,
Native American Bank,
Rosebud Sioux Tribe

SECTION FOUR
LATINO INSIGHTS

INSIGHTS

"I Became Motivated and Couldn't Wait to Go to School"

"Going to college totally changed my life. I didn't know what I wanted to do with my life or what to study. In a media buyers class I took I had a great teacher named Kathleen Haspel who exposed me to great publications like Mother Jones and The Nation. She challenged us on how this news coverage was different from what mainstream offered us. It was the first class that I truly loved – I was excited and couldn't wait to get to that class. I discovered the power of media to influence people. I became motivated and couldn't wait to go to school. The other thing about school is the friends you make who have similar interests to yours. I never thought I'd be interested in the media."

***Joseph Torres**,*
Government Relations Manager, Free Press

Latino USA

Growing Fast

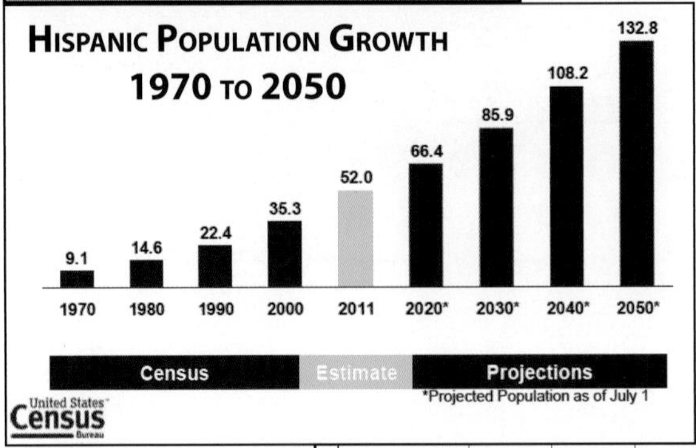

Hispanic Growth 1990 to 2050

	1990	2000	2010	2012	2017	2050	1990-2050 Change
Hispanic	22.6	35.3	50.8	54.8	66.5	132.8	488%
African American	30.6	35.7	40.4	41.4	44.2	65.7	115%
Asian American	7.5	11.1	15.9	17.2	20.8	40.6	441%
American Indian	2.1	2.7	3.8	4.0	4.9	8.6	310%
The Rest	186.8	196.6	198.4	201.3	197.6	191.3	2%
Total USA	249.6	281.4	309.3	315.9	334.0	439.0	76%
Hispanic %	9%	13%	16%	17%	20%	30%	

Population figures are in millions

SOURCE: U.S. Census Bureau, Seleg Center for Economic Growth & Latino Print Network

Country of Origin

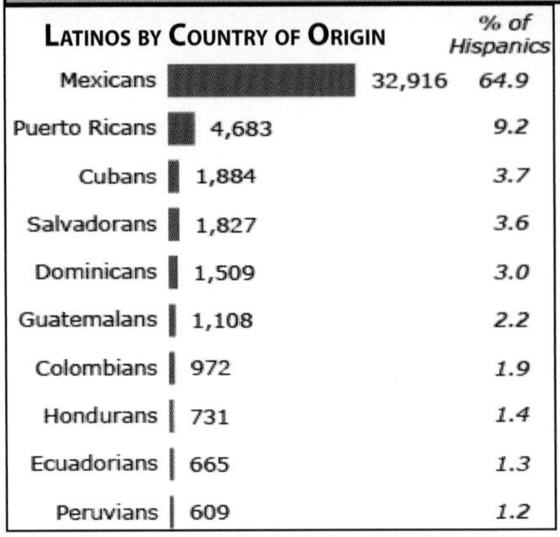

Pew Hispanic Center, The 10 Largest Hispanic Origin Groups Study, July 2012

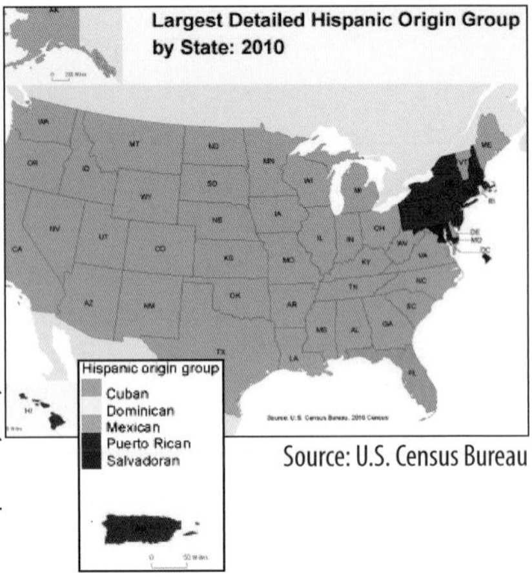

Source: U.S. Census Bureau

KEY MARKETS

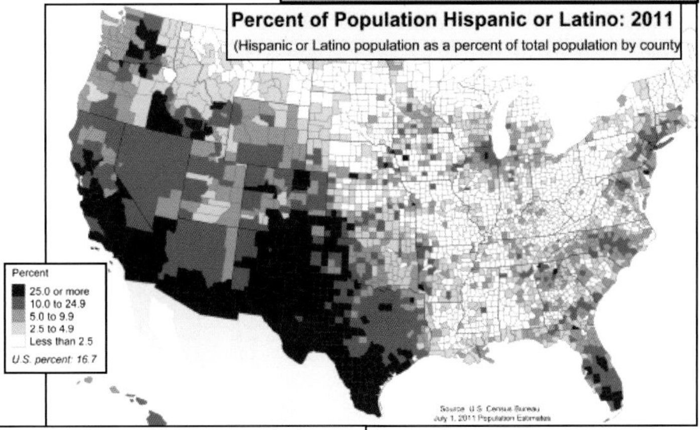

Source: U.S. Census Bureau

57% of all USA Latino Households use at least one Hispanic newspaper weekly

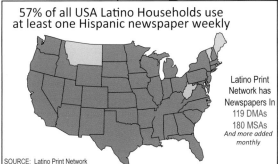

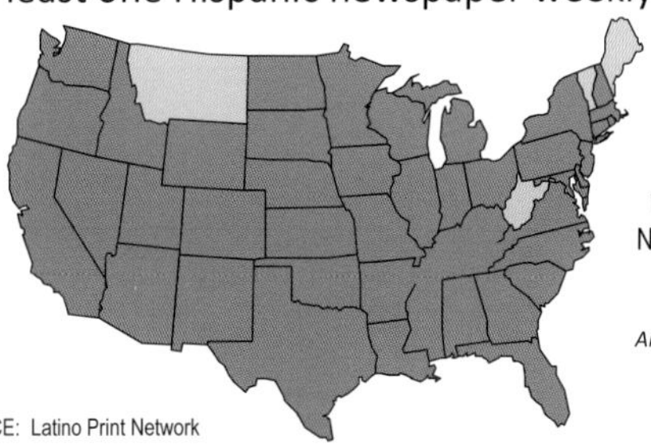

Latino Print Network has Newspapers In
119 DMAs
180 MSAs
And more added monthly

SOURCE: Latino Print Network

Hispanic Population Trends For the Top 20 DMAs in the USA

DMA: Designated Marketing Area	Hispanic Ranking			Hispanic Population			Growth	Hispanic % of Pop		
	2011	2000	1990	2011	2000	1990	90-10	2011	2000	1990
Los Angeles, CA	**1**	1	1	8,089,549	6,447,089	4,623,962	*75%*	46%	40%	32%
New York, NY-CT-NJ	**2**	2	2	4,562,986	3,750,460	2,724,521	*67%*	22%	19%	15%
Houston, TX	**3**	5	6	2,265,482	1,414,317	805,484	*181%*	35%	28%	20%
Miami-Ft. Lauderdale, FL	**4**	3	3	2,133,711	1,575,702	1,064,674	*100%*	48%	40%	33%
Dallas-Ft. Worth, TX	**5**	7	9	2,098,131	1,169,394	535,575	*292%*	28%	20%	12%
Chicago, IL-IN	**6**	4	5	2,048,440	1,498,457	873,729	*134%*	21%	16%	10%
San Francisco-Oakland-San Jose, CA	**7**	6	4	1,677,444	1,288,886	880,346	*91%*	23%	19%	15%
Phoenix, AZ	**8**	9	14	1,553,175	909,576	429,829	*261%*	30%	23%	16%
San Antonio, TX	**9**	8	7	1,355,196	1,032,035	795,760	*70%*	55%	51%	47%
Harlingen-Weslaco-Brownsville-McAllen, TX	**10**	10	8	1,142,940	856,541	593,896	*92%*	90%	88%	85%
Sacramento-Stockton-Modesto, CA	**11**	13	15	1,066,866	686,246	417,436	*156%*	26%	20%	15%
Fresno-Visalia, CA	**12**	12	13	1,034,175	743,129	470,252	*120%*	53%	45%	35%
San Diego, CA	**13**	11	10	995,127	750,896	498,330	*100%*	32%	27%	20%
Denver, CO	**14**	16	16	901,453	574,316	304,384	*196%*	22%	17%	12%
Washington, DC-MD-VA	**15**	18	19	815,253	441,782	225,837	*261%*	13%	8%	5%
El Paso, TX-NM	**16**	14	12	793,481	650,786	492,695	*61%*	79%	75%	67%
Albuquerque-Santa Fe, NM-AZ-CO	**17**	15	11	786,969	639,411	490,967	*60%*	41%	38%	35%
Philadelphia, PA-DE-NJ	**18**	17	17	743,601	468,251	275,893	*170%*	9%	6%	4%
Atlanta, GA-AL-NC	**19**	23	46	737,520	323,746	64,309	*1047%*	11%	6%	2%
Orlando-Daytona Beach-Melbourne, FL	**20**	22	27	709,826	342,070	133,309	*432%*	19%	12%	6%

Created by Latino Print Network © 2012 760-434-1223. Source: 1990, 2000, 2010 Censuses; American Marketscape DataStream 2011.

EDUCATION

Changes in the Characteristics of the U.S. Hispanic Population, by Origin, 2000 and 2010

	Median Age		Less than high school[1]		High school diploma only[1]		Bachelor's degree or more[1]		Proficient in English[2]		U.S. citizens[3]		Poverty[4]		Home-owners[5]	
	2000	2010	2000	2010	2000	2010	2000	2010	2000	2010	2000	2010	2000	2010	2000	2010
	(years)		*(%)*		*(%)*		*(%)*		*(%)*		*(%)*		*(%)*		*(%)*	
All Hispanics	25	27	48	38	22	26	10	13	59	65	71	74	23	25	46	46
Mexicans	24	25	54	43	21	26	7	9	57	64	68	73	23	27	48	50
Puerto Ricans	27	27	37	25	26	30	12	16	73	82	99	99	26	27	34	38
Cubans	40	40	37	24	20	29	21	24	54	58	73	74	14	18	58	57
Salvadorans	28	29	64	53	17	24	5	7	38	46	43	55	20	20	32	42
Dominicans	29	29	49	34	21	26	11	15	46	55	57	70	28	26	20	24
Guatemalans	27	27	61	54	17	22	7	8	36	41	38	49	22	26	27	30
Colombians	33	34	26	15	25	27	23	32	50	59	54	66	17	13	41	49
Hondurans	28	28	55	47	21	26	9	10	39	42	40	47	26	27	24	29
Ecuadorians	31	31	36	30	25	26	14	18	45	50	49	60	17	18	31	39
Peruvians	33	34	18	11	27	27	25	30	53	59	50	62	12	14	42	49

[1]Based on adults ages 25 and older. [2]Based on population ages 5 and older and includes those who speak only English at home or speak English very well. [3]Includes U.S. citizens by birth or naturalization. [4]Poverty status is determined for individuals in housing units and non-institutional group quarters. The poverty universe excludes children under age 15 who are not related to the householder, people living in institutional group quarters and people living in college dormitories or military barracks. For detailed information on how poverty status is determined, see http://usa.ipums.org/usa-action/variables/POVERTY#description_tab. Due to the way in which the IPUMS assigns poverty values, these data will differ from those that might be provided by the U.S. Census Bureau. [5]Includes household heads living in owner-occupied homes. The household population excludes persons living in institutions, group quarters, college dormitories and other group quarters.

Pew Hispanic Center, The 10 Largest Hispanic Origin Groups Study, July 2012

Share of U.S. Hispanic Population Ages 25 and Older with a Bachelor's Degree or More, by Origin, 2010

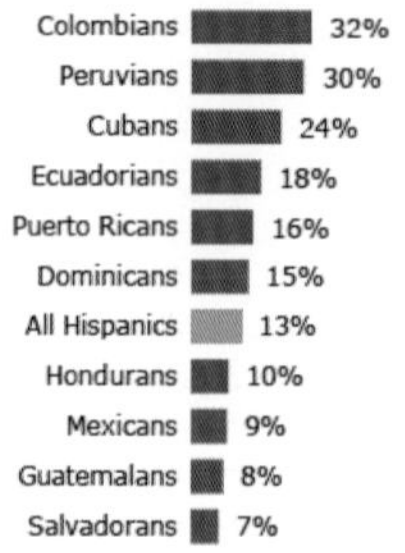

Note: Total U.S. share is 28%.

Pew Hispanic Center, The 10 Largest Hispanic Origin Groups Study, July 2012

Share of U.S. Hispanic Population Ages 25 and Older With Only a High School Diploma, by Origin, 2010

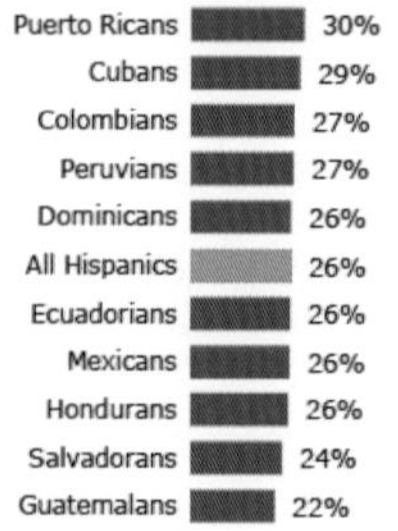

Note: Total U.S. share is 28%.

Pew Hispanic Center, The 10 Largest Hispanic Origin Groups Study, July 2012

LANGUAGE

Hispanics By Language Ability

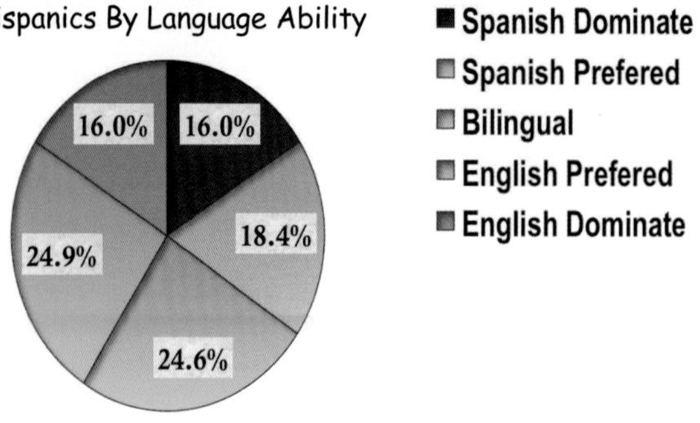

SOURCE: Latino Print Network 2011

BUYING POWER

	1990	2000	2010	2012	2017	1990-2017 Change
Hispanic	$210	$488	$1,014	$1,179	$1,677	699%
African American	$316	$600	$947	$1,038	$1,307	314%
Asian American	$115	$273	$609	$718	$1,023	790%
American Indian	$20	$40	$87	$103	$148	651%
The Rest	$3,579	$5,923	$8,507	$9,153	$10,929	205%
Total USA	$4,240	$7,324	$11,164	$12,191	$15,084	256%
Hispanic %	5%	7%	9%	10%	11%	

Dollar figures are in billions

SOURCE: U.S. Census Bureau, Seleg Center for Economic Growth & Latino Print Network

Median Household Income among U.S. Hispanic Population, by Origin, 2010

Pew Hispanic Center, The 10 Largest Hispanic Origin Groups Study, July 2012

FAMILIES

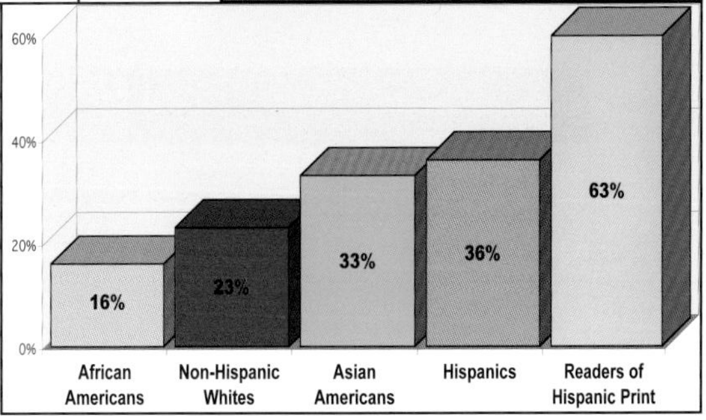

BUSINESSES

Hispanic Owned Businesses

	1997	2002	2007
Number of Businesses (in millions)	1.2	1.6	2.26
Change		33%	41%
Total Revenues (in billions)	$190.0	$222.0	$350.7
Change		17%	58%
Total Employees (in millions)	1	1.5	1.9
Change		50%	27%

Source: U.S. Census Bureau 1997, 2002 & 2007 surveys

FOREIGN BORN

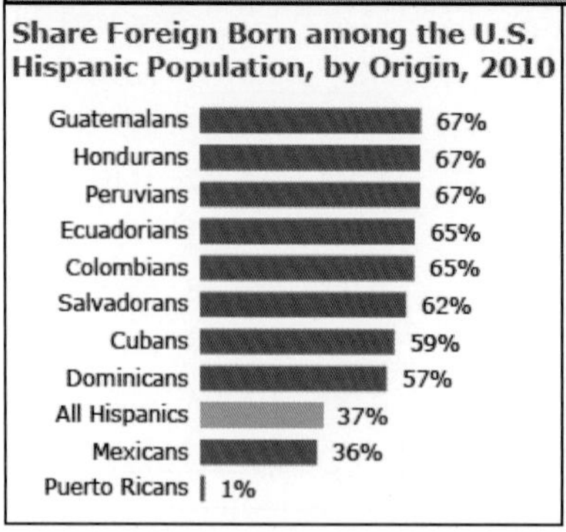

Pew Hispanic Center, The 10 Largest Hispanic Origin Groups Study, July 2012

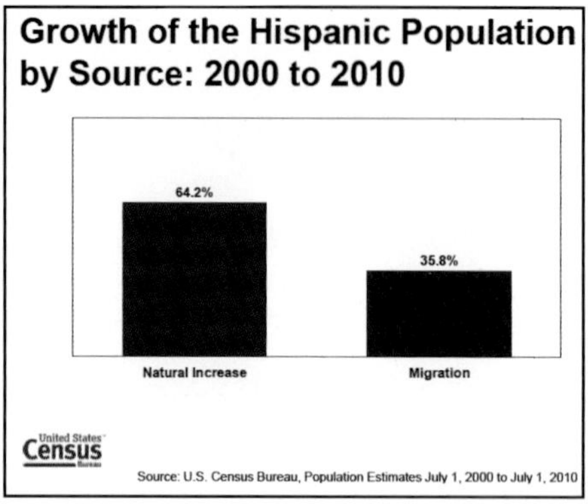

CITIZENSHIP

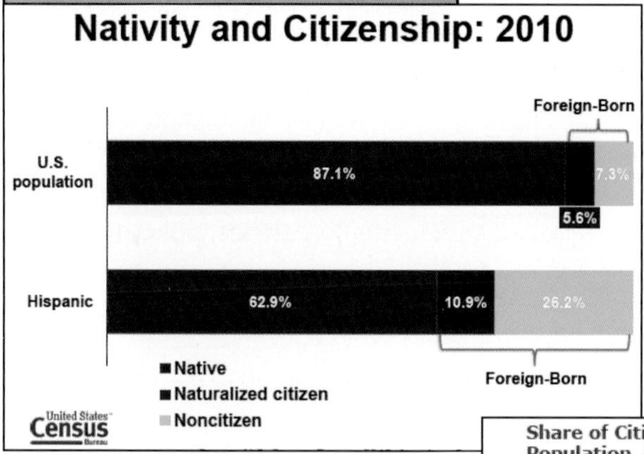

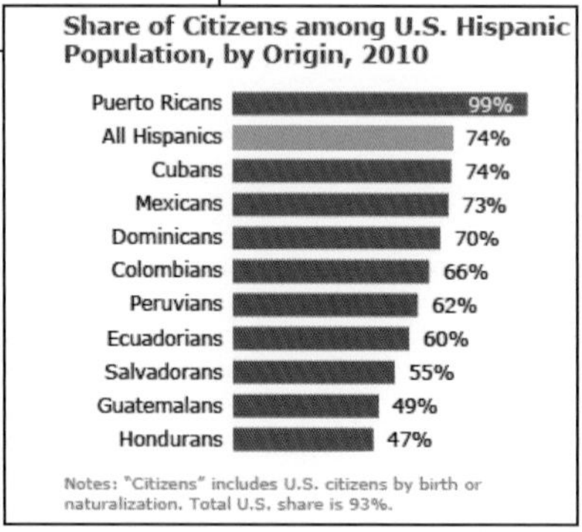

Pew Hispanic Center, The 10 Largest Hispanic Origin Groups Study, July 2012

HOMEOWNERS

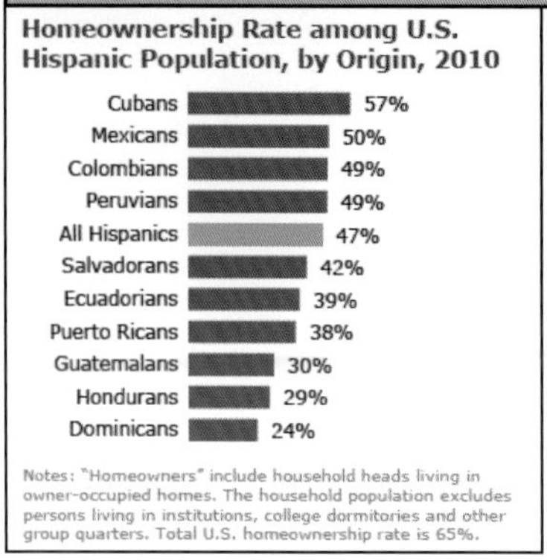

Pew Hispanic Center, The 10 Largest Hispanic Origin Groups Study, July 2012

GOVERNMENT OF THE DISTRICT OF COLUMBIA

Executive Office of the Mayor
Office on Latino Affairs

The Executive Office of the Mayor, Office on Latino Affairs (OLA), established in 1976, provides a wide range of vital support services to the Latino community of District of Columbia.

The mission of the Office on Latino Affairs is to improve the quality of life of the District's Latino residents by addressing a broad range of social and economic needs through strategic management of public and private partnerships, expertise on policy, community relations, civic engagement and community-based grants.

OLA employs the cooperation of District government agencies, policy makers, community organizations, the private sector, and others in order to empower the Latino community and build a stronger partnership for future growth.

We are proud to support the ***Latino and American Indian Scholarship Directory***. As the fastest growing minority group, our young generation of Latinos must be prepared to fill the ranks of the new and changing economy. This directory serves to connect the next generation of leaders to financial resources so that they may achieve their academic potential.

For more information visit us at www.ola.dc.gov
Office on Latino Affairs (OLA)
200 14th Street N.W., |Suite 206
Washington DC 20009

Phone| (202) 671-2825
Fax| (202) 672-4557
Web| www.ola.dc.gov

Follow Mayor OLA on Facebook and Twitter!

Follow OLA on Twitter at http://www.twitter.com/oladcgov
and on Facebook at http://www.facebook.com/olagovdc

The Hispanic Scholarship Fund Supports Latino Scholars

A College Degree in Every Household

by Katharine A. Diaz

Since 1975, the San Francisco–based Hispanic Scholarship Fund (HSF) has worked to fulfill a dream that in the future every Latino family will be able to boast at least one college graduate.

To date, the HSF has awarded more than $360 million in scholarships, representing more than 100,000 awards. It continues to build relationships with foundations and corporations, to educate parents and families about the importance of a higher education, and to reach out to students to help them secure the needed resources to pay for a college education. Most of its scholars are

Insights

"We Have a 100% Graduation Rate with Our Scholars"

"An education is a leveler of the playing field. It's the credentials to move ahead, not only in your capabilities, your knowledge, and your effectiveness; but also to have the credentials to be accepted in certain areas of our community and professions. Community College was extremely important to get me ready for a four year university, Cal State Los Angeles. We have 500 TELACU Scholars on an annual basis going to colleges across the USA. We set aside 20% of our net profit for that purpose. We believe in the importance of keeping our young people in school and giving them options in terms of various professions, concentrating on the STEM fields. We have a 100% graduation rate with our Scholars. We may be the largest Latino regional scholarship program, but we need many, many scholarship programs to help our young people. When have you educated too many? When have you prevented too many dropouts? There is a lot to do for a lot of us."

David Lizárraga, *CEO TELACU, one of the largest non-profits in the USA, and former USHCC Chair*

low income and are the first in their family to attend college.

Yet, the challenge remains great. According to the Center for Education Statistics, Latino students represent the second-largest, ethnic minority population in the United States but are less likely to enroll in colleges and universities compared with their non-Hispanic white counterparts. And their high school dropout rates remain considerably higher than for non-Hispanic whites.

Fortunately, the fund has seen a steady increase in scholarship funding despite the current economic climate. According to Cathy Makunga, vice president of Scholarship Programs for the HSF, "Shifting demographics tell us that if we don't support this group of students, we are going to be in trouble in the future. We have to pay more attention to this student population."

She points out that there is ever-increasing interest in funding scholarships in the areas of science, technology, engineering and mathematics (STEM). "We see more of an increase [in funding] in that area because of workforce development."

This clearly correlates to the fact that the great majority of scholarship funding comes from corporations that are clearly interested in building an educated and qualified workforce.

"We are always looking for new markets and partners," says Makunga, "but we are heavily focused on corporate funding. The majority of our funding comes from the corporate realm; as much as 80 percent."

Still, there are other markets that the HSF is trying to capture as potential funders. An important one is individual giving. "We are trying to evolve our alumni base and individual giving," explains Makunga. "We recognize that there is a need in cultivating that environment."

For 2011-12, 5,116 scholarships (out of more than 15,000 applications accepted for consideration) were awarded by the HSF to the tune of more than $33.6 million.

Latino students looking for college funding will appreciate the broad base of programs managed by the HSF. Makunga and her staff of 11 administer 150 HSF scholarship programs that include high school to college, community college transfer and college scholarship programs. Some programs award as few as two to three scholarships, others as many as 300.

INSIGHTS

"College Made My Dreams a Reality"

"College made my dreams a reality because I wanted to be a journalist and to be a journalist you need to go to college. I went to the University of Guayaquil in Ecuador and got my degree. The University at that time in Ecuador was free except for a small registration fee and for my books. It was a very good education."

Mary Andrade, *Award winning author and co-publisher of La Oferta.*

Funding partners include AT&T, Goya, Procter & Gamble, Staples, Toyota and many, many others.

In addition, she manages the HSF's major national core programs as well as such specialized, co-branded scholarships as the Gates Millennium Scholars Program (GMS). "This is the Cadillac of scholarships," explains Makunga. GMS scholarships guarantee a recipient five years of funding for their undergraduate studies. Then if they continue their post-graduate studies in STEM, education, public health or library studies, they can get continued funding to work toward masters' and doctoral degrees.

The HSF employs several strategies to reach students. It outreaches to former applicants and recipients and utilizes social media to network with students. There are also direct-marketing campaigns to target various groups, academic departments at colleges and universities, and other institutions. In addition, the fund hosts events throughout the year to build awareness of the scholarships.

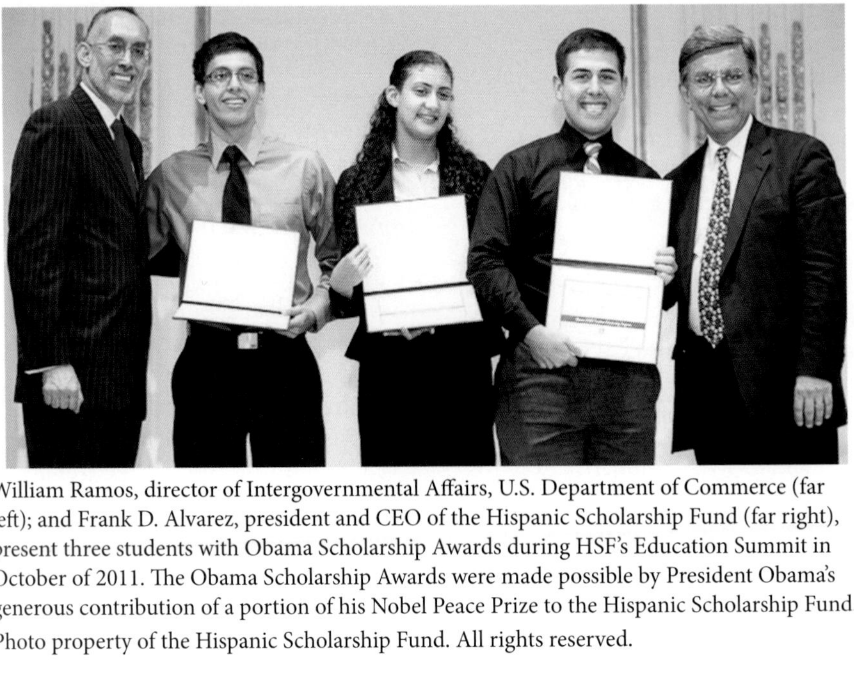

William Ramos, director of Intergovernmental Affairs, U.S. Department of Commerce (far left); and Frank D. Alvarez, president and CEO of the Hispanic Scholarship Fund (far right), present three students with Obama Scholarship Awards during HSF's Education Summit in October of 2011. The Obama Scholarship Awards were made possible by President Obama's generous contribution of a portion of his Nobel Peace Prize to the Hispanic Scholarship Fund.

Another important piece is outreach to parents and families. Makunga notes that it is very important to educate parents and families about what it means to send a child to college. "Too often the family has not been included in that conservation," emphasizes Makunga. They need to understand how important it is for their children to attend college, and to learn about available resources in order to spare them sticker shock.

HSF scholarships are available for a broad range of areas of study. Regardless, Makunga observes that there are a few general tips that can help you, an interested student, ensure that your application reaches reviewers.

You need to complete everything on the application and submit it by the deadline. You should try to make it clear what areas of study you are interested in. "Very few scholarships are open-ended," notes Makunga.

For example, even if you know you want to obtain a degree in business, if you can be more specific about where yours interests lie—such as in actuarial sciences or accounting—that might give you an edge over other applicants.

Finally, you should look at those areas of study or professions where there is a deficit. If there is a lack students studying engineering, then there might be more scholarships available in that field.

And, yes, grades do matter.

Students, to learn more about the HSF and its scholarships, visit its Web site at http://www.hsf.net. Pay close attention to the requirements to make sure the scholarship is a match to you and your interests. Is preference given to a specific area of study? Is enrollment in specific colleges or universities preferred? And pay close attention to deadlines, which vary. Remember, an incomplete application or a late one is not likely to reach a reviewer.

Parents can also learn about programs and events that are directed at them on the Web site. These include publications and workshops and seminars. Potential donors—whether individual, corporate or foundation—can learn all about the many ways to donate to the HSF.

Hispanic Scholarship Fund
1411 W. 190th Street, Ste. 325
Gardena, CA 90248
310-359-6042
www.hsf.net

INSIGHTS

"I Was One Step Closer To Having A Mind That Could Be Just As Free As My Spirit"

"I had to drop out of college four times because I didn't get any financial aid or enough scholarships. . . but when I finally got my diploma I felt so proud of myself. I had obtained something so valuable that no one could take away and I was one step closer to having a mind that could be just as free as my spirit."

Josefina Lopez, *Award winning playwright for "Real Women Have Curves"*

Resource Center
Latino Organizations

These are some of the key national Latino organizations. For more, go to www.EmpoweringStudents.com.

AAHHE, American Association of Hispanics in Higher Education,
www.aahhe.org
ALAS, Association of Latino Administrators & Superintendents
www.alasedu.net
CABE, California Association for Bilingual Education
www.bilingualeducation.org
HACU, Hispanic Association of Colleges & Universities
www.hacu.net
Latino Literacy Now
www.LBFF.us
PIQE, Parent Institute for Quality Education
www.piqe.org
USHLI, United States Hispanic Leadership Institute
www.USHLI.org

Other Key Latino Organizations
American GI Forum, civil rights
www.agifusa.org
ASPIRA Association, civil rights
www.aspira.org
AHAA, **Association of Hispanic Ad Agencies**, business trade
www.ahaa.org
ALPFA, **Association of Latino Professionals in Finance and Accounting**,
www.alpfa.org
CHCI, **Congressional Hispanic Caucus Institute**, political
www.chci.org
CHLI, **Congressional Hispanic Leadership Institute**, political
www.chli.org
Cuban American National Council
www.cnc.org
Dolores Huerta Foundation, community
www.DoloresHuerta.org
HACR, Hispanic Association on Corporate Responsibility, economic development
www.hacr.org
Hispanic National Bar Association, business/trade
www.HNBA.com
Las Comadres para Las Americas, women's issues
www.lascomadres.org
LULAC, League of United Latin American Citizens, civil rights
www.LULAC.org
MALDEF, Mexican American Legal Defense & Education Fund, legal
www.maldef.org
MANA, women's issues
www.hermana.org
MAOF, Mexican American Opportunity Foundation, community development
www.MAOF.org
MFHA, Multicultural Foodservice & Hospitality Association, business/trade
www.mfha.net
National Alliance for Hispanic Health,
www.hispanichealth.org
NAHP, National Association of Hispanic Publications, business/trade
www.NAHP.org
NAHREP, Nat'l Association of Hispanic Real Estate Professionals, business/trade
www.nahrep.org
NALAC, Nat'l Association of Latino Arts & Culture, cultural
www.nalac.org
NALEO, Nat'l Association of Latino Elected & Appointed Officials, political
www.naleo.org
NALIP, National Association of Latino Independent Producers, business/trade
www.NALIP.org

NCLR, National Council of La Raza, www.NCLR.org
NDAC, National Dominican American Roundtable, community development www.danr.org
NHLI, National Hispana Leadership Institute, women's issues www.NHLI.org
NHCC, Nat'l Hispanic Corporate Council, business/trade www.nhcchq.org
National Hispanic Cultural Center, www.nhccnm.org
National Puerto Rican Coalition www.bateylink.org
NSHMBA, Nat'l Society of Hispanic MBAs, business/trade www.nshmba.org
New Economics for Women, www.NewEconomicsforWomen.org
SER, Jobs for Progress, economic development www.ser-national.org
SHPE, Society of Hispanic Professional Engineers, business/trade www.shpe.org
SVREP, Southwest Voter Registration & Education Project, political www.svrep.org
TELACU, economic development www.TELACU.com
USHCC, United States Hispanic Chamber of Commerce, business/trade www.USHCC.org
Voto Latino, political www.votolatino.org

To have your organization considered for this list, please email kirk@whisler.com *and put ORGANIZATION in the subject box.*

Helpful Latino Websites

For the report ***College Knowledge What Latino Parents Need to Know and Why They Don't Know It***, Tomás Rivera Policy Institute: http://www.trpi.org/PDFs/College_Knowledge.pdf
The White House and the Hispanic Community: http://www.whitehouse.gov/hispanic
Congressional Hispanic Caucus Internship information: http://www.chci.org/education_center/page/6th-edition-national-directory-of-scholarships-internships-and-fellowships-for-latino-youth
Latino Book & Family Festivals: www.LBFF.us
LULAC's educational programs: http://lulac.org/programs/education/
MALDEF education information: http://maldef.org/education/index.html
NALIP serving the entertainment industry: www.NALIP.org
NCLR's educational programs: http://www.nclr.org/index.php/issues_and_programs/education/

Helpful Research: These studies are available on the enclosed CD and on www.EmpoweringStudents.com; plus more studies are available on ES+, where you can find 336 additional pages of information:

- Hispanic College Enrollment Spikes, PEW
- Hispanic data from the 2010 Census, U.S. Census Bureau
- Hispanic-Student-Enrollments-Reach-New-Highs-in-2011 Pew
- Hispanicity and Educational Inequality- Risks, Opportunities and the Nation's Future, ETS
- Hispanics in the USA, U.S. Census Bureau
- No dreamers left behind study, North American Integration and Development Center, UCLA

DREAM ACT INSIGHTS

Education Becoming a Reality for Undocumented Students.
The Dream Act, also known as the Development, Relief and Education of Alien Minors Act, was first introduced in Congress in 2001 to provide a pathway for undocumented youth to legally stay in the U.S., go to college, and ultimately gain legal status after fulfilling certain requirements such as attending college or enlisting in the U.S. Armed Forces. Supporters of the DREAM Act believe it is imperative not only to the individuals who would benefit from this important legislation, but also to the country, which would benefit in many ways, including economically. The Act offers an opportunity for undocumented students who have lived in the U.S. since they were children, to give back by utilizing their education and talents. Statistics from the National Immigration Law Center estimate approximately 65,000 undocumented students graduate from high school every year and this trend is expected to continue. If enacted by Congress, the DREAM Act would provide these young people the possibility of obtaining conditional permanent residency. Guidelines would be established that set out the path to qualify for conditional permanent residency under the DREAM Act. Two of the options under the DREAM Act guidelines would be to attend college or enlist in the U.S. military; fulfilling either of these requirements would eventually allow these young people to apply for U.S. citizenship.

What are the eligibility requirements under the proposed DREAM Act?
Individuals must have been 15 years old or younger when they entered the United States. If a student were 16 when he or she entered the United States, that student would not qualify under the DREAM Act. Individuals must have resided in the United States for at least five consecutive years prior to the passing of the DREAM Act. Individuals must have graduated from a U.S. high school, or have obtained a GED, or have been accepted into an institution of higher education, such as a college or university. Individuals must be between 12 and 35 years of age when they apply for conditional permanent residency. Individual must have demonstrated good moral character. What will be considered good moral character? While the DREAM Act does not specifically outline the guideline in regards to good moral character, it can be best described as a law-abiding person of the United States.

And if the DREAM Act passes?
If this immigration legislation is to become law, eligible, undocumented young men and women may apply for conditional permanent residency through the DREAM Act. Conditional Permanent Residency

is similar in some ways to Legal Permanent Residency in that you would be able to work, drive, and travel in the United States. Individuals would not be able to travel abroad for long periods of time for a period of six years.

What would it mean if Conditional Permanent Residency is approved under the proposed DREAM Act?
Individuals would need to enroll in an institution of higher learning in order to obtain a bachelor's degree or higher graduate degree, such as a Ph.D., M.D., etc.; or enlist in one of the branches of the U.S. Armed Services. Individuals will also be eligible for student loans and federal work-study programs. It is also important to note that within six years of being granted conditional permanent residency, the individual must complete at least two years of college or military service. If this requirement is not met, the individual will be disqualified from the process. Once five and a half years of the six years have passed, the individual can file for adjustment of status in order to remove the conditionality of their permanent residency. Eventually, the person can file for U.S. citizenship once all requirements are fulfilled.

Consideration of DACA (Deferred Action for Childhood Arrivals Process)
On June 15, 2012, the Secretary of Homeland Security announced that certain people who came to the United States as children and meet several key guidelines may request consideration of deferred action for a period of two years, subject to renewal, and would then be eligible for work authorization. Deferred action is a discretionary determination to defer removal action of an individual as an act of prosecutorial discretion. Deferred action does not provide an individual with lawful status. If you need further information and cannot find it on this Web page or in our Frequently Asked Questions, you may contact our National Customer Service Center at 1-800-375-5283.

Guidelines:
You may request consideration of deferred action for childhood arrivals if you:
1. Were under the age of 31 as of June 15, 2012;
2. Came to the United States before reaching your 16th birthday;
3. Have continuously resided in the United States since June 15, 2007, up to the present time;
4. Were physically present in the United States on June 15, 2012, and at the time of making your request for consideration of deferred action with USCIS;
5. Entered without inspection before June 15, 2012, or your lawful immigration status expired as of June 15, 2012;
6. Are currently in school, have graduated or obtained a certificate of completion from high school, have obtained a general education development (GED) certificate, or are an honorably discharged veteran of the Coast Guard or Armed Forces of the United States; and
7. Have not been convicted of a felony, significant misdemeanor, three or more other misdemeanors, and do not otherwise pose a threat to national security or public safety.

For additional information, go to U.S. CIS website at
http://www.uscis.gov/

HACU

Championing Hispanic Higher Education Success

The Hispanic Association of Colleges and Universities (HACU) has awarded more than $3.8 million in scholarships to students at HACU-member institutions in the United States and Puerto Rico since 1992. Students can find information on the HACU Scholarship Program in this directory or by visiting www.hacu.net.

Founded in 1986 with a charter membership of 18 colleges and universities, the Association now counts more than 400 institutions of higher learning among its members in ten countries.

In the beginning

The idea for the Hispanic Association of Colleges and Universities was born in late 1985. Dr. Antonio Rigual, then vice president for institutional advancement at Our Lady of the Lake University (OLLU) in San Antonio, Texas, and Sister Elizabeth Anne Sueltenfuss, OLLU president at the time, visited the Xerox Corporation headquarters to request support for the establishment of a "Center for Hispanic Higher Education."

After being referred to Gus Cardenas, Xerox national liaison for Hispanic affairs, and with the collaboration of others, the initial idea of forming an association of colleges and universities with high Hispanic enrollments took shape. In January 1986, a meeting of higher education administrators from various institutions took place to attempt to define the purpose of the unnamed association.

On May 23-24, 1986, HACU was formed at a meeting attended by representatives from 19 institutions in six states and five educational associations. Officers were elected for the Association, which became the first organization of colleges and universities committed to Hispanic education.

The newly-formed group established a set of bylaws and defined its mission to engage in activities that heightened the awareness among corporations, foundations, governmental agencies and individuals about the role that member colleges and universities play in educating the nation's Hispanic youth.

HACU Today

Today, HACU's more than 380 U.S. member institutions, although they represent less than 10% of all higher education institutions nationwide, are home to more than two-thirds of all Hispanic college students, enrolling a total 4.5 million students.

In 1992, HACU led the effort to convince Congress to formally recognize campuses with high Hispanic enrollment as federally-designated Hispanic-Serving Institutions (HSIs) and to begin targeting federal appropriations to those campuses. These institutions, defined (in part) by their minimum 25 percent Hispanic enrollment, educate half the Hispanics in higher education in the U.S. but are severely constrained by persisting underfunding.

Soon after, HACU and its allies were instrumental in convincing Congress to appropriate money specifically for HSIs. For the first time ever, HSIs were granted $12 million in 1995 from federal resources. Since then, funding has increased significantly because of HACU's persistent advocacy. In 2011, for example, $104.3 million were appropriated for the HSI undergraduate program under Title V of the Higher Education Act. HACU's efforts have led to over $2 billion being set aside for HSIs. See the accompanying chart for total appropriations for federal HSI programs to date.

HACU has launched an innovative effort to foster collaboration between HSIs and Hispanic-Serving School Districts (HSSDs). By 2011, 35 major K-12 school districts had become affiliated with HACU to this end. HACU was advocating with Congress for amendments to the Elementary and Secondary Education Act (ESEA) to incorporate a series of new interventions and authorized funding to support such collaboration. The aim is

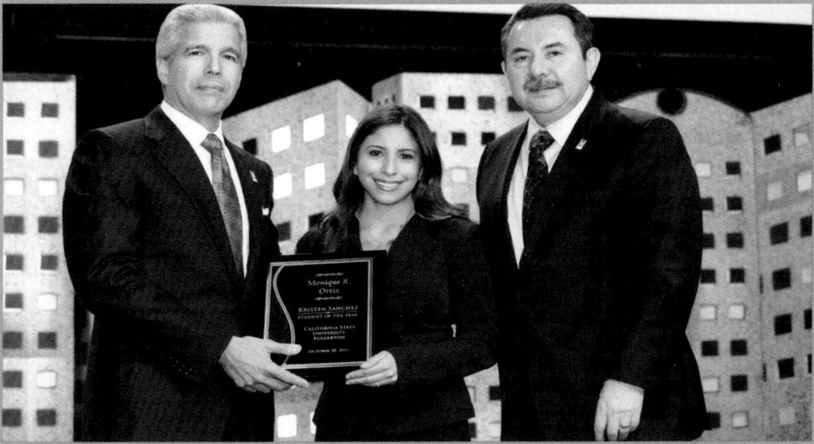

Monique R. Ortiz, a student at California State University-Fullerton, received the Kristin A. Sanchez Student of the Year award from Deloitte in 2011, along with a $10,000 scholarship. Presenting the award at HACU's 25th Annual Conference were Jorge Caballero of Deloitte (left) and HACU President and CEO Antonio R. Flores. (Photo courtesy of the Hispanic Association of Colleges and Universities)

to create a seamless pipeline for student success from kindergarten through graduate school. The proposed amendments include the creation of centers of excellence for teacher education, especially in STEM (science, technology, engineering and mathematics) fields, and for administrator leadership development at HSIs.

HACU's collaborative approach has produced more than 30 formal Memoranda of Understanding (MOUs) and Partnership Agreements with federal agencies, offices, and business organizations. HACU has also hosted technical assistance workshops for HSIs throughout the country on federal program grants and other resources available.

The HACU National Internship Program (HNIP), which in 2012 celebrates its 20th anniversary, has placed more than 9,500 student interns with corporations around the country or federal agencies in Washington or field offices. HNIP has been recognized by the federal Office of Personnel Management as a key strategy in increasing Hispanic employment in the federal government.

HACU also conducts policy analyses and research on issues affecting Hispanic higher educational success and HSIs. Through 2011, the association provided leadership with several ongoing grant-funded programs, including the Walmart MSI Student Success Project, the American Legacy Foundation's Tobacco Use Survey, and a productive National Umbrella Cooperative Agreement with the Office of Minority Health in the U.S. Department of Health and Human Services.

For students attending HACU-member institutions, HACU offers not only the HACU Scholarship program, but also study-abroad partnerships and other student programs. Thousands of young Hispanics benefit from HACU with internships, scholarships, college retention and advancement programs, pre-collegiate support, and career development opportunities and programs. Since 2005, Southwest Airlines has partnered with HACU to create the "Dándole Alas a Tu Éxito/Giving Flight to Your Success" travel award program which provides Southwest Airline tickets to students with socio-economic need who travel away from home to pursue higher education.

Each spring higher education administrators, students and supporters of Hispanic higher education gather in Washington, DC, for the annual National Capitol Forum on Hispanic Higher Education, to learn the

Insights

"It Made Me A New Person"

"Going to college and getting a college education changed my life. It introduced me to another world I would never would have access to. It made me a new person- one that allowed me to discover who I was, where I came from, and where I was going. It made an enormous difference in my life."

Jesus Nieto,
Ph.D.

latest in federal education policy and legislation and to visit their legislators on the Hill.

The annual conference in the fall is HACU's premier conference on Hispanic higher education, attracting approximately 1,500 participants, and designed to address the improvement of Hispanic higher education, to forge linkages between K-12 and higher education, and to explore international partnerships in education. Since 1998, HACU's annual conference has included a Student Track, a two-and-a-half-day career-development program for undergraduate students. The Student Track has provided participants with career advice on such topics as communications skills and interview techniques, resume-writing and networking, and federal and corporate career opportunities. Most students are supported either by their home institutions as Student Ambassadors or by federal or corporate sponsors as Student Conference Scholars.

HACU's biennial International Conference focuses on opportunities for cross-border educational collaborations, addressing the critical issues in international education.

Advocating for Hispanic higher education success for the fastest-growing and youngest population will be crucial over the next two and a half decades to ensure greater access and success in higher education, and to strengthen support for the colleges and universities where Latinos enroll. To regain the global lead in college degree attainment, Latinos must reach parity with the rest of America in degree completion. HACU will continue to advocate

The HACU National Internship Program has placed more than 9,500 student interns with federal agencies in Washington, D.C. and field offices throughout the country, as well as with corporations nationwide.
(Photo courtesy of the Hispanic Association of Colleges and Universities)

Federal Appropriations for Hispanic-Serving Institutions, 1995-2012

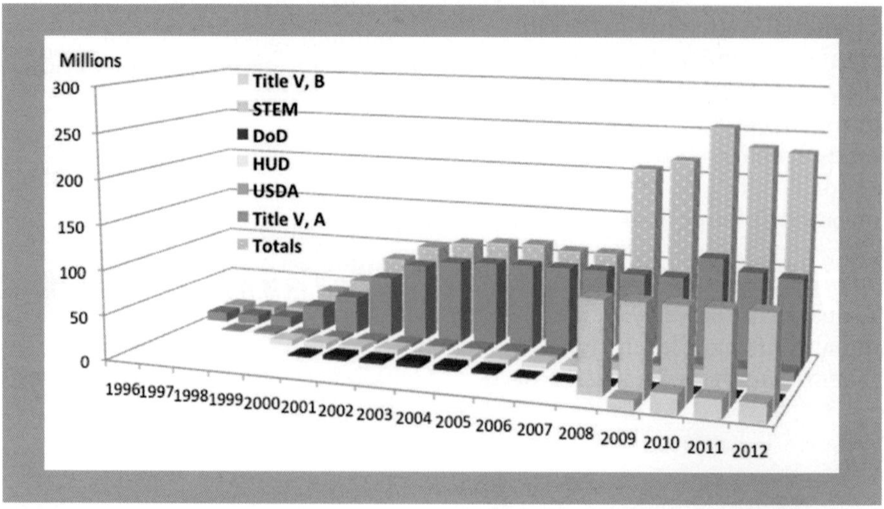

for HSIs, emerging HSIs, and Hispanic-Serving School Districts to be supported by all levels of government, the business community, and the philanthropic sector on par with the rest of higher education institutions and to fulfill its mission of "Championing Hispanic Success in Higher Education."

Since the first $12 million appropriation in Fiscal Year 1995 for HSI capacity building, HACU and its allies in Congress have been able to add U.S. Department of Agriculture (USDA) funding in Fiscal Year 1997 and more than double Title V funding in Fiscal Year 1999. Since then, other packets of federal funding have been created by Congress for some fiscal years including the U.S. Department of Housing and Urban Development (HUD) and the Department of Defense (DoD), for example. The College Cost Reduction and Access Act (CCRAA) legislation in 2008 added $100 million for STEM degree completion through articulation programs between HSI community colleges and 4-year degree institutions; this funding is committed at $100 million per year through 2019-20 fiscal year, which represents a cumulative investment in STEM Hispanic higher education of $1.2 billion over a period of 12 years. The combined grand total of federal funding granted to HSIs since 1995-96 fiscal year to date is more than $2 billion without counting the $800 million mandated through 2019 for STEM education. HACU and its supporters continue to advocate for increased investment in Hispanic-Serving Institutions.

HACU

HISPANIC ASSOCIATION OF COLLEGES & UNIVERSITIES

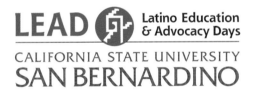

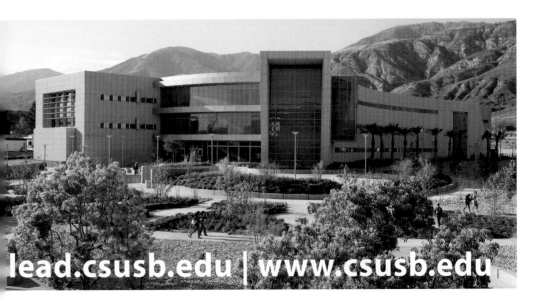

Section Five
American Indian Insights

Insights

"We Need to Be Smart Business Owners"

"When I was in high school I didn't know what types of career paths were available for me, as a Navajo woman. All of my family members were tradesmen doing everything from carpentry to plumbing to painters. In my childhood they all said don't go into construction. I looked at every other path from architecture to aerospace, but 10 years later I'm in construction management – and I love it. It has enabled me to work with tribal communities. We try to expose students who are considering trade school careers to reroute them into construction management. We need to build our own Native American construction businesses, to build our own housing, casinos, hotels and shopping centers. We need to be smart business owners. Going to college has really helped me by meeting the right people who have motivated me."

Kammy Harding,
Alternative Energy & Federal Projects, Kitchell Contractors, Navajo

American Indian USA

Growing Fast

American Indian Growth 1990 to 2050

	1990	2000	2010	2012	2017	2050	1990-2050 Change
Hispanic	22.6	35.3	50.8	54.8	66.5	132.8	488%
African American	30.6	35.7	40.4	41.4	44.2	65.7	115%
Asian American	7.5	11.1	15.9	17.2	20.8	40.6	441%
American Indian	2.1	2.7	3.8	4.0	4.9	8.6	310%
The Rest	186.8	196.6	198.4	201.3	197.6	191.3	2%
Total USA	249.6	281.4	309.3	315.9	334.0	439.0	76%
Hispanic %	9%	13%	16%	17%	20%	30%	

Population figures are in millions

SOURCE: U.S. Census Bureau, Seleg Center for Economic Growth & Latino Print Network

American Indian and Alaska Native Population: 2000 and 2010
(For information on confidentiality protection, nonsampling error, and definitions, see *www.census.gov/prod/cen2010/doc/pl94-171.pdf*)

Race	2000		2010		Change, 2000 to 2010	
	Number	Percentage of total population	Number	Percentage of total population	Number	Percent
Total population	281,421,906	100.0	308,745,538	100.0	27,323,632	9.7
American Indian and Alaska Native alone or in combination	4,119,301	1.5	5,220,579	1.7	1,101,278	26.7
American Indian and Alaska Native alone	2,475,956	0.9	2,932,248	0.9	456,292	18.4
American Indian and Alaska Native in combination	1,643,345	0.6	2,288,331	0.7	644,986	39.2
American Indian and Alaska Native; White	1,082,683	0.4	1,432,309	0.5	349,626	32.3
American Indian and Alaska Native; Black or African American	182,494	0.1	269,421	0.1	86,927	47.6
American Indian and Alaska Native; White; Black or African American	112,207	–	230,848	0.1	118,641	105.7
American Indian and Alaska Native; Some Other Race	93,842	–	115,752	–	21,910	23.3
American Indian and Alaska Native; Asian	52,429	–	58,829	–	6,400	12.2
All other combinations including American Indian and Alaska Native	119,690	–	181,172	0.1	61,482	51.4

Source: U.S. Census Bureau

Tribes

There are currently 566 federally recognized tribes in the USA. Source: BIA

Percentage Distribution of the Largest American Indian Tribal Groupings by Response Type: 2010
(For information on confidentiality protection, nonsampling error, and definitions, see *www.census.gov/prod/cen2010/doc/sf1.pdf*)

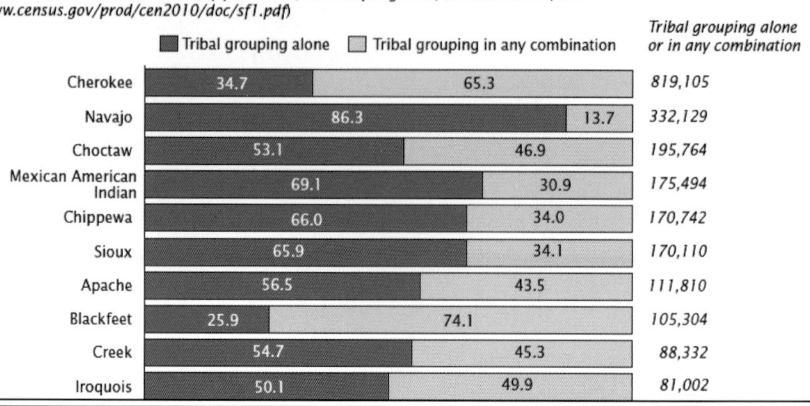

KEY MARKETS

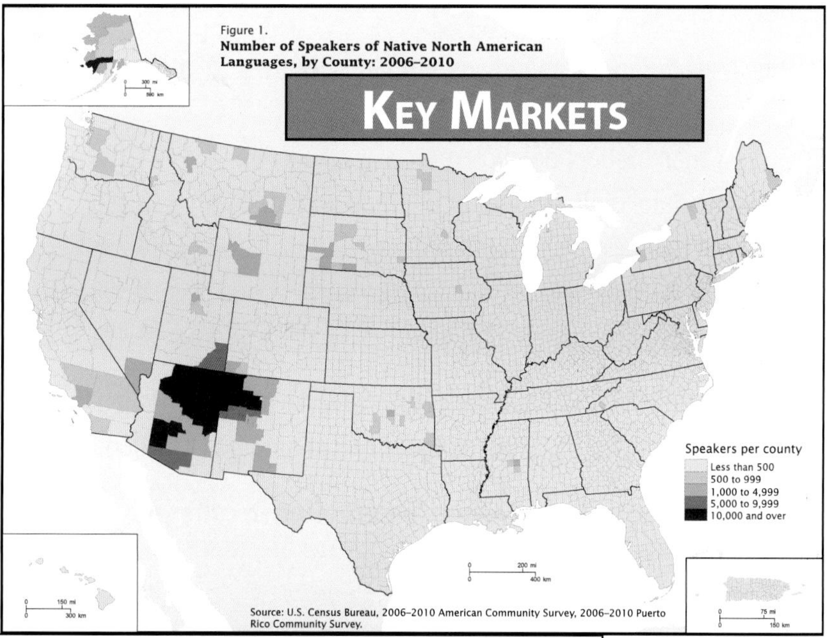

Percentage Distribution of the American Indian and Alaska Native Population by Region: 2000 and 2010

(For information on confidentiality protection, nonsampling error, and definitions, see *www.census.gov/prod/cen2010/doc/pl94-171.pdf*)

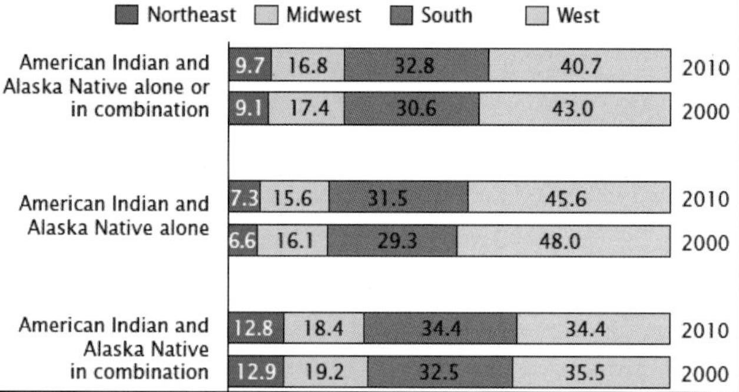

Place	Total population	Alone or in combination	
		Rank	Number
New York, NY	8,175,133	1	111,749
Los Angeles, CA	3,792,621	2	54,236
Phoenix, AZ	1,445,632	3	43,724
Oklahoma City, OK	579,999	4	36,572
Anchorage, AK	291,826	5	36,062
Tulsa, OK	391,906	6	35,990
Albuquerque, NM	545,852	7	32,571
Chicago, IL	2,695,598	8	26,933
Houston, TX	2,099,451	9	25,521
San Antonio, TX	1,327,407	10	20,137
Tucson, AZ	520,116	11	19,903
Philadelphia, PA	1,526,006	13	17,495
San Diego, CA	1,307,402	12	17,865

EDUCATION

Education level for American Indians and Alaska Natives 25 and older in 2011:

• Less than high school diploma	21.1%
• High school diploma, GED or alternative credential	31.4%
• Some college or Associate's degree	34.2%
• Bachelor's degree	8.9%
• Graduate or professional degree	4.4%

In 1976 there were 76,100 American Indians/Alaska Natives enrolled in college and universities. By 2006 the number had grown to 181,000.

Percentage of youth 18 to 24 who are enrolled in college:

Asian Americans	60.1%
Whites (non-Hispanic)	44.7%
African American	37.1%
Hispanics	34.8%
American Indians/Alaska Natives	23.5%

Source: U.S. Department of Education

LANGUAGE

27% percent of American Indians and Alaska Natives alone 5 and older spoke a language other than English at home, compared with 20.8 percent for the nation as a whole. Source: 2011 American Community Survey

Language spoken	Estimate
All Native North American language speakers	**372,095**
Navajo	169,471
Yupik	18,950
Dakota	18,616
Apache	13,063
Keres	12,945
Cherokee	11,610
Choctaw	10,343
Zuni	9,686
Ojibwa	8,371
Pima	7,270
Inupik	7,203
Hopi	6,634
Tewa	5,176
Muskogee	5,064

Buying Power

American Indian Growth 1990 to 2050

	1990	2000	2010	2012	2017	1990-2017 Change
Hispanic	$210	$488	$1,014	$1,179	$1,677	699%
African American	$316	$600	$947	$1,038	$1,307	314%
Asian American	$115	$273	$609	$718	$1,023	790%
American Indian	$20	$40	$87	$103	$148	651%
The Rest	$3,579	$5,923	$8,507	$9,153	$10,929	205%
Total USA	$4,240	$7,324	$11,164	$12,191	$15,084	256%
American Indian %	0.45%	0.55%	0.77%	0.85%	0.98%	

Dollar figures are in billions

SOURCE: U.S. Census Bureau, Seleg Center for Economic Growth & Latino Print Network

Businesses

American Indian & Alaskan Native Owned Businesses

	1997	2002	2007
Number of Businesses (in thousands)	197.3	201.4	237.0
Change		2%	18%
Total Revenues (in billions)	$34.3	$26.9	$34.4
Change		-22%	28%
Total Employees (in millions)	298.7	191.3	184.4
Change		-36%	-4%

Source: U.S. Census Bureau 1997, 2002 & 2007 surveys

Homeowners

54% of American Indians and Alaska Natives own their own home. For the USA overall home ownership is 65%.

American Indian and Alaska Native Areas and Population Distribution Overlay : 2010

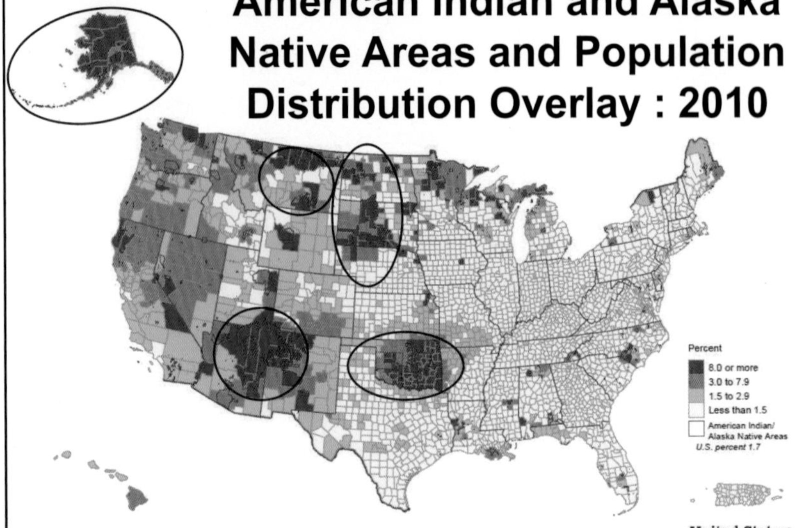

Note: AIAN refers to American Indian and Alaska Native.
Source: 2010 Census

21

American Indian Reservation	
Navajo Nation Reservation and Off-Reservation Trust Land, AZ–NM–UT	173,667
Pine Ridge Reservation, SD–NE	18,834
Fort Apache Reservation, AZ	13,409
Gila River Indian Reservation, AZ	11,712
Osage Reservation, OK	47,472
San Carlos Reservation, AZ	10,068
Rosebud Indian Reservation and Off-Reservation Trust Land, SD	10,869
Tohono O'odham Nation Reservation and Off-Reservation Trust Land, AZ	10,201
Blackfeet Indian Reservation and Off-Reservation Trust Land, MT	10,405
Flathead Reservation, MT	28,359
Alaska Native Village Statistical Area	
Knik Alaska Native village statistical area	65,768
Bethel Alaska Native village statistical area	6,080
Kenaitze Alaska Native village statistical area	32,902
Barrow Alaska Native village statistical area	4,212
Ketchikan Alaska Native village statistical area	12,742
Kotzebue Alaska Native village statistical area	3,201
Nome Alaska Native village statistical area	3,681
Chickaloon Alaska Native village statistical area	23,087
Dillingham Alaska Native village statistical area	2,378
Sitka Alaska Native village statistical area	4,480

coalición
RURAL
coalition

GET INVOLVED

34 Years **70 Organizations** **1 Voice**

Supporting Youth, Diverse, and New-Beginning Farmers and Ranchers succeed as Fair Food and Farm Policy Leaders across the Nation

FOR VOLUNTEER INTERNSHIP AND FELLOWSHIP OPPORTUNITIES

contact: angela@ruralco.org

http://twitter.com/RuralCo

http://www.youtube.com/RuralCoalition

http://Facebook.com/RuralCoalition

http://flickr.com/RuralCoalition

DONATE: http://ruralco.org

1029 Vermont Avenue, NW Suite 601, Washington, DC, 20005 Tel: (202) 628-7160

Educating the Mind and Spirit

The American Indian College Fund Makes a Difference for Native Scholars

By Katharine A. Díaz

Cherokee, Choctaw, Sioux, Navajo, Kiowa, Osage, Wampanoag . . . whatever their nation or tribe, American Indian students who want to go to college can rest assured that the American Indian College Fund (the Fund) has their back.

The Denver-based national scholarship fund is the largest, private provider of scholarships for American Indian students in the United States and supports the nation's 33 accredited, tribal colleges and universities (TCU's). The Fund was created in 1989 after tribal college presidents recognized the need to establish an organization to raise private-sector funds for these colleges serving Indian Country that receive little or no local or state tax support.

Insights

"Tribe Has Scholarships That Pay Everything for School"

"Going to college gave me the skill set and the knowledge to be able to help my tribe compete in the business world. In Native America, especially in the business arena, there's a lack of skills and knowledge. It hurts our tribes because our tribes rely so much on economic development and creating business enterprises to create jobs for. Our tribe has scholarships that pay everything for school and outside that I leveraged traditional financial aid products – loans, grants set up for any student. It was never a matter of funding – it was getting in there and applying myself, having the work ethic and the desire to get through college. While a lot of my tribe attempt to go to college, only about 3% get a bachelors and 0.3% get an advanced degree like a masters."

Kahseuss Jackson, *Economic Development Coordinator, Confederated Tribes of the Warm Springs Reservation of Oregon*

The American Indian College Fund's mission is to transform Indian higher education by funding and creating awareness of the tribal colleges and universities, and to offer students access to knowledge, skills and cultural values that enhance their communities and the country.
In addition to scholarships, the Fund also provides capital support to the TCU; funding for culture and language preservation; intellectual capital development at the TCU; culturally sensitive early childhood development programs; and leadership development for Native students.

But back to scholarships . . .

More than 83,000 scholarship awards have been made to Native students since the fund's founding. In 2010-11, the fund distributed close to $4.9 million in scholarships and program support, which directly translated into 6,410 awards to more than 3,500 scholarships recipients. For 2011-12, $5.6 million made it possible to support 4,218 scholarship recipients. According to Patrick McTee, director of Scholarships for the American Indian College Fund, there are two major scholarship programs—the Full Circle Scholarship program and the TCU Scholarship program.
The Full Circle program applies to students attending a public, private nonprofit, or tribal college. The TCU program is open to students who attend tribal colleges only. They are funded by the American Indian College Fund and awarded by the colleges.

To attract more dollars to the fund, McTee explains that a new public service announcement campaign

has been launched. Called "Help a Student Help a Tribe," the campaign

Insights

"That's Where You Decide Who You Want To Be in the Future"

"I funded college two ways: I had a scholarship through the American Indian Science & Engineering Society. I was a biology major when I entered college and wanted to go into the pre-dentistry track and be an orthodontist. The other half was paid through personal funds. I later switched over to being a communications major and that's how I ended up at the museum. Going to college was incredibly life changing because when you go to a large college like Penn State you're just a number to them. But as you delve into your major and classes get smaller and more personal, that's where you decide who you want to be in the future."

Leonda Levchuk,
Public Affairs Officer, National Museum of the American Indian, Navajo

One very happy graduate from the *Institute of American Indian Arts* received scholarship funding from the *American Indian College Fund.*

has been getting a lot of attention nationally. As with other scholarship funds, corporate, foundation and individual donations are sought. "We are tapping every source, but the biggest evolution is in the corporate world," says McTee. "Corporations are becoming more and more astute with their giving and couple it with their corporate efforts. It is more about recipients as a potential pool for internships and employees."

On the other hand, points out McTee, foundations want the scholarships to impact the geographic area they serve. They too are looking at the whole picture.

To date, corporate and foundation partners range from Allstate to the National Indian Gaming Association to Morgan Stanley and Wrigley and hundreds more.

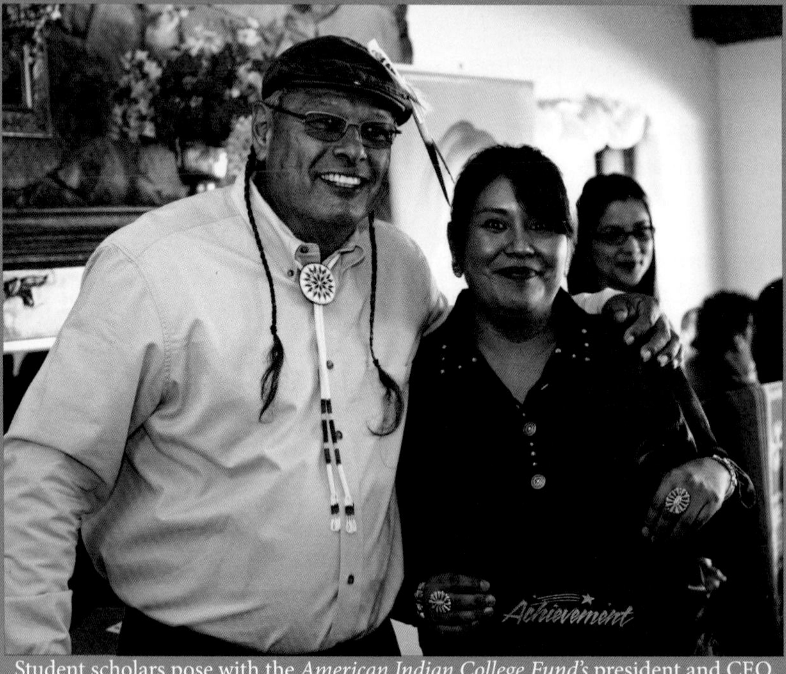

Student scholars pose with the *American Indian College Fund's* president and CEO, Richard B. Williams (Lakota/Northern Cheyenne) (left), at an awards banquet.

INSIGHTS

"It Was Hard, But the Results Were Worth It a Million Times Over"

"College got my life in order. It changed my life entirely. Teachers and coaches took time to help me. All I wanted to do was to be somebody and to make a difference in this world – and it took college for me to find that path. My tribe funded a little of my college expenses, but most came through student loans. My wife and I paid student loans until we were in our mid forties. It was hard, but the results were worth it a million times over. Through my efforts with my tribe, we created a priority with our education funds and with gaming dollars, now all tribal members can go to school up to $20,000 annually."

Ernest L. Stevens, Jr., *Chair, National Indian Gaming Association, Oneida Tribe of Indians of Wisconsin*

McTee and his scholarship team—four in the organization's 40+ staff of nonprofit professionals—are aggressive about reaching out to students to inform them about scholarship opportunities. "We visit high schools and tribal colleges," says McTee. "We do direct mail campaigns and hit Native American conferences, such as those of the American Indian Science and Engineering Society and National Indian Education Association, as well as state association conferences." His team also maintains an active profile on Facebook and YouTube and other social media.

Scholarships are offered in pretty much every field, including trade and technical fields, notes McTee. But the top fields are business, health-related fields (nursing, nutrition, dental, pre-medicine, etc.), sciences, engineering, mathematics, technology, liberal arts and education.

Interestingly, 1 in 5 American Indian College Fund scholarship recipients major in business or business-related fields; and according to a 2010 fund survey, 36 percent express interest in internships in the gaming and hospitality fields.

How competitive is the scholarship review process? According to McTee, for the Full Circle scholarships for 2011-12, approximately 2,000 applications were received for some 500 awards. As a result, it is very important that students take care with their applications.

So, if you are a student looking into scholarships, McTee shares these tips if you are applying for scholarships through the American Indian College Fund:

- Grades are important. The scholarships may be needs based, but good grades are a key factor.
- Show involvement in your community, your culture or tribe. This shows that you are interested in Native American culture.
- Pay particular attention to your essay. Write and rewrite it as many times as it takes to polish it.
- And, finally and most importantly, finish the application and send it in.

Interested students can visit the Fund's Web site at www.collegefund.org. Click on the "Student & Alumni" link and you will be where you need to be to learn about scholarship opportunities. Note that the Full Circle Scholarship applications are accepted from January 1 through May 31. The application period for TCU Scholarships varies. The fall semester application period starts on August 1, while the spring semester application period opens January 1.

In addition, you will find information on jobs and internships as well as a list of tribal colleges. Check out the "Resource" pages for excellent guides and handbooks and contacts for other organizations. You will also like the Fund's Facebook page created especially for students with the latest announcements about scholarships at facebook.com/nativescholars.

Overall, McTee is optimistic about the future. Corporations and foundations are increasing their giving. But the future looks particularly bright for Native scholars due to the Individual Indian Trust Settlement.

In December 2010, federal legislation provided $3.4 billion to settle the class-action lawsuit, Corbell v. Salazar, which was filed in 1996 by Elouise Corbell and others over the government's handling of Individual Indian Trust Accounts. It claimed that the federal government had cheated American Indian tribes for more than 100 years of royalties for oil, mineral and other leases. Although appeals have been filed, up to $60 million from the settlement have been designated to fund higher education scholarships for American Indian youth.

The American Indian College Fund will benefit from the settlement and, in fact, is one of the organizations being considered to administer the settlement funds set aside for these scholarships.

American Indian College Fund
8333 Greenwood Blvd.
Denver, Colorado 80221
800-776-3863
303-426-8900
www.collegefund.org

Insights

"I Struggled To Go To College"

"Most of my life I was a bookkeeper and secretary – I had to support my four sons. I struggled to go to college. I was able to go because of my tribal scholarships, but the biggest help I got was from our credit enterprise. One day I opened my mail and there was a check for $2,600. I was the only one that had applied. I just cried because I couldn't believe that I'd actually won something. I graduated from Heritage College, now Heritage University, with a BA in Business. I'm glad I had my education because it's allowed me to get the position of Treasurer for Legends Casino."

JoAnn Wahpat*,*
Yakama Nation,
Washington

Resource Center
American Indian Organizations

These are some of the key national American Indian organizations. For more, go to www.EmpoweringStudents.com

AIANTA, American Indian Alaska Native Tourism Association, business/trade
www.aianta.org
American Indian Film Festival, cultural
www.AIFISF.com
American Indian Graduate Center, educational
www.AIGCS.org
American Indian Higher Education Consortium, educational
www.aihec.org
Gathering of Nations Pow Wow, cultural
www.GatheringOfNations.com
Haskell Indian Nations University, educational
http://www.haskell.edu/
Nat'l Center for American Indian Enterprise Development, business
www.ncaied.org
National Congress of American Indians, civil rights
www.ncai.org
NIEA, National Indian Education Association, educational
www.niea.org
National Indian Gaming Association, business/trade
www.IndianGaming.org
National Tribal Environmental Council, business/trade
www.ntec.org
NACDC, Native American Community Development Corporation, business/trade
www.NACDC.org
NAJA, Native American Journalist Association, business/trade
www.naja.com
Smithsonian Nat'l Museum of the American Indian, cultural
www.AmericanIndian.si.com

To have your organization considered for this list, please email kirk@whisler.com *and put ORGANIZATION in the subject box.*

Fighting for Access and Equity

The National Indian Education Association Advocates for Educational Opportunities for Native Students

By Katharine A. Díaz

In 1970, the National Indian Education Association (NIEA) was incorporated. Since then, its goal has been to advance comprehensive educational opportunities for American Indians, Alaska Natives, and Native Hawaiians throughout the United States.

Through advocacy, research and capacity building, NIEA assists tribes and communities to control and choose excellent education for its Native students, promotes culturally based education that allows Native students to preserve languages and traditions of their tribes and nations, and expands equal educational opportunity for every Native student regardless of where they live.

Adrienne Tsikewa (Hopi, Tewa), a 2012 John C. Rouillard and Alice Tonemah Memorial Scholarship winner, is a master's degree student at the University of Oklahoma.

Recently, NIEA has met with success in various arenas:
- NIEA worked with the U.S. Department of Education on consulting tribal leaders and holding listening sessions with tribal communities across this country. The resulting report, Tribal Leaders Speak, was instrumental in articulating the educational needs of tribal communities.
- NIEA successfully advocated for President Obama to sign Executive Order 13592, which established a White House Initiative in support of American Indian and Alaska Native students, as well as for tribal colleges.
- Working with the U.S. Senate Committee on Indian Affairs

and with House members, NIEA is advocating for the passage of the Native CLASS Act, which offers opportunities for Native communities to choose education that best serves their children.
- Its new research efforts have helped federal agencies and education researchers learn more about the challenges faced by American Indian, Alaska Native, and Native Hawaiian students—and how to overcome them.

According to RiShawn Biddle, director of Communications for NIEA, the bottom line for the association is the education of Native students. While NIEA has always focused on K–12 education, it has recognized the need to address higher education too.

"If you can't graduate from high school, you can't go to college," notes Biddle. "And in this knowledge-based economy, students have to gain a college education in order to succeed. "[At NIEA] we believe in a cradle-to-career continuum," adds Biddle. That means also supporting Native students not only at the beginning of their college education, but through it and after it with access to scholarships, scholarship management, internships and career guidance.

Every year, NIEA awards John C. Rouillard and Alice Tonemah Memorial Scholarships to deserving full-time undergraduate, master's or doctoral Native students regardless of major. Awards range from $1,000–$2,000 and are supported by various sponsors. In 2012, two scholarships, funded by the Cherokee Nation, were awarded to students.

Jessica Vigil (Yakama Nation), a 2012 John C. Rouillard and Alice Tonemah Memorial Scholarship winner, is a graduate student at Eastern Washington University

The scholarships were initiated in the 1980's and two to three scholarships are awarded annually. Biddle notes that the scholarship is well known among the Native community and is marketed at the association's

Insights

"I Encourage Everyone To Go To College"

"Going to college gave me the ability to think. The most decisive thing in college was that I met my wife there and we've been married now 39 years. I encourage everyone to get a higher education. The biggest deal is that college gives you the ability to think though challenges and opportunities that life presents."

Joe Williams, Jr,
Commissioner, Tlingit-Haida Regional Housing Authority, The Saxman Village of the Chilkat Tribe in Southeast Alaska

Amanda Shirey (Cheyenne), a 2008 John C. Rouillard and Alice Tonemah Memorial Scholarship winner, attended Seninole State College.

conference and on its Web site. Applications are generally available in April and are due the beginning of August. "About 40 to 50 students apply each year," explains Biddle. To compete for scholarships, Biddle says the number one thing they look for is a student who is "at the very least dedicated to helping his or her Native community or other Native communities . . . to giving back. "We also try to reach people who are in need and are excellent. The 'more excellent' you are," states Biddle, "the more likely you are to receive funding." (For more John C. Rouillard and Alice Tonemah Memorial Scholarship information: http://www.niea.org/Scholarships/NIEA-Scholarships-and-Internships.aspx)

On its Web site, NIEA also posts information on other scholarships available to Native scholars. It also provides a listing of tribal colleges and universities and a listing of colleges that offer degrees in Native American Studies.
Biddle is aware that securing resources for a college education is always challenging and that institutions for higher learning are going through tremendous changes that impact Native students. That's why the NIEA is placing a "huge focus on ensuring that Native students gain access to higher education."

Still, there are reasons to be optimistic says Biddle. Executive Order 13592 will boost support of Native students and for tribal colleges. An example is recent accreditation of the Comanche Nation College, which is a big plus for the Native community. Tribes understand that college is important for their youth and there is a renewed focus on improving the college to career pipeline.

"Native students are not invisible," states Biddle. "NIEA constantly beats the drum to say that these are our students and they need access to high quality and [culturally based] education so that they can be leaders in the tribes and in this nation."
National Indian Education Association
110 Maryland Ave., NE, Suite 104
Washington, D.C. 20002
202-544-7290
www.niea.org

NATIONAL INDIAN EDUCATION ASSOCIATION
Advancing Excellence for Our Native Students

Resource Center
American Indian Research & Websites

These are some of the key national American Indian organizations. For more, go to www.EmpoweringStudents.com

AIANTA, American Indian Alaska Native Tourism Association, business/trade
www.aianta.org
American Indian Film Festival, cultural
www.AIFISF.com
American Indian Graduate Center, educational
www.AIGCS.org
American Indian Higher Education Consortium, educational
www.aihec.org
Gathering of Nations Pow Wow, cultural
www.GatheringOfNations.com
Haskell Indian Nations University, educational
http://www.haskell.edu/
Nat'l Center for American Indian Enterprise Development, business
www.ncaied.org
National Congress of American Indians, civil rights
www.ncai.org
NIEA, National Indian Education Association, educational
www.niea.org
National Indian Gaming Association, business/trade
www.IndianGaming.org
National Tribal Environmental Council, business/trade
www.ntec.org
NACDC, Native American Community Development Corporation, business/trade
www.NACDC.org
NAJA, Native American Journalist Association, business/trade
www.naja.com
Smithsonian Nat'l Museum of the American Indian, cultural
www.AmericanIndian.si.com

To have your organization considered for this list, please email kirk@whisler.com *and put ORGANIZATION in the subject box.*

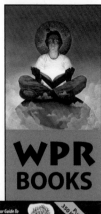

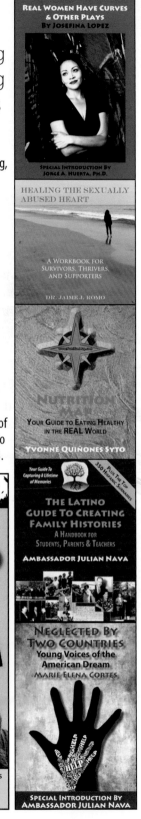

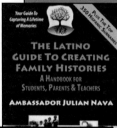

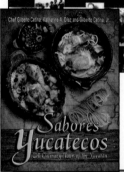

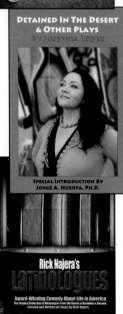

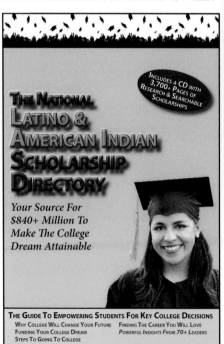

Section Six
Major Scholarships

No database is ever perfect and within hours of 'being updated' at least one of the records will have become outdated. We spent several thousand hours updating these records, but we want you to be aware that some of these records will have become outdated and some of these scholarships will no longer be available. We apologize in advance for any problems this might cause. For updates as they happen please go to www.EmpoweringStudents.com

Insights
"In College I Became Involved"

"College affected my life enormously. Before college in the community I was from everyone went into the Army and went off to fight in Viet Nam. My teachers raised some money to give me a scholarship and my folks changed my mind and I went to college. I was involved in politics to some degree in high school, but in college I really became involved. I became involved in the civil rights, anti-war, environmental, and farm worker movements. All of these types of causes. That dramatically changed my life. I always have advocated on behalf of the underserved. I'm still involved today with the Chamber in generating economic wealth for Latino owned businesses."

Jorge Corralejo, *CEO, Latino Business Chamber of Greater Los Angeles*

Major Scholarships

These 132 scholarship offer on average over $500,000 a year in scholarships.
For these & 1,770+ more searchable scholarships see the enclosed CD.

AAUW Educational Foundation Career

Organization	Foundation	Grant

Organization **Association of University Women Educational Foundation**
Department
Address 1111 16th St. NW
Washington State DC Zip code 20036

Websites — Where to apply: Online
Organization www.aauw.org
Scholarship

Annual Opportunities (estimated)

Scholarships Offered Annually	20-49
Average per Scholarship	$10,638

Field of Study: Various — Nontraditional fields

Target Audiences

									Tribe	X	Overall Diverse
Aimed At	X	Am. Indian	X	Latino	X	African Am	X	Asian Am	X	Women	X	Open to all
College Level		Pre College		1st Yr.		2nd Yr.		3rd Yr.		4th Yr.	X	Graduate Studies

Area Served: National
Citizenship requirements: U.S. Citizenship required

Basis For Award

							Extracurricular Activities
	Financial Need		Grades		Interviews		Community Involvement
	Essays		Minimum G.P.A.		SAT ACT		Letters of Recommendation

AAUW International Fellowship

Organization	Non-Profit	Fellowship

Organization **American Association of University Women (AAUW)**
Department AAUW Fellowships and Grants
Address P.O. Box 4030
Iowa City State IA Zip code 52243-4030

Websites — Where to apply: Online
Organization www.aauw.org
Scholarship www.aauw.org/learn/fellowships_grants/international.cfm

Annual Opportunities (estimated)

Scholarships Offered Annually	20-49
Average per Scholarship	$19,959

Field of Study: General — All Fields of Study.

Target Audiences

									Tribe		Overall Diverse
Aimed At		Am. Indian		Latino		African Am		Asian Am	X	Women		Open to all
College Level		Pre College		1st Yr.		2nd Yr.		3rd Yr.		4th Yr.		Graduate Studies

Area Served: International
Citizenship requirements: Non-citizens only

Basis For Award

							Extracurricular Activities
	Financial Need		Grades		Interviews		Community Involvement
	Essays		Minimum G.P.A.		SAT ACT		Letters of Recommendation

Academic Competitiveness Grants (ACG)

Organization | Government | Grant

Organization
Department U.S. Department of Education
Address 400 Maryland Avenue, SW
Washington State DC Zip code 20202

Websites Where to apply: Online

Organization www.ed.gov/
Scholarship www2.ed.gov/programs/smart/index.html

Annual Opportunities (estimated)

Scholarships Offered Annually: Over 1,000
Average per Scholarship: $1,000

Field of Study: Various — Major in physical, life or computer science, engineering, mathematics, technology, or a critical foreign

Target Audiences

					Tribe		Overall Diverse
Aimed At	Am. Indian	Latino	African Am	Asian Am	Women	X	Open to all
College Level	Pre College	X 1st Yr.	X 2nd Yr.	3rd Yr.	4th Yr.		Graduate Studies

Area Served: National
Citizenship requirements: Must be permanent resident or citizen

Basis For Award

			Extracurricular Activities
X Financial Need	X Grades	Interviews	Community Involvement
Essays	3.0 Minimum G.P.A.	SAT ACT	Letters of Recommendation

Academic Scholarship

Organization | College Program | Scholarship

Organization **Loyola Marymount University**
Department Financial Aid
Address Xavier Hall, One Lmu Drive, Ste. 200
Los Angeles State CA Zip code 90045

Websites Where to apply: Online

Organization
Scholarship www.lmu.edu/financialaid

Annual Opportunities (estimated)

Scholarships Offered Annually: Over 1,000
Average per Scholarship: $1,100

Field of Study: General — Open

Target Audiences

					Tribe		Overall Diverse
Aimed At	Am. Indian	Latino	African Am	Asian Am	Women	X	Open to all
College Level	Pre College	X 1st Yr.	X 2nd Yr.	X 3rd Yr.	X 4th Yr.		Graduate Studies

Area Served: Regional
Citizenship requirements: Must be permanent resident or citizen

Basis For Award

			X Extracurricular Activities
X Financial Need	X Grades	X Interviews	X Community Involvement
Essays	3.7 Minimum G.P.A.	X SAT ACT	X Letters of Recommendation

More scholarships are added every month: Go to ***www.EmpoweringStudents.com***

Achievement Awards

Organization	College Program	Award

Organization **University of Redlands**
Department Office of Admissions
Address 1200 E. Colton Ave.
Redlands State CA Zip code 92373

Websites — Where to apply: Online

Organization
Scholarship http://www.redlands.edu

Annual Opportunities (estimated)

Scholarships Offered Annually	500-999
Average per Scholarship	$7,000

Field of Study: General — All Fields of Study

Target Audiences

Aimed At	Am. Indian	Latino	African Am	Asian Am	Tribe / Women	X Overall Diverse / Open to all	
College Level	Pre College	X 1st Yr.	2nd Yr.	3rd Yr.	4th Yr.	Graduate Studies	

Area Served: Regional
Citizenship requirements: Must be permanent resident or citizen

Basis For Award

X Financial Need	X Grades	Interviews	X Extracurricular Activities
Essays	3.5 Minimum G.P.A.	X SAT ACT	Community Involvement
			X Letters of Recommendation

Air Force ROTC 4-Year Scholarship

Organization	Government	Scholarship

Organization **Air Force Reserve Officers Training Corps**
Department
Address HQ AFROTC, 551 East Maxwell Blvd.
Maxwell AFB State AL Zip code 36112-6106

Websites — Where to apply: Online

Organization
Scholarship http://afrotc.com/home.htm?flash=yes

Annual Opportunities (estimated)

Scholarships Offered Annually	500-999
Average per Scholarship	$14,000

Field of Study: Various

Target Audiences

Aimed At	Am. Indian	Latino	African Am	Asian Am	Tribe / Women	X Overall Diverse / Open to all
College Level	Pre College	X 1st Yr.	2nd Yr.	3rd Yr.	4th Yr.	Graduate Studies

Area Served: National
Citizenship requirements: U.S. Citizenship required

Basis For Award

Financial Need	X Grades	X Interviews	X Extracurricular Activities
Essays	Minimum G.P.A.	SAT ACT	Community Involvement
			Letters of Recommendation

America's Junior Miss Scholarship Program

Organization | Non-Profit | Scholarship

Organization **America's Junior Miss**
Department
Address P.O. Box 2786
Mobile State Al Zip code 36652

Websites | Where to apply: Online

Organization http://www.ajm.org
Scholarship

Annual Opportunities (estimated)

Scholarships Offered Annually	Over 1,000
Average per Scholarship	$1,000

Field of Study: GENERAL

Target Audiences

Tribe:

Aimed At		Am. Indian		Latino		African Am		Asian Am	X	Women		Overall Diverse / Open to all
College Level	X	Pre College		1st Yr.		2nd Yr.		3rd Yr.		4th Yr.		Graduate Studies

Area Served: National
Citizenship requirements:

Basis For Award

	Financial Need	X	Grades	X	Interviews	X	Extracurricular Activities
X	Essays		Minimum G.P.A.	X	SAT ACT	X	Community Involvement
						X	Letters of Recommendation

American Indian College Fund

Organization | Non-Profit | Scholarship

Organization **American Indian College Fund**
Department
Address 8333 Greenwood Blvd.
Denver State CO Zip code 80221

Websites | Where to apply: Online

Organization www.collegefund.org
Scholarship

Annual Opportunities (estimated)

Scholarships Offered Annually	Over 1,000
Average per Scholarship	$2,500

Field of Study: All Fields of Study — GENERAL

Target Audiences

Tribe: All tribes

Aimed At	X	Am. Indian		Latino		African Am		Asian Am		Women		Overall Diverse / Open to all
College Level		Pre College	X	1st Yr.	X	2nd Yr.	X	3rd Yr.	X	4th Yr.	X	Graduate Studies

Area Served: National
Citizenship requirements: U.S. Citizenship required

Basis For Award

X	Financial Need	X	Grades		Interviews		Extracurricular Activities
	Essays		Minimum G.P.A.		SAT ACT		Community Involvement
						X	Letters of Recommendation

MAJOR SCHOLARSHIPS

More scholarships are added every month: Go to ***www.EmpoweringStudents.com***

AMERICAN INDIAN SCHOLARSHIPS

ORGANIZATION | **GOVERNMENT** | **SCHOLARSHIP**

Organization
Department
Address 1776 D Street NW
Washington State DC Zip code 20006-5303

WEBSITES — Where to apply: By mail

Organization http://www.dar.org
Scholarship To assist Native American students

ANNUAL OPPORTUNITIES (ESTIMATED)

Scholarships Offered Annually	Over 1,000
Average per Scholarship	$1,000

FIELD OF STUDY: GENERAL

TARGET AUDIENCES

All tribes | Tribe

Aimed At	X	Am. Indian		Latino		African Am		Asian Am		Women	Overall Diverse / Open to all
College Level		Pre College	X	1st Yr.	X	2nd Yr.	X	3rd Yr.	X	4th Yr.	X Graduate Studies

Area Served: National
Citizenship requirements:

BASIS FOR AWARD

X	Financial Need	X	Grades		Interviews		Extracurricular Activities
	Essays	2.75	Minimum G.P.A.		SAT ACT		Community Involvement
							Letters of Recommendation

AMERICAN INDIAN SERVICES SCHOLARSHIPS

ORGANIZATION | **NON-PROFIT** | **SCHOLARSHIP**

Organization **American Indian Services**
Department
Address 1902 North Canyon Road Suite 100
Provo State UT Zip code 84604

WEBSITES — Where to apply: Online

Organization www.americanindianservices.org/
Scholarship www.americanindianservices.org/students.html

ANNUAL OPPORTUNITIES (ESTIMATED)

Scholarships Offered Annually	Over 1,000
Average per Scholarship	$2,000

FIELD OF STUDY: GENERAL

TARGET AUDIENCES

All tribes | Tribe

Aimed At	X	Am. Indian		Latino		African Am		Asian Am		Women	Overall Diverse / Open to all
College Level		Pre College	X	1st Yr.	X	2nd Yr.	X	3rd Yr.	X	4th Yr.	Graduate Studies

Area Served: National
Citizenship requirements: Must be permanent resident or citizen

BASIS FOR AWARD

X	Financial Need	X	Grades		Interviews		Extracurricular Activities
	Essays	2.25	Minimum G.P.A.		SAT ACT		Community Involvement
							Letters of Recommendation

AmeriCorps VISTA

Organization	Government	Grant

Organization **AmeriCorps Recruitment**
Department
Address 1201 New York Ave., N.W.
Washington State DC Zip code 20525

Websites — Where to apply: Online
Organization americorps.gov
Scholarship

Annual Opportunities (estimated)

Scholarships Offered Annually	Over 1,000
Average per Scholarship	$4,720

Field of Study: General — Open

Target Audiences

					Tribe	X Overall Diverse
Aimed At	Am. Indian	Latino	African Am	Asian Am	Women	Open to all
College Level	Pre College	1st Yr.	X 2nd Yr.	X 3rd Yr.	X 4th Yr.	Graduate Studies

Area Served: National
Citizenship requirements: Must be permanent resident or citizen

Basis For Award

			Extracurricular Activities
Financial Need	X Grades	Interviews	Community Involvement
Essays	N/A Minimum G.P.A.	SAT ACT	Letters of Recommendation

Annual Grant Competition

Organization	Government	Grant

Organization **United States Institute of Peace**
Department
Address 2301 Constitution Avenue, NW
Washington State DC Zip code 20037

Websites — Where to apply: Online
Organization www.usip.org
Scholarship www.usip.org/grants-fellowships/annual-grant-competition

Annual Opportunities (estimated)

Scholarships Offered Annually	20-49
Average per Scholarship	$50,000

Field of Study: General — Social Justice

Target Audiences

					Tribe	Overall Diverse
Aimed At	Am. Indian	Latino	African Am	Asian Am	Women	X Open to all
College Level	Pre College	X 1st Yr.	X 2nd Yr.	X 3rd Yr.	X 4th Yr.	X Graduate Studies

Area Served: International
Citizenship requirements: Doesn't matter

Basis For Award

			Extracurricular Activities
X Financial Need	Grades	Interviews	X Community Involvement
X Essays	Minimum G.P.A.	SAT ACT	Letters of Recommendation

MAJOR SCHOLARSHIPS

More scholarships are added every month: Go to **www.EmpoweringStudents.com**

Bailey Scholarship

Organization | College Program | **Scholarship**

Organization **Mary Baldwin College (MBC)**
Department Office of Admissions
Address P.O. Box 1500
Staunton State VA Zip code 24401

Websites — Where to apply: Online

Organization
Scholarship http://www.mbc.edu

Annual Opportunities (estimated)

Scholarships Offered Annually	20-49
Average per Scholarship	$15,000

Field of Study: General — All Fields of Study

Target Audiences

Aimed At	Am. Indian	Latino	African Am	Asian Am	Women	Tribe	Overall Diverse
							X Open to all
College Level	Pre College	X 1st Yr.	X 2nd Yr.	X 3rd Yr.	X 4th Yr.		Graduate Studies

Area Served: Regional
Citizenship requirements: Doesn't matter

Basis For Award

Financial Need	Grades	Interviews	Extracurricular Activities
Essays	Minimum G.P.A.	SAT ACT	Community Involvement
			Letters of Recommendation

Barat College Presidential Scholarships

Organization | College Program | **Scholarship**

Organization **Barat College**
Department Office of Financial Aid
Address 700 E. Westleigh Rd.
Lake Forest State IL Zip code 60045

Websites — Where to apply: Online

Organization
Scholarship http://www.barat.edu

Annual Opportunities (estimated)

Scholarships Offered Annually	100-499
Average per Scholarship	$6,000

Field of Study: General — Open

Target Audiences

Aimed At	Am. Indian	Latino	African Am	Asian Am	Women	Tribe	Overall Diverse
							X Open to all
College Level	Pre College	X 1st Yr.	X 2nd Yr.	X 3rd Yr.	X 4th Yr.		Graduate Studies

Area Served: Regional
Citizenship requirements: Must be permanent resident or citizen

Basis For Award

Financial Need	X Grades	Interviews	X Extracurricular Activities
Essays	3.0 Minimum G.P.A.	X SAT ACT	X Community Involvement
			X Letters of Recommendation

More scholarships are added every month: Go to ***www.EmpoweringStudents.com***

Barry M. Goldwater Scholarship

Organization | Foundation | Scholarship

Organization **Barry M. Goldwater Scholarship**
Department Barry M. Goldwater Scholarship & Excellence In Education Foundation
Address 6225 Brandon Ave., Suite 315
Springfield State VA Zip code 22150-2519

Websites — Where to apply: Online

Organization
Scholarship www.act.org/goldwater/

Annual Opportunities (estimated)

Scholarships Offered Annually	100-499
Average per Scholarship	$7,500

Field of Study: STEM — Science & Mathematics

Target Audiences

					Tribe	Overall Diverse
Aimed At	Am. Indian	Latino	African Am	Asian Am	Women	X Open to all
College Level	Pre College	X 1st Yr.	X 2nd Yr.	X 3rd Yr.	X 4th Yr.	Graduate Studies

Area Served: National
Citizenship requirements: Must be permanent resident or citizen

Basis For Award

Financial Need	Grades	Interviews	Extracurricular Activities
Essays	Minimum G.P.A.	SAT ACT	Community Involvement
			Letters of Recommendation

Becapel

Organization | College Program | Program

Organization **Colegio Regional de la Montana**
Department Financial Aid
Address Box 2500
Utuado State PR Zip code 00641

Websites — Where to apply: Online

Organization
Scholarship http://www.suagm.edu/umet/

Annual Opportunities (estimated)

Scholarships Offered Annually	Over 1,000
Average per Scholarship	$2,308

Field of Study: General — All Fields of Study

Target Audiences

					Tribe	Overall Diverse
Aimed At	Am. Indian	X Latino	African Am	Asian Am	Women	Open to all
College Level	Pre College	X 1st Yr.	X 2nd Yr.	X 3rd Yr.	X 4th Yr.	Graduate Studies

Area Served: International
Citizenship requirements: Must be permanent resident or citizen

Basis For Award

X Financial Need	X Grades	Interviews	Extracurricular Activities
Essays	Minimum G.P.A.	X SAT ACT	Community Involvement
			Letters of Recommendation

More scholarships are added every month: Go to ***www.EmpoweringStudents.com***

Benjamin A. Gilman International Scholarship

Organization	Government	Scholarship

Organization **U.S Department of State: Adminstered by the Ins. of International**
Department Gilman Scholarship Program
Address 1800 West Loop South, Suite 250
Houston State TX Zip code 77027

Websites — Where to apply: Online

Organization
Scholarship www.iie.org/Programs/Gilman-Scholarship-Program

Annual Opportunities (estimated)

Scholarships Offered Annually: Over 1,000
Average per Scholarship: $5,000

Field of Study: GENERAL — All Fields of Study

Target Audiences

Aimed At: Am. Indian [ ], Latino [ ], African Am [ ], Asian Am [ ], Women [ ], Tribe [ ], Overall Diverse [X], Open to all [X]

College Level: Pre College [ ], 1st Yr. [X], 2nd Yr. [X], 3rd Yr. [X], 4th Yr. [X], Graduate Studies [ ]

Area Served: International
Citizenship requirements: U.S. Citizenship required

Basis For Award

Financial Need [X], Essays [X], Grades [X], Minimum G.P.A. [ ], Interviews [ ], SAT ACT [ ], Extracurricular Activities [ ], Community Involvement [ ], Letters of Recommendation [ ]

Best Buy Scholarship Program

Organization	Business	Program

Organization **Best Buy Co., Inc.**
Department Scholarship Management Services, Scholarship America
Address One Scholarship Way
Saint Peter State MN Zip code 56082

Websites — Where to apply: Online

Organization http://pr.bby.com/
Scholarship https://bestbuy.scholarshipamerica.org

Annual Opportunities (estimated)

Scholarships Offered Annually: Over 1,000
Average per Scholarship: $1,000

Field of Study: VARIOUS — Varies

Target Audiences

Aimed At: Am. Indian [ ], Latino [ ], African Am [ ], Asian Am [ ], Women [ ], Tribe [ ], Overall Diverse [ ], Open to all [X]

College Level: Pre College [X], 1st Yr. [X], 2nd Yr. [ ], 3rd Yr. [ ], 4th Yr. [ ], Graduate Studies [ ]

Area Served: National
Citizenship requirements: Must be permanent resident or citizen

Basis For Award

Financial Need [ ], Essays [ ], Grades [X], Minimum G.P.A. 2.5, Interviews [ ], SAT ACT [ ], Extracurricular Activities [X], Community Involvement [X], Letters of Recommendation [ ]

BIA Higher Education Grant

Organization	Government
	Scholarship
Organization	**Bureau of Indian Affairs**
Department	
Address	1849 C st NW/MS-3512 MIB
	Washington — State DC — Zip code 20240-0001

Websites	Where to apply: Either by mail or online
Organization	http://www.bia.gov/
Scholarship	

Annual Opportunities (estimated)		**Field of Study**
Scholarships Offered Annually	100-499	General
Average per Scholarship	$2,500	All Fields of Study

Target Audiences

Tribe: All tribes

Aimed At	X	Am. Indian		Latino		African Am		Asian Am	X	Women		Open to all
												Overall Diverse
College Level	X	Pre College	X	1st Yr.	X	2nd Yr.	X	3rd Yr.	X	4th Yr.		Graduate Studies

Area Served	National
Citizenship requirements	Doesn't matter

Basis For Award

X	Financial Need		Grades		Interviews		Extracurricular Activities
	Essays		Minimum G.P.A.		SAT ACT		Community Involvement
							Letters of Recommendation

Boren Scholarships

Organization	Foundation
	Scholarship
Organization	**National Security Education Program**
Department	
Address	1400 K Street, NW, 7th Floor
	Washington — State DC — Zip code 20005

Websites	Where to apply: Online
Organization	
Scholarship	http://borenawards.org/boren_scholarship/basics.html

Annual Opportunities (estimated)		**Field of Study**
Scholarships Offered Annually	100-499	Various
Average per Scholarship	$15,000	

Target Audiences

Tribe:

Aimed At		Am. Indian		Latino		African Am		Asian Am		Women	X	Open to all
												Overall Diverse
College Level		Pre College	X	1st Yr.	X	2nd Yr.	X	3rd Yr.	X	4th Yr.		Graduate Studies

Area Served	National
Citizenship requirements	Must be permanent resident or citizen

Basis For Award

	Financial Need		Grades		Interviews		Extracurricular Activities
	Essays		Minimum G.P.A.		SAT ACT		Community Involvement
							Letters of Recommendation

More scholarships are added every month: Go to **www.EmpoweringStudents.com**

Breakthrough To Nursing Scholarships For Ethnic

Organization — Foundation — **Scholarship**

Organization **National Student Nurses' Association, Inc. (NSNA)**
Department
Address 110 William Street
New York State NY Zip code 10038

Websites — Where to apply: Online

Organization www.nsna.org
Scholarship

Annual Opportunities (estimated)

Scholarships Offered Annually: Over 1,000
Average per Scholarship: $1,500

Field of Study: Medicine — Pre-Nursing and Nursing Students

Target Audiences

Aimed At: [ ] Am. Indian [X] Latino [X] African Am [X] Asian Am [ ] Women [ ] Open to all [ ] Tribe [X] Overall Diverse

College Level: [ ] Pre College [X] 1st Yr. [X] 2nd Yr. [X] 3rd Yr. [X] 4th Yr. [ ] Graduate Studies

Area Served: National
Citizenship requirements: Must be permanent resident or citizen

Basis For Award

[X] Financial Need [X] Grades [ ] Interviews [ ] Extracurricular Activities [X] Community Involvement
[ ] Essays [ ] Minimum G.P.A. [ ] SAT ACT [X] Letters of Recommendation

Buick Achievers Scholarship Program

Organization — Other — **Scholarship**

Organization **Buick Achievers**
Department Buick Customer Assistance Center
Address P.O. Box 33136
Detroit State MI Zip code 48232-5136

Websites — Where to apply: Online

Organization www.buickachievers.com
Scholarship

Annual Opportunities (estimated)

Scholarships Offered Annually: Over 1,000
Average per Scholarship: $4,091

Field of Study: Various — Engineering/Technology or select Design and Business-related programs of study (See website for

Target Audiences

Aimed At: [ ] Am. Indian [ ] Latino [ ] African Am [ ] Asian Am [ ] Women [X] Open to all [ ] Tribe [ ] Overall Diverse

College Level: [ ] Pre College [X] 1st Yr. [X] 2nd Yr. [X] 3rd Yr. [X] 4th Yr. [ ] Graduate Studies

Area Served: National
Citizenship requirements: Must be permanent resident or citizen

Basis For Award

[X] Financial Need [X] Grades [ ] Interviews [X] Extracurricular Activities [X] Community Involvement
[X] Essays [ ] Minimum G.P.A. [ ] SAT ACT [ ] Letters of Recommendation

More scholarships are added every month: Go to ***www.EmpoweringStudents.com***

BURGER KING SCHOLARS PROGRAM

ORGANIZATION NON-PROFIT | PROGRAM

Organization **The BURGER KING McLAMORE Foundation**
Department Scholarship Management Services
Address One Scholarship Way
St. Peter State MN Zip code 56082

WEBSITES Where to apply: Online

Organization http://www.bkmclamorefoundation.org/Home
Scholarship http://www.bkmclamorefoundation.org/WhatWeDo/ScholarsProgram

ANNUAL OPPORTUNITIES (ESTIMATED)

Scholarships Offered Annually: Over 1,000
Average per Scholarship: $1,113

FIELD OF STUDY Varies — VARIOUS

TARGET AUDIENCES

Aimed At		Am. Indian		Latino		African Am		Asian Am		Women	X	Open to all
College Level		Pre College	X	1st Yr.		2nd Yr.		3rd Yr.		4th Yr.		Graduate Studies

Tribe: — Overall Diverse: —

Area Served: International
Citizenship requirements: Must be permanent resident or citizen

BASIS FOR AWARD

X	Financial Need	X	Grades		Interviews		Extracurricular Activities
	Essays	2.0	Minimum G.P.A.		SAT ACT		Community Involvement
							Letters of Recommendation

CAL GRANT UNDERGRADUATE SCHOLARSHIP PROGRAM

ORGANIZATION COLLEGE PROGRAM | GRANT

Organization **California Student Aid Commission**
Department Customer Service Division
Address PO Box 419027
Rancho Cordova State CA Zip code 95741- 9027

WEBSITES Where to apply: Online

Organization
Scholarship http://www.csac.ca.gov

ANNUAL OPPORTUNITIES (ESTIMATED)

Scholarships Offered Annually: Over 1,000
Average per Scholarship: $4,000

FIELD OF STUDY All Fields of Study — GENERAL

TARGET AUDIENCES

Aimed At		Am. Indian		Latino		African Am		Asian Am		Women	X	Open to all
College Level		Pre College	X	1st Yr.	X	2nd Yr.	X	3rd Yr.	X	4th Yr.	X	Graduate Studies

Tribe: — Overall Diverse: —

Area Served: Regional
Citizenship requirements: Doesn't matter

BASIS FOR AWARD

X	Financial Need	X	Grades	X	Interviews	X	Extracurricular Activities
	Essays	3.0	Minimum G.P.A.	X	SAT ACT	X	Community Involvement
						X	Letters of Recommendation

More scholarships are added every month: Go to **www.EmpoweringStudents.com**

CAMP Scholarship

Organization | **Non-Profit** | **Scholarship**

Organization **College Assistance Migrant Program (CAMP) / Migrant Students**
Department Migrant Students Foundation, Inc.
Address 305 Prospect Ave, Suite 4
Lewiston State ID Zip code 83501

Websites — Where to apply: Online

Organization www.migrantstudents.org
Scholarship www.migrantstudents.org/scholarships/campscholarship

Annual Opportunities (estimated)

Scholarships Offered Annually	Over 1,000
Average per Scholarship	$1,000

Field of Study: All Fields of Study — GENERAL

Target Audiences

									Tribe		Overall Diverse
Aimed At		Am. Indian	X	Latino		African Am		Asian Am	Women		Open to all
College Level		Pre College	X	1st Yr.		2nd Yr.		3rd Yr.	4th Yr.		Graduate Studies

Area Served: Regional
Citizenship requirements: Doesn't matter

Basis For Award

X	Financial Need	X	Grades		Interviews		Extracurricular Activities
X	Essays		Minimum G.P.A.		SAT ACT		Community Involvement
							Letters of Recommendation

Center for Student Opportunity Scholarship

Organization | **Non-Profit** | **Scholarship**

Organization **Center for Student Opportunity**
Department
Address PO Box 30370
Bethesda State MD Zip code 20824

Websites — Where to apply: Online

Organization www.csopportunity.org
Scholarship

Annual Opportunities (estimated)

Scholarships Offered Annually	Over 1,000
Average per Scholarship	$2,000

Field of Study: All Fields of Study — GENERAL

Target Audiences

									Tribe	X	Overall Diverse
Aimed At		Am. Indian	X	Latino		African Am		Asian Am	Women		Open to all
College Level		Pre College	X	1st Yr.		2nd Yr.		3rd Yr.	4th Yr.		Graduate Studies

Area Served: National
Citizenship requirements: Must be permanent resident or citizen

Basis For Award

X	Financial Need		Grades	X	Interviews		Extracurricular Activities
	Essays		Minimum G.P.A.		SAT ACT		Community Involvement
							Letters of Recommendation

Chancellor's Scholarships for Outstanding

Organization	College Program	Scholarship

Organization **Vanderbilt University**

Department Office of Undergraduate Admissions

Address 2305 West End Ave.

Nashville State TN Zip code 37203

Websites — Where to apply: Online

Organization

Scholarship http://www.vanderbilt.edu

Annual Opportunities (estimated)

Scholarships Offered Annually	20-49
Average per Scholarship	$20,000

Field of Study Open: GENERAL

Target Audiences

Aimed At: [ ] Am. Indian [ ] Latino [ ] African Am [ ] Asian Am [ ] Women [ ] Tribe [X] Overall Diverse [ ] Open to all

College Level: [ ] Pre College [X] 1st Yr. [X] 2nd Yr. [X] 3rd Yr. [X] 4th Yr. [ ] Graduate Studies

Area Served: Regional

Citizenship requirements: Must be permanent resident or citizen

Basis For Award

[ ] Financial Need [ ] Grades [ ] Interviews [ ] Extracurricular Activities [ ] Community Involvement

[ ] Essays [ ] Minimum G.P.A. [ ] SAT ACT [ ] Letters of Recommendation

City Year & AmeriCorps

Organization	Foundation	Award

Organization **City Year, Inc.**

Department

Address 285 Columbus Ave.

Boston State MA Zip code 02116

Websites — Where to apply: Online

Organization www.cityyear.org

Scholarship

Annual Opportunities (estimated)

Scholarships Offered Annually	Over 1,000
Average per Scholarship	$4,725

Field of Study: GENERAL

Target Audiences

Aimed At: [ ] Am. Indian [ ] Latino [ ] African Am [ ] Asian Am [ ] Women [ ] Tribe [ ] Overall Diverse [X] Open to all

College Level: [ ] Pre College [ ] 1st Yr. [ ] 2nd Yr. [ ] 3rd Yr. [ ] 4th Yr. [ ] Graduate Studies

Area Served: National

Citizenship requirements: Must be permanent resident or citizen

Basis For Award

[ ] Financial Need [ ] Grades [ ] Interviews [ ] Extracurricular Activities [ ] Community Involvement

[ ] Essays [ ] Minimum G.P.A. [ ] SAT ACT [ ] Letters of Recommendation

Civil Engineering Corps (CEC)

Organization	Government	Scholarship

Organization **United States Department of the Navy**

Department

Address

Washington State DC Zip code

Websites — Where to apply: Online

Organization

Scholarship http://www.cec.navy.mil/

Annual Opportunities (estimated)	
Scholarships Offered Annually	20-49
Average per Scholarship	$30,000

Field of Study: STEM

Target Audiences

										Tribe		Overall Diverse
Aimed At		Am. Indian		Latino		African Am		Asian Am		Women	X	Open to all
College Level		Pre College		1st Yr.		2nd Yr.		3rd Yr.		4th Yr.		Graduate Studies

Area Served: National

Citizenship requirements: U.S. Citizenship required

Basis For Award

							Extracurricular Activities
	Financial Need	X	Grades		Interviews		Community Involvement
	Essays	3.0	Minimum G.P.A.	X	SAT ACT		Letters of Recommendation

Coca-Cola Clemson Scholars Program

Organization	College Program	Program

Organization **Clemson University**

Department Office of Financial Aid

Address G-01 Sikes Hall, Box 345123

Clemson State SC Zip code 29634-5123

Websites — Where to apply: Online

Organization

Scholarship www.clemson.edu/finaide

Annual Opportunities (estimated)	
Scholarships Offered Annually	100-499
Average per Scholarship	$2,500

Field of Study: Open — GENERAL

Target Audiences

										Tribe	X	Overall Diverse
Aimed At		Am. Indian		Latino		African Am		Asian Am		Women		Open to all
College Level		Pre College	X	1st Yr.	X	2nd Yr.	X	3rd Yr.	X	4th Yr.		Graduate Studies

Area Served: Regional

Citizenship requirements: Must be permanent resident or citizen

Basis For Award

							Extracurricular Activities
	Financial Need	X	Grades		Interviews		Community Involvement
	Essays	2.5	Minimum G.P.A.	X	SAT ACT		Letters of Recommendation

COCA-COLA SCHOLARS PROGRAM

ORGANIZATION	NON-PROFIT	PROGRAM

Organization **Coca-Cola Scholars Foundation, Inc.**
Department
Address 1 Coca-Cola Plaza
Atlanta State GA Zip code 30313

WEBSITES — Where to apply: Online

Organization www.coca-colascholars.org
Scholarship www.coca-colascholars.org/page.aspx?pid=388

ANNUAL OPPORTUNITIES (ESTIMATED)

Scholarships Offered Annually	100-499
Average per Scholarship	$15,000

FIELD OF STUDY: GENERAL — All Fields of Study

TARGET AUDIENCES

					Tribe	Overall Diverse
Aimed At	Am. Indian	Latino	African Am	Asian Am	Women	X Open to all
College Level	Pre College	X 1st Yr.	X 2nd Yr.	X 3rd Yr.	X 4th Yr.	Graduate Studies

Area Served: National
Citizenship requirements: Must be permanent resident or citizen

BASIS FOR AWARD

			X Extracurricular Activities
Financial Need	X Grades	Interviews	X Community Involvement
Essays	3.0 Minimum G.P.A.	X SAT ACT	X Letters of Recommendation

COLLEGE RETENTION/GENERAL SCHOLARSHIP PROGRAM

ORGANIZATION	OTHER	SCHOLARSHIP

Organization **Hispanic Scholarship Fund**
Department
Address One Sansome St., Suite 1000
San Francisco State CA Zip code 94104

WEBSITES — Where to apply: Online

Organization
Scholarship http://www.hsf.net

ANNUAL OPPORTUNITIES (ESTIMATED)

Scholarships Offered Annually	100-499
Average per Scholarship	$2,000

FIELD OF STUDY: GENERAL — All Fields of Study

TARGET AUDIENCES

					Tribe	Overall Diverse
Aimed At	Am. Indian	X Latino	African Am	Asian Am	Women	Open to all
College Level	Pre College	1st Yr.	2nd Yr.	3rd Yr.	4th Yr.	Graduate Studies

Area Served: National
Citizenship requirements: Must be permanent resident or citizen

BASIS FOR AWARD

			Extracurricular Activities
Financial Need	X Grades	Interviews	Community Involvement
Essays	2.7 Minimum G.P.A.	SAT ACT	Letters of Recommendation

MAJOR SCHOLARSHIPS

More scholarships are added every month: Go to **www.EmpoweringStudents.com**

Community Builders Fellowship Program

Organization | Government | Fellowship

Organization **U.S. Department of Housing and Urban Development**
Department
Address 451 7th St. SW
Washington State DC Zip code 20410

Websites — Where to apply: Online

Organization
Scholarship www.hud.gov/cb/

Annual Opportunities (estimated)

Scholarships Offered Annually: 100-499
Average per Scholarship: $65,217

Field of Study: Various — See comments

Target Audiences

Aimed At	[ ] Am. Indian	[ ] Latino	[ ] African Am	[ ] Asian Am	[ ] Women	[X] Open to all
					[ ] Tribe	[ ] Overall Diverse
College Level	[ ] Pre College	[ ] 1st Yr.	[ ] 2nd Yr.	[ ] 3rd Yr.	[ ] 4th Yr.	[X] Graduate Studies

Area Served: National
Citizenship requirements: Doesn't matter

Basis For Award

[ ] Financial Need	[ ] Grades	[ ] Interviews	[ ] Extracurricular Activities
[ ] Essays	[ ] Minimum G.P.A.	[ ] SAT ACT	[ ] Community Involvement
			[ ] Letters of Recommendation

Community Enrichment Scholarship Program

Organization | College Program | Scholarship

Organization **Bluffton College**
Department Office of Admissions
Address 280 West College Ave.
Bluffton State OH Zip code 45817-1196

Websites — Where to apply: Online

Organization
Scholarship http://www.bluffman.edu

Annual Opportunities (estimated)

Scholarships Offered Annually: 10-19
Average per Scholarship: $112,500

Field of Study: General — Open

Target Audiences

Aimed At	[ ] Am. Indian	[ ] Latino	[ ] African Am	[ ] Asian Am	[ ] Women	[X] Open to all
					[ ] Tribe	[ ] Overall Diverse
College Level	[ ] Pre College	[X] 1st Yr.	[X] 2nd Yr.	[X] 3rd Yr.	[X] 4th Yr.	[ ] Graduate Studies

Area Served: Regional
Citizenship requirements: Must be permanent resident or citizen

Basis For Award

[X] Financial Need	[X] Grades	[ ] Interviews	[X] Extracurricular Activities
[ ] Essays	[ ] Minimum G.P.A.	[ ] SAT ACT	[X] Community Involvement
			[ ] Letters of Recommendation

More scholarships are added every month: Go to ***www.EmpoweringStudents.com***

DANA COLLEGE HONOR SCHOLARSHIP

ORGANIZATION | COLLEGE PROGRAM | SCHOLARSHIP

Organization **Dana College**
Department Financial Aid Office
Address 2848 College Dr.
Blair State NE Zip code 68008

WEBSITES Where to apply: Online

Organization
Scholarship http://www.dana.edu.

ANNUAL OPPORTUNITIES (ESTIMATED)

Scholarships Offered Annually	
Average per Scholarship	?

FIELD OF STUDY All Fields of Study
GENERAL

TARGET AUDIENCES

						Tribe	Overall Diverse
Aimed At	Am. Indian	Latino	African Am	Asian Am	Women	X	Open to all
College Level	Pre College	X 1st Yr.	X 2nd Yr.	X 3rd Yr.	X 4th Yr.		Graduate Studies

Area Served: Regional
Citizenship requirements: Must be permanent resident or citizen

BASIS FOR AWARD

			X Extracurricular Activities
Financial Need	X Grades	X Interviews	X Community Involvement
Essays	Minimum G.P.A.	X SAT ACT	X Letters of Recommendation

DEANS' SCHOLARSHIP

ORGANIZATION | COLLEGE PROGRAM | SCHOLARSHIP

Organization **University of Southern California**
Department Financial Aid
Address University Park Campus
Los Angeles State CA Zip code 90007

WEBSITES Where to apply: Online

Organization
Scholarship http://www.usc.edu

ANNUAL OPPORTUNITIES (ESTIMATED)

Scholarships Offered Annually	100-499
Average per Scholarship	$6,000

FIELD OF STUDY Open
GENERAL

TARGET AUDIENCES

						Tribe	Overall Diverse
Aimed At	Am. Indian	Latino	African Am	Asian Am	Women	X	Open to all
College Level	Pre College	X 1st Yr.	X 2nd Yr.	X 3rd Yr.	X 4th Yr.		Graduate Studies

Area Served: Regional
Citizenship requirements: Must be permanent resident or citizen

BASIS FOR AWARD

			X Extracurricular Activities
Financial Need	X Grades	X Interviews	X Community Involvement
Essays	3.6 Minimum G.P.A.	X SAT ACT	X Letters of Recommendation

More scholarships are added every month: Go to **www.EmpoweringStudents.com**

DELL SCHOLARS PROGRAM

ORGANIZATION	FOUNDATION	PROGRAM

Organization **Michael & Susan Dell Foundation**

Department

Address PO Box 163867

Austin State TX Zip code 78716

WEBSITES

Where to apply Online

Organization www.dellscholars.org

Scholarship www.dellscholars.org/Criteria.aspx

ANNUAL OPPORTUNITIES (ESTIMATED) — FIELD OF STUDY Varies

Scholarships Offered Annually	100-499	VARIOUS
Average per Scholarship	$20,000	

TARGET AUDIENCES

Aimed At		Am. Indian	Latino	African Am	Asian Am	Women	Tribe	Overall Diverse
							X	Open to all

College Level		Pre College	X 1st Yr.	2nd Yr.	3rd Yr.	4th Yr.	Graduate Studies

Area Served National

Citizenship requirements Must be permanent resident or citizen

BASIS FOR AWARD

						Extracurricular Activities
X	Financial Need	X	Grades		Interviews	Community Involvement
X	Essays	2.4	Minimum G.P.A.		SAT ACT	X Letters of Recommendation

---

DEPARTMENTAL SCHOLARSHIP

ORGANIZATION	COLLEGE PROGRAM	SCHOLARSHIP

Organization **University of Southern Indiana**

Department Office of Student Financial Assistance

Address 8600 University Blvd.

Evansville State IN Zip code 47712

WEBSITES

Where to apply Online

Organization

Scholarship http://www.usi.edu

ANNUAL OPPORTUNITIES (ESTIMATED) — FIELD OF STUDY Open

Scholarships Offered Annually	500-999	GENERAL
Average per Scholarship	$1,000	

TARGET AUDIENCES

Aimed At		Am. Indian	Latino	African Am	Asian Am	Women	Tribe	Overall Diverse
							X	Open to all

College Level		Pre College	X 1st Yr.	X 2nd Yr.	X 3rd Yr.	X 4th Yr.	Graduate Studies

Area Served Regional

Citizenship requirements Must be permanent resident or citizen

BASIS FOR AWARD

						X Extracurricular Activities
	Financial Need	X	Grades		Interviews	X Community Involvement
	Essays	3.6	Minimum G.P.A.		SAT ACT	X Letters of Recommendation

More scholarships are added every month: Go to **www.EmpoweringStudents.com**

Distinguished Achievement Academic Scholarship

Organization: College Program | **Scholarship**

Organization **Prairie View A & M University**
Department Office of Student Affairs - Scholarship Division
Address PO Box 519; MS 1005
Prairie View State TX Zip code 77446

Websites
Where to apply: Online
Organization www.pvamu.edu
Scholarship

Annual Opportunities (estimated)
Scholarships Offered Annually	100-499
Average per Scholarship	$6,400

Field of Study
Open
GENERAL

Target Audiences
					Tribe	Overall Diverse
Aimed At	Am. Indian	Latino	African Am	Asian Am	Women	X Open to all
College Level	Pre College	X 1st Yr.	X 2nd Yr.	X 3rd Yr.	X 4th Yr.	Graduate Studies

Area Served: Regional
Citizenship requirements: Doesn't matter

Basis For Award
			X Extracurricular Activities
Financial Need	X Grades	X Interviews	X Community Involvement
Essays	3.0 Minimum G.P.A.	X SAT ACT	X Letters of Recommendation

Elks Most Valuable Student Awards

Organization: Foundation | **Award**

Organization **Elks National Foundation**
Department
Address 2750 North Lakeview Ave.
Chicago State IL Zip code 60614-1889

Websites
Where to apply: Online
Organization
Scholarship www.elks.org/enf/

Annual Opportunities (estimated)
Scholarships Offered Annually	500-999
Average per Scholarship	$1,000

Field of Study
GENERAL

Target Audiences
					Tribe	Overall Diverse
Aimed At	Am. Indian	Latino	African Am	Asian Am	X Women	X Open to all
College Level	X Pre College	1st Yr.	2nd Yr.	3rd Yr.	4th Yr.	Graduate Studies

Area Served: National
Citizenship requirements: U.S. Citizenship required

Basis For Award
			Extracurricular Activities
Financial Need	Grades	Interviews	Community Involvement
Essays	Minimum G.P.A.	SAT ACT	Letters of Recommendation

Established Investigator Grant

Organization	Non-Profit	Grant

Organization **American Heart Association**
Department Division of Research Administration
Address 7272 Greenville Ave.
Dallas State TX Zip code 75231-4596

Websites — Where to apply: Online

Organization
Scholarship http://www.americanheart.org

Annual Opportunities (estimated)

Scholarships Offered Annually	50-99
Average per Scholarship	$75,000

Field of Study: General

Target Audiences

										Tribe		Overall Diverse
Aimed At		Am. Indian		Latino		African Am		Asian Am		Women	X	Open to all
College Level		Pre College		1st Yr.		2nd Yr.		3rd Yr.		4th Yr.	X	Graduate Studies

Area Served: National
Citizenship requirements: Must be permanent resident or citizen

Basis For Award

							Extracurricular Activities
	Financial Need		Grades		Interviews		Community Involvement
	Essays		Minimum G.P.A.		SAT ACT		Letters of Recommendation

Fifth Year Accounting Student Scholarship

Organization	College Program	Scholarship

Organization **Texas Higher Education Coordinating Board**
Department Student Services Division
Address P. O. Box 12788,
Austin State TX Zip code 78711

Websites — Where to apply: Online

Organization
Scholarship www.collegefortexans.com

Annual Opportunities (estimated)

Scholarships Offered Annually	100-499
Average per Scholarship	$3,000

Field of Study: Business — Accounting

Target Audiences

										Tribe		Overall Diverse
Aimed At		Am. Indian		Latino		African Am		Asian Am		Women	X	Open to all
College Level		Pre College		1st Yr.		2nd Yr.		3rd Yr.		4th Yr.	X	Graduate Studies

Area Served: Regional
Citizenship requirements: Must be permanent resident or citizen

Basis For Award

						X	Extracurricular Activities
X	Financial Need		Grades		Interviews	X	Community Involvement
	Essays		Minimum G.P.A.		SAT ACT	X	Letters of Recommendation

More scholarships are added every month: Go to **www.EmpoweringStudents.com**

FORD FOUNDATION DISSERTATION FELLOWSHIPS

ORGANIZATION NON-PROFIT | FELLOWSHIP

Organization **National Research Council**
Department Fellowship Office, GR 346A
Address 500 Fifth St., N.W.
Washington State DC Zip code 20001

WEBSITES Where to apply: Online

Organization
Scholarship www.national-academies.org

ANNUAL OPPORTUNITIES (ESTIMATED)

Scholarships Offered Annually	20-49
Average per Scholarship	$21,500

FIELD OF STUDY STEM — Behavioral Sciences, Humanities, Engineering, Mathematics

TARGET AUDIENCES

					Tribe	X	Overall Diverse
Aimed At	Am. Indian	Latino	African Am	Asian Am	Women		Open to all
College Level	Pre College	1st Yr.	2nd Yr.	3rd Yr.	4th Yr.	X	Graduate Studies

Area Served: National
Citizenship requirements: Must be permanent resident or citizen

BASIS FOR AWARD

							Extracurricular Activities
	Financial Need		Grades		Interviews		Community Involvement
	Essays		Minimum G.P.A.		SAT ACT		Letters of Recommendation

FORD FOUNDATION POSTDOCTORAL FELLOWSHIPS

ORGANIZATION NON-PROFIT | FELLOWSHIP

Organization **National Research Council**
Department Fellowship Office/GR 346A
Address 500 Fifth St, N.W.
Washington State DC Zip code 20001

WEBSITES Where to apply: Online

Organization
Scholarship www.national-academies.org

ANNUAL OPPORTUNITIES (ESTIMATED)

Scholarships Offered Annually	20-49
Average per Scholarship	$37,500

FIELD OF STUDY STEM — Behavioral & Social Sciences, Humanities, Engineering, Mathematics

TARGET AUDIENCES

					Tribe	X	Overall Diverse
Aimed At	Am. Indian	Latino	African Am	Asian Am	Women		Open to all
College Level	Pre College	1st Yr.	2nd Yr.	3rd Yr.	4th Yr.	X	Graduate Studies

Area Served: National
Citizenship requirements: Must be permanent resident or citizen

BASIS FOR AWARD

						X	Extracurricular Activities
	Financial Need		Grades	X	Interviews	X	Community Involvement
	Essays		Minimum G.P.A.		SAT ACT	X	Letters of Recommendation

MAJOR SCHOLARSHIPS

More scholarships are added every month: Go to ***www.EmpoweringStudents.com***

FORD FOUNDATION PREDOCTORAL & DISSERTATION

ORGANIZATION NON-PROFIT — FELLOWSHIP

Organization **National Research Council**
Department Office of Scientific and Engineering Personnel
Address 2101 Constitution Ave. N.W.
Washington State DC Zip code 20418

WEBSITES Where to apply: Online

Organization
Scholarship www.fellowships.nas.edu

ANNUAL OPPORTUNITIES (ESTIMATED)

Scholarships Offered Annually	50-99
Average per Scholarship	$21,500

FIELD OF STUDY STEM — Behavioral Sciences, Humanities, Engineering, Mathematics

TARGET AUDIENCES

					Tribe	X	Overall Diverse
Aimed At	Am. Indian	Latino	African Am	Asian Am	Women		Open to all
College Level	Pre College	1st Yr.	2nd Yr.	3rd Yr.	4th Yr.	X	Graduate Studies

Area Served: National
Citizenship requirements: Must be permanent resident or citizen

BASIS FOR AWARD

			Extracurricular Activities
Financial Need	Grades	Interviews	Community Involvement
Essays	Minimum G.P.A.	SAT ACT	Letters of Recommendation

FULBRIGHT GRANT

ORGANIZATION FOUNDATION — GRANT

Organization
Department
Address 3007 Tilden St., NW, Suite L-500
Washington State DC Zip code 20008

WEBSITES Where to apply: Online

Organization
Scholarship www.cies.org

ANNUAL OPPORTUNITIES (ESTIMATED)

Scholarships Offered Annually	50-99
Average per Scholarship	$50,000

FIELD OF STUDY VARIOUS — International Study

TARGET AUDIENCES

					Tribe		Overall Diverse
Aimed At	Am. Indian	Latino	African Am	Asian Am	Women	X	Open to all
College Level	Pre College	1st Yr.	2nd Yr.	X 3rd Yr.	X 4th Yr.		Graduate Studies

Area Served: Regional
Citizenship requirements: U.S. Citizenship required

BASIS FOR AWARD

			Extracurricular Activities
Financial Need	Grades	Interviews	Community Involvement
Essays	Minimum G.P.A.	SAT ACT	Letters of Recommendation

More scholarships are added every month: Go to ***www.EmpoweringStudents.com***

GOOD NEIGHBOR SCHOLARSHIP PROGRAM

ORGANIZATION	GOVERNMENT	SCHOLARSHIP

Organization Texas Higher Education Coordinating Board
Department Student Services Division
Address P.O. Box 12788
Austin   **State** TX   **Zip code** 78711-2788

WEBSITES

Where to apply Online

Organization
Scholarship www.collegefortexans.com

ANNUAL OPPORTUNITIES (ESTIMATED)	FIELD OF STUDY	Open
Scholarships Offered Annually	100-499	GENERAL
Average per Scholarship	$8,511	

TARGET AUDIENCES

							Tribe	X	Overall Diverse
Aimed At	Am. Indian	X	Latino		African Am		Asian Am		Women		Open to all

College Level		Pre College	X	1st Yr.	X	2nd Yr.	X	3rd Yr.	X	4th Yr.	X	Graduate Studies

Area Served International
Citizenship requirements Non-citizens only

BASIS FOR AWARD

						Extracurricular Activities
X	Financial Need	X	Grades	X	Interviews	Community Involvement
	Essays		Minimum G.P.A.	X	SAT ACT	Letters of Recommendation

GRANT-IN-AID

ORGANIZATION	NON-PROFIT	GRANT

Organization American Heart Association
Department Division of Research Administration
Address 7272 Greenville Ave.
Dallas   **State** TX   **Zip code** 75231-4596

WEBSITES

Where to apply Online

Organization
Scholarship http://www.americanheart.org

ANNUAL OPPORTUNITIES (ESTIMATED)	FIELD OF STUDY	Cardiovascular function disease,
Scholarships Offered Annually	STEM	stroke or related basic science.
Average per Scholarship	?	

TARGET AUDIENCES

							Tribe		Overall Diverse
Aimed At	Am. Indian		Latino		African Am		Asian Am		Women	X	Open to all

College Level		Pre College		1st Yr.		2nd Yr.		3rd Yr.		4th Yr.	X	Graduate Studies

Area Served National
Citizenship requirements Must be permanent resident or citizen

BASIS FOR AWARD

						Extracurricular Activities
	Financial Need		Grades		Interviews	Community Involvement
	Essays		Minimum G.P.A.		SAT ACT	Letters of Recommendation

MAJOR SCHOLARSHIPS

More scholarships are added every month: Go to **www.EmpoweringStudents.com**

HACU National Internship Program (HNIP)

Organization: Non-Profit | **Internship**

Organization **Hispanic Association of Colleges and Universities**
Department
Address One Dupont Circle, N.W., Suite 430
Washington State DC Zip code 20036

Websites

Where to apply: Online

Organization www.hacu.net
Scholarship www.hacu.net/hnip

Annual Opportunities (estimated)

Scholarships Offered Annually	500-999
Average per Scholarship	$3,000

Field of Study

All Fields of Study

GENERAL

Target Audiences

Aimed At	Am. Indian	X Latino	African Am	Asian Am	Tribe	Women	Overall Diverse / Open to all
College Level	Pre College	1st Yr.	X 2nd Yr.	X 3rd Yr.	X 4th Yr.	X Graduate Studies	

Area Served: National
Citizenship requirements: Must be permanent resident or citizen

Basis For Award

X Financial Need	X Grades	X Interviews	X Extracurricular Activities
Essays	3.0 Minimum G.P.A.	SAT ACT	X Community Involvement
			X Letters of Recommendation

Harry S. Truman Scholarship

Organization: Government | **Scholarship**

Organization **Truman Scholarship Foundation**
Department
Address 712 Jackson Place, N.W.
Washington State DC Zip code 20006

Websites

Where to apply: Online

Organization
Scholarship http://www.truman.gov

Annual Opportunities (estimated)

Scholarships Offered Annually	50-99
Average per Scholarship	$10,000

Field of Study

Public Policy/Public Service

LIBRAL

Target Audiences

Aimed At	Am. Indian	Latino	African Am	Asian Am	Tribe	Women	X Overall Diverse / Open to all
College Level	Pre College	1st Yr.	2nd Yr.	3rd Yr.	X 4th Yr.	X Graduate Studies	

Area Served: National
Citizenship requirements: U.S. Citizenship required

Basis For Award

Financial Need	X Grades	X Interviews	X Extracurricular Activities
Essays	3.0 Minimum G.P.A.	SAT ACT	X Community Involvement
			X Letters of Recommendation

HEALTH PROFESSIONS PREPARATORY SCHOLARSHIP

ORGANIZATION	NON-PROFIT	SCHOLARSHIP

Organization **Indian Health Service**

Department IHS Scholarship Program

Address The Reyes Building, 801 Thompson Avenue, Suite 400

Rockville　　　　　　　　State MD　　　　Zip code 20852

WEBSITES

Where to apply Online

Organization www.ihs.gov

Scholarship www.scholarship.ihs.gov

ANNUAL OPPORTUNITIES (ESTIMATED)

FIELD OF STUDY	Health profession

Scholarships Offered Annually	50-99
Average per Scholarship	$10,000

MEDICINE

TARGET AUDIENCES

						All tribes		Tribe		Overall Diverse
Aimed At	X	Am. Indian		Latino		African Am		Asian Am		Women		Open to all

College Level		Pre College	X	1st Yr.	X	2nd Yr.	X	3rd Yr.	X	4th Yr.		Graduate Studies

Area Served National

Citizenship requirements U.S. Citizenship required

BASIS FOR AWARD

							Extracurricular Activities
	Financial Need	X	Grades		Interviews		Community Involvement
X	Essays	2.0	Minimum G.P.A.		SAT ACT	X	Letters of Recommendation

---

HISPANIC COLLEGE FUND

ORGANIZATION	NON-PROFIT	SCHOLARSHIP

Organization **Hispanic College Fund, Inc.**

Department Scholarship Selection Committee

Address 1300 L Street, NW, Suite 975

Washington　　　　　　　State DC　　　　Zip code 20005

WEBSITES

Where to apply Online

Organization

Scholarship www.hispanicfund.org

ANNUAL OPPORTUNITIES (ESTIMATED)

FIELD OF STUDY	Business related major

Scholarships Offered Annually	100-499
Average per Scholarship	$1,667

BUSINESS

TARGET AUDIENCES

								Tribe		Overall Diverse
Aimed At		Am. Indian	X	Latino		African Am		Asian Am		Women		Open to all

College Level		Pre College	X	1st Yr.	X	2nd Yr.	X	3rd Yr.	X	4th Yr.		Graduate Studies

Area Served National

Citizenship requirements Must be permanent resident or citizen

BASIS FOR AWARD

							Extracurricular Activities
X	Financial Need	X	Grades		Interviews	X	Community Involvement
	Essays	3.0	Minimum G.P.A.	X	SAT ACT	X	Letters of Recommendation

MAJOR SCHOLARSHIPS

More scholarships are added every month: Go to **www.EmpoweringStudents.com**

Hispanic Office of Planning & Evaluation (Talent Program)

Organization | College Program | Program

Organization **Hispanic Office of Planning and Evaluation**
Department
Address 165 Brookside Ave.
Jamaica Plain State MA Zip code 02130

Websites | Where to apply: Online

Organization www.hsph.harvard.edu/hyvpc/files/profile_hope.pd
Scholarship

Annual Opportunities (estimated)

Scholarships Offered Annually	Over 1,000
Average per Scholarship	$1,000

Field of Study: General — All Fields of Study

Target Audiences

Aimed At	[ ] Am. Indian	[X] Latino	[ ] African Am	[ ] Asian Am	[ ] Tribe / Women	[ ] Overall Diverse / Open to all
College Level	[X] Pre College	[ ] 1st Yr.	[ ] 2nd Yr.	[ ] 3rd Yr.	[ ] 4th Yr.	[ ] Graduate Studies

Area Served: Regional
Citizenship requirements: Must be permanent resident or citizen

Basis For Award

[X] Financial Need	[ ] Grades	[ ] Interviews	[ ] Extracurricular Activities
[ ] Essays	[ ] Minimum G.P.A.	[ ] SAT ACT	[ ] Community Involvement
			[ ] Letters of Recommendation

Hispanic Scholarship Fund

Organization | Non-Profit | Scholarship

Organization **Hispanic Scholarship Fund (HSF)**
Department
Address 1411 W. 190th Street, Suite 325
Gardena State CA Zip code 90248

Websites | Where to apply: Online

Organization www.hsf.net
Scholarship

Annual Opportunities (estimated)

Scholarships Offered Annually	Over 1,000
Average per Scholarship	$4,000

Field of Study: General — All Fields of Study

Target Audiences

Aimed At	[ ] Am. Indian	[X] Latino	[ ] African Am	[ ] Asian Am	[ ] Tribe / Women	[ ] Overall Diverse / Open to all
College Level	[ ] Pre College	[X] 1st Yr.	[X] 2nd Yr.	[X] 3rd Yr.	[X] 4th Yr.	[X] Graduate Studies

Area Served: National
Citizenship requirements: Must be permanent resident or citizen

Basis For Award

[X] Financial Need	[X] Grades	[ ] Interviews	[X] Extracurricular Activities
[ ] Essays	3.0 Minimum G.P.A.	[X] SAT ACT	[ ] Community Involvement
			[X] Letters of Recommendation

More scholarships are added every month: Go to ***www.EmpoweringStudents.com***

Hopi Scholarship

Organization | Tribe | Scholarship

Organization **Hopi Tribe Grants and Scholarship Program**
Department
Address Box 123
Kykotsmovi State AZ Zip code 86039

Websites — Where to apply: By mail

Organization
Scholarship http://www.HopiEducationFund.org

Annual Opportunities (estimated)

Scholarships Offered Annually	500-999
Average per Scholarship	$1,680

Field of Study: GENERAL

Target Audiences

Hopi Tribe

Aimed At	X Am. Indian	Latino	African Am	Asian Am	Women	Overall Diverse / Open to all
College Level	Pre College	X 1st Yr.	X 2nd Yr.	X 3rd Yr.	X 4th Yr.	X Graduate Studies

Area Served: National
Citizenship requirements: Doesn't matter

Basis For Award

X Financial Need	X Grades	Interviews	Extracurricular Activities
Essays	3.0 Minimum G.P.A.	X SAT ACT	Community Involvement
			Letters of Recommendation

Howard Hughes Medical Institute Fellowships &

Organization | Other | Grant

Organization **Howard Hughes Medical Institute**
Department Office of Grants & Special Programs
Address 4000 Jones Bridge Rd.
Chevy Chase State MD Zip code 20815-6789

Websites — Where to apply: Online

Organization
Scholarship http://www.hhmi.org/grants

Annual Opportunities (estimated)

Scholarships Offered Annually	100-499
Average per Scholarship	$37,000

Field of Study: MEDICINE — Research support in biomedical sciences. Medical, Dental, and Osteopathic

Target Audiences

Tribe

Aimed At	Am. Indian	Latino	African Am	Asian Am	Women	Overall Diverse / X Open to all
College Level	Pre College	1st Yr.	2nd Yr.	3rd Yr.	4th Yr.	X Graduate Studies

Area Served: International
Citizenship requirements: Doesn't matter

Basis For Award

X Financial Need	X Grades	X Interviews	X Extracurricular Activities
Essays	Minimum G.P.A.	X SAT ACT	X Community Involvement
			X Letters of Recommendation

MAJOR SCHOLARSHIPS

More scholarships are added every month: Go to **www.EmpoweringStudents.com**

Howard Hughes Medical Institute Pre Doctoral

Organization | Non-Profit | Fellowship

Organization **National Research Council**
Department Office of Scientific and Engineering Personnel
Address 2101 Constitution Ave. N.W.
Washington State DC Zip code 20418

Websites Where to apply: Online

Organization
Scholarship http://fellowships.nas.edu

Annual Opportunities (estimated)

Scholarships Offered Annually	20-49
Average per Scholarship	$31,000

Field of Study Biological Sciences — STEM

Target Audiences

										Tribe		Overall Diverse
Aimed At		Am. Indian		Latino		African Am		Asian Am		Women	X	Open to all
College Level		Pre College		1st Yr.		2nd Yr.		3rd Yr.		4th Yr.	X	Graduate Studies

Area Served: National
Citizenship requirements: Doesn't matter

Basis For Award

							Extracurricular Activities
	Financial Need		Grades		Interviews		Community Involvement
	Essays		Minimum G.P.A.		SAT ACT		Letters of Recommendation

HSF/ General College Scholarships

Organization | Non-Profit | Scholarship

Organization **Hispanic Scholarship Fund**
Department
Address 1411 W. 190th Street, Suite 325
Gardena State CA Zip code 90248

Websites Where to apply: Online

Organization www.hsf.net
Scholarship www.hsf.net/scholarships

Annual Opportunities (estimated)

Scholarships Offered Annually	Over 1,000
Average per Scholarship	$3,119

Field of Study All Fields of Study — General

Target Audiences

										Tribe		Overall Diverse
Aimed At		Am. Indian	X	Latino		African Am		Asian Am		Women		Open to all
College Level		Pre College	X	1st Yr.	X	2nd Yr.	X	3rd Yr.	X	4th Yr.	X	Graduate Studies

Area Served: National
Citizenship requirements: Must be permanent resident or citizen

Basis For Award

						X	Extracurricular Activities
X	Financial Need	X	Grades		Interviews		Community Involvement
	Essays	3.0	Minimum G.P.A.	X	SAT ACT		Letters of Recommendation

More scholarships are added every month: Go to ***www.EmpoweringStudents.com***

HSF/General Scholarships

Organization	Non-Profit
Type	Scholarship
Organization	**Hispanic Scholarship Fund**
Department	
Address	1411 W. 190th Street, Suite 325
City	Gardena
State	CA
Zip code	90248

Websites

Where to apply	Online
Organization	
Scholarship	www.hsf.net

Annual Opportunities (estimated)

Scholarships Offered Annually	Over 1,000
Average per Scholarship	$3,000

Field of Study: General — All Fields of Study

Target Audiences

Tribe						
Aimed At	Am. Indian	X Latino	African Am	Asian Am	Women	Overall Diverse / Open to all
College Level	Pre College	X 1st Yr.	X 2nd Yr.	X 3rd Yr.	X 4th Yr.	X Graduate Studies

Area Served	National
Citizenship requirements	Must be permanent resident or citizen

Basis For Award

X	Financial Need	X	Grades		Interviews
	Essays	3.0	Minimum G.P.A.	X	SAT ACT

	Extracurricular Activities
	Community Involvement
	Letters of Recommendation

IHS Scholarship Program

Organization	Government
Type	Scholarship
Organization	**Indian Health Service**
Department	
Address	801 Thompson Ave., Ste. 400
City	Rockville
State	MD
Zip code	20852

Websites

Where to apply	Either by mail or online
Organization	http://www.ihs.gov
Scholarship	http://www.ihs.gov/scholarship/index.cfm

Annual Opportunities (estimated)

Scholarships Offered Annually	100-499
Average per Scholarship	$20,000

Field of Study: Medicine — Health

Target Audiences

Tribe	All tribes					
Aimed At	X Am. Indian	Latino	African Am	Asian Am	Women	Overall Diverse / Open to all
College Level	Pre College	X 1st Yr.	X 2nd Yr.	X 3rd Yr.	X 4th Yr.	X Graduate Studies

Area Served	National
Citizenship requirements	Must be permanent resident or citizen

Basis For Award

	Financial Need		Grades		Interviews
	Essays		Minimum G.P.A.		SAT ACT

	Extracurricular Activities
	Community Involvement
	Letters of Recommendation

Inter-American University of Puerto Rico-San

Organization | College Program | Scholarship

Organization **Inter-American University of Puerto Rico-San German**
Department
Address 5100 C40 Fangernan Campus
San German State PR Zip code 00683

Websites — Where to apply: By mail

Organization www.sg.inter.edu
Scholarship

Annual Opportunities (estimated)

Scholarships Offered Annually: Over 1,000
Average per Scholarship: $1,000

Field of Study: General — All Fields of Study

Target Audiences

Aimed At		Am. Indian	X	Latino		African Am		Asian Am		Women	Tribe / Overall Diverse / Open to all
College Level		Pre College	X	1st Yr.	X	2nd Yr.	X	3rd Yr.	X	4th Yr.	Graduate Studies

Area Served: International
Citizenship requirements: Must be permanent resident or citizen

Basis For Award

X	Financial Need	X	Grades	X	Interviews	X	Extracurricular Activities
	Essays	2.25	Minimum G.P.A.	X	SAT ACT	X	Community Involvement
						X	Letters of Recommendation

Jack Kent Cooke Foundation Scholarship

Organization | Foundation | Scholarship

Organization **Jack Kent Cooke Foundation**
Department
Address 44325 Woodridge Parkway
Lansdowne State VA Zip code 20176

Websites — Where to apply: Online

Organization www.jackkentcookefoundation.org
Scholarship www.jkcf.org/scholarships

Annual Opportunities (estimated)

Scholarships Offered Annually: 50-99
Average per Scholarship: $30,000

Field of Study: General — All Fields of Study

Target Audiences

Aimed At		Am. Indian		Latino		African Am		Asian Am		Women	X	Tribe / Overall Diverse / Open to all
College Level	X	Pre College	X	1st Yr.	X	2nd Yr.	X	3rd Yr.	X	4th Yr.	X	Graduate Studies

Area Served: National
Citizenship requirements: Must be permanent resident or citizen

Basis For Award

X	Financial Need	X	Grades		Interviews		Extracurricular Activities
	Essays	3.5	Minimum G.P.A.		SAT ACT		Community Involvement
							Letters of Recommendation

Jacob K. Javits Fellowships Program

Organization	Government	Fellowship

Organization **U.S. Department of Education, OPE**
Department Jacob K. Javits Fellowships Program
Address 1990 K Street, N.W., 6th Floor
Washington State DC Zip code 20006-8524

Websites — Where to apply: Online
Organization
Scholarship www.ed.gov/programs/jacobjavits/index.html

Annual Opportunities (estimated)

Scholarships Offered Annually	20-49
Average per Scholarship	$30,000

Field of Study: VARIOUS — Arts, Humanities, adn Social Sciences

Target Audiences

										Tribe		Overall Diverse
Aimed At		Am. Indian		Latino		African Am		Asian Am		Women	X	Open to all
College Level		Pre College		1st Yr.		2nd Yr.		3rd Yr.		4th Yr.	X	Graduate Studies

Area Served: National
Citizenship requirements: Must be permanent resident or citizen

Basis For Award

							Extracurricular Activities
X	Financial Need	X	Grades	X	Interviews		Community Involvement
X	Essays		Minimum G.P.A.		SAT ACT		Letters of Recommendation

Joseph E. Pogue Scholarships

Organization	College Program	Scholarship

Organization **University of North Carolina at Chapel Hill**
Department Office of Scholarships and Student Aid
Address P. O. Box 1080
Chapel Hill State NC Zip code 27514

Websites — Where to apply: Online
Organization
Scholarship http://www.jomc.unc.edu

Annual Opportunities (estimated)

Scholarships Offered Annually	50-99
Average per Scholarship	$7,500

Field of Study: GENERAL — Open

Target Audiences

										Tribe		Overall Diverse
Aimed At		Am. Indian		Latino		African Am		Asian Am		Women	X	Open to all
College Level		Pre College	X	1st Yr.	X	2nd Yr.	X	3rd Yr.	X	4th Yr.		Graduate Studies

Area Served: Regional
Citizenship requirements: Must be permanent resident or citizen

Basis For Award

						X	Extracurricular Activities
	Financial Need	X	Grades	X	Interviews	X	Community Involvement
	Essays		Minimum G.P.A.	X	SAT ACT	X	Letters of Recommendation

Major Scholarships

More scholarships are added every month: Go to ***www.EmpoweringStudents.com***

KFC Colonel's Scholars Program

Organization | **Business** | **Scholarship**

Organization **KFC Foundation**
Department KFC's Corporate Address for Customer Comments
Address P.O. Box 725489
Atlanta State GA Zip code 31139

Websites — Where to apply: Online

Organization www.kfcscholars.org
Scholarship www.kfcscholars.org/scholarships

Annual Opportunities (estimated)

Scholarships Offered Annually	50-99
Average per Scholarship	$10,000

Field of Study: GENERAL — All Fields of Study

Target Audiences

Aimed At		Am. Indian		Latino		African Am		Asian Am		Women	X	Open to all (Tribe / Overall Diverse)
College Level		Pre College	X	1st Yr.	X	2nd Yr.	X	3rd Yr.	X	4th Yr.		Graduate Studies

Area Served: Regional
Citizenship requirements: Must be permanent resident or citizen

Basis For Award

X	Financial Need	X	Grades		Interviews		Extracurricular Activities
X	Essays	2.75	Minimum G.P.A.		SAT ACT		Community Involvement
							Letters of Recommendation

Leadership Scholarship

Organization | **College Program** | **Scholarship**

Organization **Loyola Marymount University**
Department Financial Aid
Address Xavier Hall, One Lmu Drive, Ste. 200
Los Angeles State CA Zip code 90045

Websites — Where to apply: Online

Organization
Scholarship www.lmu.edu/financialaid

Annual Opportunities (estimated)

Scholarships Offered Annually	20-49
Average per Scholarship	$36,000

Field of Study: GENERAL — Open

Target Audiences

Aimed At		Am. Indian		Latino		African Am		Asian Am		Women	X	Open to all (Tribe / Overall Diverse)
College Level		Pre College	X	1st Yr.	X	2nd Yr.	X	3rd Yr.	X	4th Yr.		Graduate Studies

Area Served: Regional
Citizenship requirements: Must be permanent resident or citizen

Basis For Award

X	Financial Need	X	Grades	X	Interviews	X	Extracurricular Activities
	Essays		Minimum G.P.A.	X	SAT ACT	X	Community Involvement
						X	Letters of Recommendation

Los Diablos Scholarship

Organization | College Program | Scholarship

Organization **Arizona State University**
Department Los Diablos Latino Alumni Association
Address
Tempe State AZ Zip code 85287-4305

Websites Where to apply: Online

Organization http://www.asu.edu
Scholarship http://www.asu.edu/alumni/chapters/special/los_diablos.shtml

Annual Opportunities (estimated)

Scholarships Offered Annually	100-499
Average per Scholarship	$10,000

Field of Study: General — All Fields of Study

Target Audiences

										Tribe		Overall Diverse
Aimed At		Am. Indian	X	Latino		African Am		Asian Am		Women		Open to all
College Level		Pre College	X	1st Yr.	X	2nd Yr.	X	3rd Yr.	X	4th Yr.		Graduate Studies

Area Served: Regional
Citizenship requirements: Must be permanent resident or citizen

Basis For Award

							Extracurricular Activities
X	Financial Need	X	Grades		Interviews	X	Community Involvement
	Essays	3.0	Minimum G.P.A.		SAT ACT		Letters of Recommendation

Mayor's Graduate Scholarship Program

Organization | Government | Scholarship

Organization **Admission Referral and Information Center**
Department NYC Department of Citywide Administrative Services
Address One Centre Street, Room 1340
New York State NY Zip code 10007

Websites Where to apply: By mail

Organization www.nyc.gov
Scholarship www.nyc.gov/mgsp

Annual Opportunities (estimated)

Scholarships Offered Annually	Over 1,000
Average per Scholarship	$650

Field of Study: General — Open

Target Audiences

										Tribe	X	Overall Diverse
Aimed At		Am. Indian		Latino		African Am		Asian Am		Women		Open to all
College Level		Pre College	X	1st Yr.	X	2nd Yr.	X	3rd Yr.	X	4th Yr.	X	Graduate Studies

Area Served: Regional
Citizenship requirements: Must be permanent resident or citizen

Basis For Award

							Extracurricular Activities
	Financial Need	X	Grades		Interviews		Community Involvement
X	Essays		Minimum G.P.A.		SAT ACT		Letters of Recommendation

Major Scholarships

More scholarships are added every month: Go to **www.EmpoweringStudents.com**

MEDI-CORPS

Organization | College Program | Program

Organization **UC Davis School of Medicine**
Department Office of Research and Education for the Medically Underserved
Address Office of the Dean
Davis State CA Zip code 95616

Websites — Where to apply: Online

Organization
Scholarship http://www.ucdavis.edu

Annual Opportunities (estimated)

Scholarships Offered Annually	50-99
Average per Scholarship	$10,000

Field of Study: MEDICINE — Medicine

Target Audiences

Aimed At		Am. Indian	X	Latino		African Am		Asian Am		Women		Open to all
								Tribe				Overall Diverse
College Level		Pre College	X	1st Yr.	X	2nd Yr.	X	3rd Yr.	X	4th Yr.		Graduate Studies

Area Served: Regional
Citizenship requirements: Must be permanent resident or citizen

Basis For Award

X	Financial Need	X	Grades	X	Interviews		Extracurricular Activities
							Community Involvement
	Essays		Minimum G.P.A.		SAT ACT	X	Letters of Recommendation

MICROSOFT SCHOLARSHIP PROGRAM

Organization | Business | Scholarship

Organization **Microsoft Corporation**
Department
Address One Microsoft Way
Redmond State WA Zip code 98052-8303

Websites — Where to apply: Online

Organization
Scholarship http://careers.microsoft.com/careers/en/us/collegescholarship.aspx

Annual Opportunities (estimated)

Scholarships Offered Annually	50-99
Average per Scholarship	$14,000

Field of Study: STEM — Computer science, computer engineering, or a related technical discipline

Target Audiences

Aimed At	X	Am. Indian	X	Latino	X	African Am		Asian Am	X	Women		Open to all
								Tribe			X	Overall Diverse
College Level		Pre College	X	1st Yr.	X	2nd Yr.	X	3rd Yr.	X	4th Yr.		Graduate Studies

Area Served: National
Citizenship requirements: Doesn't matter

Basis For Award

X	Financial Need	X	Grades		Interviews		Extracurricular Activities
							Community Involvement
X	Essays	3.0	Minimum G.P.A.	X	SAT ACT	X	Letters of Recommendation

MINORITY GRANTS

ORGANIZATION	COLLEGE PROGRAM	GRANT

Organization **Michigan Technological University**
Department Financial Aid Office
Address 1400 Townsend Dr.
Houghton State MI Zip code 49931-1295

WEBSITES Where to apply: Online

Organization
Scholarship http://www.mtu.edu

ANNUAL OPPORTUNITIES (ESTIMATED) | **FIELD OF STUDY**: All Fields of Study — GENERAL

Scholarships Offered Annually	100-499
Average per Scholarship	$4,939

TARGET AUDIENCES

				Tribe	X	Overall Diverse
Aimed At	Am. Indian	Latino	African Am	Asian Am	Women	Open to all
College Level	Pre College	X 1st Yr.	X 2nd Yr.	X 3rd Yr.	X 4th Yr.	Graduate Studies

Area Served: Regional
Citizenship requirements: U.S. Citizenship required

BASIS FOR AWARD

			Extracurricular Activities
Financial Need	Grades	Interviews	Community Involvement
Essays	Minimum G.P.A.	SAT ACT	Letters of Recommendation

MINORITY MEDICAL EDUCATION PROGRAM

ORGANIZATION	FOUNDATION	PROGRAM

Organization **Robert Wood Johnson Foundation**
Department College Road East and U.S. Route 1
Address P.O. Box 2316
Princeton State NJ Zip code 08543-2316

WEBSITES Where to apply: Online

Organization
Scholarship http://www.aamc.org/mmep

ANNUAL OPPORTUNITIES (ESTIMATED) | **FIELD OF STUDY**: Open — GENERAL

Scholarships Offered Annually	Over 1,000
Average per Scholarship	$25,000

TARGET AUDIENCES

				Tribe	X	Overall Diverse
Aimed At	Am. Indian	Latino	African Am	Asian Am	Women	Open to all
College Level	Pre College	X 1st Yr.	2nd Yr.	3rd Yr.	4th Yr.	Graduate Studies

Area Served: National
Citizenship requirements: U.S. Citizenship required

BASIS FOR AWARD

			Extracurricular Activities
Financial Need	Grades	Interviews	Community Involvement
Essays	Minimum G.P.A.	SAT ACT	Letters of Recommendation

MAJOR SCHOLARSHIPS

More scholarships are added every month: Go to **www.EmpoweringStudents.com**

MINORITY RESEARCH INFRASTRUCTURE SUPPORT

ORGANIZATION — GOVERNMENT — PROGRAM

Organization **The National Institute of Mental Health**
Department Office of the Director
Address 6001 Executive Blvd., Room 8184, MSC 9663
Bethesda State MD Zip code 20892

WEBSITES — Where to apply: Online

Organization
Scholarship www.nimh.nih.gov/grants

ANNUAL OPPORTUNITIES (ESTIMATED)

Scholarships Offered Annually: 100-499
Average per Scholarship: $35,000

FIELD OF STUDY: MEDICINE — Mental Health and Illness

TARGET AUDIENCES

											Tribe	X	Overall Diverse
Aimed At		Am. Indian		Latino		African Am		Asian Am		Women			Open to all
College Level		Pre College		1st Yr.		2nd Yr.		3rd Yr.		4th Yr.		X	Graduate Studies

Area Served: National
Citizenship requirements: Doesn't matter

BASIS FOR AWARD

							Extracurricular Activities
	Financial Need		Grades		Interviews		Community Involvement
	Essays		Minimum G.P.A.		SAT ACT		Letters of Recommendation

NATIONAL ACHIEVEMENT SCHOLARSHIP PROGRAM

ORGANIZATION — BUSINESS — SCHOLARSHIP

Organization **National Merit Scholarship Corporation**
Department
Address 1560 Sherman Avenue, Suite 200
Evanston State IL Zip code 60201-4897

WEBSITES — Where to apply: Online

Organization www.nationalmerit.org/index.php
Scholarship www.nationalmerit.org/nasp.php

ANNUAL OPPORTUNITIES (ESTIMATED)

Scholarships Offered Annually: 500-999
Average per Scholarship: $25,000

FIELD OF STUDY: GENERAL — All fields of Study.

TARGET AUDIENCES

											Tribe		Overall Diverse
Aimed At		Am. Indian		Latino	X	African Am		Asian Am		Women			Open to all
College Level	X	Pre College		1st Yr.		2nd Yr.		3rd Yr.		4th Yr.			Graduate Studies

Area Served: National
Citizenship requirements: Must be permanent resident or citizen

BASIS FOR AWARD

						X	Extracurricular Activities
X	Financial Need	X	Grades		Interviews	X	Community Involvement
X	Essays		Minimum G.P.A.	X	SAT ACT	X	Letters of Recommendation

More scholarships are added every month: Go to ***www.EmpoweringStudents.com***

NATIONAL HEALTH SERVICE CORPS SCHOLARSHIP

ORGANIZATION GOVERNMENT | SCHOLARSHIP

Organization **Bureau of Primary Health Care**
Department National Health Service Corps Program
Address 2070 Chain Bridge Road, Suite 450
Vienna State VA Zip code 22182-2563

WEBSITES Where to apply: By mail

Organization http://bphc.hrsa.gov
Scholarship http://nhsc.hrsa.gov/scholarships

ANNUAL OPPORTUNITIES (ESTIMATED)

Scholarships Offered Annually: 100-499
Average per Scholarship: $200,000

FIELD OF STUDY MEDICINE — Medical

TARGET AUDIENCES

					Tribe		Overall Diverse
Aimed At	Am. Indian	Latino	African Am	Asian Am	Women	X	Open to all
College Level	Pre College	X 1st Yr.	X 2nd Yr.	X 3rd Yr.	X 4th Yr.	X	Graduate Studies

Area Served: National
Citizenship requirements: U.S. Citizenship required

BASIS FOR AWARD

			Extracurricular Activities
Financial Need	Grades	Interviews	Community Involvement
Essays	Minimum G.P.A.	SAT ACT	Letters of Recommendation

NATIONAL SECURITY EDUCATION PROGRAM'S DAVID L.

ORGANIZATION NON-PROFIT | FELLOWSHIP

Organization **Academy for Educational Development, Inc.**
Department
Address 1825 Connecticut Ave., N.W.
Washington State DC Zip code 20009

WEBSITES Where to apply: Online

Organization
Scholarship http://www.aed.org/nsep

ANNUAL OPPORTUNITIES (ESTIMATED)

Scholarships Offered Annually: 50-99
Average per Scholarship: $16,667

FIELD OF STUDY GENERAL — All Fields of Study

TARGET AUDIENCES

					Tribe		Overall Diverse
Aimed At	Am. Indian	Latino	African Am	Asian Am	Women	X	Open to all
College Level	Pre College	1st Yr.	2nd Yr.	3rd Yr.	4th Yr.	X	Graduate Studies

Area Served: National
Citizenship requirements: Must be permanent resident or citizen

BASIS FOR AWARD

			X Extracurricular Activities
Financial Need	X Grades	X Interviews	X Community Involvement
Essays	Minimum G.P.A.	SAT ACT	X Letters of Recommendation

MAJOR SCHOLARSHIPS

More scholarships are added every month: Go to ***www.EmpoweringStudents.com***

National Society of Hispanic MBA's Scholarship

Organization: Foundation — **Scholarship**

Organization **National Society of Hispanic MBAS Scholarship Program**
Department Scholarship Management Services
Address One Scholarship Way
Saint Peter State MN Zip code 56082

Websites — Where to apply: Online

Organization www.nshmba.org
Scholarship www.nshmba.scholarshipamerica.org/

Annual Opportunities (estimated)

Scholarships Offered Annually	100-499
Average per Scholarship	$18,636

Field of Study: Business — BUSINESS

Target Audiences

									Tribe		Overall Diverse
Aimed At		Am. Indian	X	Latino		African Am		Asian Am		Women	X	Open to all
College Level		Pre College		1st Yr.		2nd Yr.		3rd Yr.		4th Yr.	X	Graduate Studies

Area Served: Regional
Citizenship requirements: Must be permanent resident or citizen

Basis For Award

							Extracurricular Activities
X	Financial Need	X	Grades		Interviews	X	Community Involvement
X	Essays	3.0	Minimum G.P.A.		SAT ACT	X	Letters of Recommendation

National Urban Fellowship Award

Organization: Non-Profit — **Fellowship**

Organization **National Urban Fellows, Inc.**
Department
Address 59 John St., Suite 310
New York State NY Zip code 10038

Websites — Where to apply: Online

Organization
Scholarship http://www.nuf.org

Annual Opportunities (estimated)

Scholarships Offered Annually	20-49
Average per Scholarship	$20,000

Field of Study: Public Administration — VARIOUS

Target Audiences

									Tribe	X	Overall Diverse
Aimed At		Am. Indian		Latino		African Am		Asian Am		Women		Open to all
College Level		Pre College		1st Yr.		2nd Yr.		3rd Yr.		4th Yr.	X	Graduate Studies

Area Served: National
Citizenship requirements: U.S. Citizenship required

Basis For Award

						X	Extracurricular Activities
	Financial Need	X	Grades	X	Interviews	X	Community Involvement
	Essays		Minimum G.P.A.		SAT ACT	X	Letters of Recommendation

More scholarships are added every month: Go to ***www.EmpoweringStudents.com***

Navajo Generating Station Navajo Scholarship

Organization | **Other** | **Scholarship**

Organization **SRP/Navajo Generating Station (NGS)**

Department

Address P.O. Box 850

Page State AZ Zip code 86040

Websites

Where to apply: By mail

Organization

Scholarship www.srpnet.com/education/grants/navajo.aspx

Annual Opportunities (estimated)

Scholarships Offered Annually	100-499
Average per Scholarship	$10,000

Field of Study: STEM

Math, engineering and environmental studies (preferred)

Target Audiences

Navajo Tribe

Aimed At	X	Am. Indian		Latino		African Am		Asian Am		Women		Open to all / Overall Diverse	
College Level		Pre College		1st Yr.		2nd Yr.	X	3rd Yr.		4th Yr.		Graduate Studies	

Area Served: National

Citizenship requirements: U.S. Citizenship required

Basis For Award

X	Financial Need	X	Grades		Interviews		Extracurricular Activities
X	Essays		Minimum G.P.A.		SAT ACT		Community Involvement
						X	Letters of Recommendation

Navajo Nation Scholarship & Financial Assistance

Organization | **Tribe** | **Scholarship**

Organization **Navajo Nation**

Department

Address P.O. Box 9000

Window Rock State AZ Zip code 86515

Websites

Where to apply: Either by mail or online

Organization www.navajo-nsn.gov/

Scholarship www.onnsfa.org/default.aspx

Annual Opportunities (estimated)

Scholarships Offered Annually	500-999
Average per Scholarship	$5,000

Field of Study: GENERAL

Target Audiences

Tribe

Aimed At	X	Am. Indian		Latino		African Am		Asian Am		Women		Open to all / Overall Diverse	
College Level		Pre College	X	1st Yr.	X	2nd Yr.	X	3rd Yr.	X	4th Yr.		Graduate Studies	

Area Served: Regional

Citizenship requirements: Must be permanent resident or citizen

Basis For Award

X	Financial Need	X	Grades		Interviews		Extracurricular Activities
	Essays		Minimum G.P.A.		SAT ACT		Community Involvement
							Letters of Recommendation

Major Scholarships

More scholarships are added every month: Go to ***www.EmpoweringStudents.com***

NEW JERSEY EDUCATIONAL OPPORTUNITY FUND GRANTS

ORGANIZATION GOVERNMENT | GRANT

Organization **New Jersey Commission of Higher Education**
Department Educational Opportunity Fund
Address P.O. Box 542
Trenton State NJ Zip code 08625-0542

WEBSITES Where to apply: Online

Organization
Scholarship www.state.nj.us

ANNUAL OPPORTUNITIES (ESTIMATED)

Scholarships Offered Annually	Over 1,000
Average per Scholarship	$1,202

FIELD OF STUDY Open — GENERAL

TARGET AUDIENCES

Aimed At	Am. Indian	Latino	African Am	Asian Am	Women	Tribe	Overall Diverse	Open to all
								X

College Level	Pre College	1st Yr.	2nd Yr.	3rd Yr.	4th Yr.	Graduate Studies
		X	X	X	X	

Area Served: Regional
Citizenship requirements: Must be permanent resident or citizen

BASIS FOR AWARD

X Financial Need	X Grades	X Interviews	Extracurricular Activities
Essays	Minimum G.P.A.	X SAT ACT	X Community Involvement
			Letters of Recommendation

NISSAN SCHOLARSHIP PROGRAM

ORGANIZATION BUSINESS | SCHOLARSHIP

Organization **Nissan**
Department Public Relations Department
Address P. O. Box 191, Mail Stop N-3-A
Gardena State CA Zip code 90248-0191

WEBSITES Where to apply: Online

Organization
Scholarship http://www.nissanusa.com

ANNUAL OPPORTUNITIES (ESTIMATED)

Scholarships Offered Annually	20-49
Average per Scholarship	$25,000

FIELD OF STUDY Automotive — VARIOUS

TARGET AUDIENCES

Aimed At	Am. Indian	Latino	African Am	Asian Am	Women	Tribe	Overall Diverse	Open to all
							X	

College Level	Pre College	1st Yr.	2nd Yr.	3rd Yr.	4th Yr.	Graduate Studies
		X	X	X	X	

Area Served: National
Citizenship requirements: Must be permanent resident or citizen

BASIS FOR AWARD

Financial Need	Grades	Interviews	Extracurricular Activities
Essays	Minimum G.P.A.	SAT ACT	Community Involvement
			Letters of Recommendation

More scholarships are added every month: Go to ***www.EmpoweringStudents.com***

NROTC Immediate Selection Decision (ISD)

Organization: Government | **Scholarship**

Organization **United States Department of the Navy**
Department
Address
Washington State DC Zip code

Websites — Where to apply: Online
Organization
Scholarship http://www.cec.navy.mil/

Annual Opportunities (estimated)

Scholarships Offered Annually	20-49
Average per Scholarship	$30,000

Field of Study: GENERAL

Target Audiences

					Tribe		Overall Diverse
Aimed At	Am. Indian	Latino	African Am	Asian Am	Women	X	Open to all
College Level	Pre College	X 1st Yr.	2nd Yr.	3rd Yr.	4th Yr.		Graduate Studies

Area Served: National
Citizenship requirements: U.S. Citizenship required

Basis For Award

		Extracurricular Activities
Financial Need	X Grades	Interviews / Community Involvement
Essays	Minimum G.P.A.	X SAT ACT / Letters of Recommendation

NSF Graduate Research Fellowship Program (GRFP)

Organization: Foundation | **Fellowship**

Organization **National Science Foundation**
Department
Address 1818 N. Street, NW Suite 600
Washington State DC Zip code 20036

Websites — Where to apply: Online
Organization www.nsfgrfp.org
Scholarship

Annual Opportunities (estimated)

Scholarships Offered Annually	100-499
Average per Scholarship	$15,000

Field of Study: STEM — Science, technology, engineering, and math

Target Audiences

					Tribe	X	Overall Diverse
Aimed At	Am. Indian	X Latino	African Am	Asian Am	X Women		Open to all
College Level	Pre College	1st Yr.	2nd Yr.	3rd Yr.	4th Yr.	X	Graduate Studies

Area Served: National
Citizenship requirements: U.S. Citizenship required

Basis For Award

		Extracurricular Activities
Financial Need	X Grades	Interviews / Community Involvement
Essays	Minimum G.P.A.	SAT ACT / X Letters of Recommendation

More scholarships are added every month: Go to ***www.EmpoweringStudents.com***

NUCLEAR PROPULSION OFFICER (NUPOC)

ORGANIZATION | GOVERNMENT | SCHOLARSHIP

Organization **United States Department of the Navy**
Department
Address
Washington State DC Zip code

WEBSITES — Where to apply: Online

Organization www.navy.mil
Scholarship

ANNUAL OPPORTUNITIES (ESTIMATED)

Scholarships Offered Annually	20-49
Average per Scholarship	$25,000

FIELD OF STUDY: GENERAL

TARGET AUDIENCES

Tribe:

Aimed At	[ ] Am. Indian	[ ] Latino	[ ] African Am	[ ] Asian Am	[ ] Women	[ ] Overall Diverse / [X] Open to all
College Level	[ ] Pre College	[ ] 1st Yr.	[ ] 2nd Yr.	[ ] 3rd Yr.	[ ] 4th Yr.	[ ] Graduate Studies

Area Served: National
Citizenship requirements: U.S. Citizenship required

BASIS FOR AWARD

[ ] Financial Need	[X] Grades	[ ] Interviews	[ ] Extracurricular Activities
[ ] Essays	3.0 Minimum G.P.A.	[ ] SAT ACT	[ ] Community Involvement
			[ ] Letters of Recommendation

OGLALA LAKOTA COLLEGE SCHOLARSHIPS

ORGANIZATION | COLLEGE PROGRAM | SCHOLARSHIP

Organization **Oglala Lakota College**
Department Financial Aid Department
Address 3 Mile Creek Rd, Box 490
Kyle State SD Zip code 57752-0490

WEBSITES — Where to apply: Either by mail or online

Organization www.olc.edu
Scholarship

ANNUAL OPPORTUNITIES (ESTIMATED)

Scholarships Offered Annually	Over 1,000
Average per Scholarship	$1,917

FIELD OF STUDY: GENERAL

TARGET AUDIENCES

Tribe: Oglala Lakota tribe

Aimed At	[X] Am. Indian	[ ] Latino	[ ] African Am	[ ] Asian Am	[ ] Women	[ ] Overall Diverse / [ ] Open to all
College Level	[ ] Pre College	[X] 1st Yr.	[X] 2nd Yr.	[X] 3rd Yr.	[X] 4th Yr.	[ ] Graduate Studies

Area Served: Regional
Citizenship requirements: Doesn't matter

BASIS FOR AWARD

[X] Financial Need	[X] Grades	[ ] Interviews	[X] Extracurricular Activities
[X] Essays	Minimum G.P.A.	[ ] SAT ACT	[ ] Community Involvement
			[ ] Letters of Recommendation

More scholarships are added every month: Go to ***www.EmpoweringStudents.com***

Ohio State Distinction Scholarship

Organization: College Program | Scholarship

Organization **Ohio State University-Columbus**

Department

Address 1800 Cannon Dr.
Columbus State OH Zip code 43210-1200

Websites — Where to apply: Online

Organization

Scholarship www.oma.ohio-state.edu

Annual Opportunities (estimated)

Scholarships Offered Annually	100-499
Average per Scholarship	$15,000

Field of Study: GENERAL — All Fields of Study

Target Audiences

									Tribe		Overall Diverse		
Aimed At		Am. Indian		Latino		African Am		Asian Am		Women	X	Open to all
College Level		Pre College	X	1st Yr.		2nd Yr.		3rd Yr.		4th Yr.		Graduate Studies

Area Served: Regional

Citizenship requirements: Must be permanent resident or citizen

Basis For Award

	Financial Need		Grades		Interviews		Extracurricular Activities
	Essays		Minimum G.P.A.		SAT ACT		Community Involvement
							Letters of Recommendation

Patty Iron Cloud National Native American

Organization: Non-Profit | Program

Organization **The Association of American Indian Physicians**

Department

Address 1225 Sovereign Row, Suite 103
Oklahoma City State OK Zip code 73108405-946-7651

Websites — Where to apply: Either by mail or online

Organization http://www.aaip.org/

Scholarship http://www.aaip.org/?NNAYISTUDENT

Annual Opportunities (estimated)

Scholarships Offered Annually	100-499
Average per Scholarship	$7,000

Field of Study: MEDICINE — Health sciences or biomedical research

Target Audiences

									Tribe		Overall Diverse		
Aimed At	X	Am. Indian		Latino		African Am		Asian Am		Women		Open to all
College Level	X	Pre College		1st Yr.		2nd Yr.		3rd Yr.		4th Yr.		Graduate Studies

Area Served: National

Citizenship requirements: Must be permanent resident or citizen

Basis For Award

X	Financial Need	X	Grades		Interviews		Extracurricular Activities
	Essays		Minimum G.P.A.		SAT ACT		Community Involvement
							Letters of Recommendation

Major Scholarships

More scholarships are added every month: Go to **www.EmpoweringStudents.com**

PRESIDENTS ACHIEVEMENT SCHOLARSHIP

ORGANIZATION | COLLEGE PROGRAM | SCHOLARSHIP

Organization **University of Texas at Austin**
Department Office of Student Financial Services
Address P. O. Box 7758, U. T. Station
Austin State TX Zip code 78713-7758

WEBSITES Where to apply Online

Organization
Scholarship www.utexas.edu/student/finaid/

ANNUAL OPPORTUNITIES (ESTIMATED) | **FIELD OF STUDY** Open

GENERAL

Scholarships Offered Annually	500-999
Average per Scholarship	$2,143

TARGET AUDIENCES

Aimed At	Am. Indian	Latino	African Am	Asian Am	Women	X Open to all
College Level	Pre College	X 1st Yr.	X 2nd Yr.	X 3rd Yr.	X 4th Yr.	Graduate Studies

Tribe | Overall Diverse

Area Served: Regional
Citizenship requirements: Must be permanent resident or citizen

BASIS FOR AWARD

X Financial Need	Grades	Interviews	X Extracurricular Activities
Essays	Minimum G.P.A.	SAT ACT	X Community Involvement
			X Letters of Recommendation

PRIORITY GRANT COMPETITION

ORGANIZATION | GOVERNMENT | GRANT

Organization **United States Institute of Peace**
Department
Address 2301 Constitution Avenue, NW
Washington State DC Zip code 20037

WEBSITES Where to apply Online

Organization www.usip.org
Scholarship http://www.usip.org/grants-fellowships/priority-grant-competition

ANNUAL OPPORTUNITIES (ESTIMATED) | **FIELD OF STUDY** Interest and involvement in social justice, and/or peace issues

GENERAL

Scholarships Offered Annually	20-49
Average per Scholarship	$45,000

TARGET AUDIENCES

Aimed At	Am. Indian	Latino	African Am	Asian Am	Women	X Open to all
College Level	Pre College	X 1st Yr.	X 2nd Yr.	X 3rd Yr.	X 4th Yr.	X Graduate Studies

Tribe | Overall Diverse

Area Served: International
Citizenship requirements: Doesn't matter

BASIS FOR AWARD

X Financial Need	Grades	Interviews	Extracurricular Activities
X Essays	Minimum G.P.A.	SAT ACT	X Community Involvement
			Letters of Recommendation

RANDOLPH MACON MINORITY SCHOLARSHIPS

ORGANIZATION | COLLEGE PROGRAM | SCHOLARSHIP

Organization **Randolph-Macon College**
Department Dean of Admissions and Financial Aid
Address P. O. Box 5005
Ashland State VA Zip code 23005

WEBSITES — Where to apply: Online

Organization
Scholarship http://www.rmc.edu

ANNUAL OPPORTUNITIES (ESTIMATED)

Scholarships Offered Annually	500-999
Average per Scholarship	$4,000

FIELD OF STUDY: Open — GENERAL

TARGET AUDIENCES

					Tribe	X Overall Diverse
Aimed At	Am. Indian	Latino	African Am	Asian Am	Women	Open to all
College Level	Pre College	X 1st Yr.	X 2nd Yr.	X 3rd Yr.	X 4th Yr.	Graduate Studies

Area Served: Regional
Citizenship requirements: Doesn't matter

BASIS FOR AWARD

			X Extracurricular Activities
X Financial Need	X Grades	X Interviews	X Community Involvement
Essays	3.2 Minimum G.P.A.	X SAT ACT	X Letters of Recommendation

RESEARCH TRAINING & CAREER DEVELOPMENT PROGRAM

ORGANIZATION | GOVERNMENT | PROGRAM

Organization **The National Institute of Mental Health**
Department Parklawn Bldg
Address 6001 Executive Blvd., Room 8184, MSC 9663
Bethesda State MD Zip code 20892

WEBSITES — Where to apply: Online

Organization
Scholarship www.nimh.nih.gov/grants/

ANNUAL OPPORTUNITIES (ESTIMATED)

Scholarships Offered Annually	100-499
Average per Scholarship	$30,000

FIELD OF STUDY: Mental Health and Illness — MEDICINE

TARGET AUDIENCES

					Tribe	Overall Diverse
Aimed At	Am. Indian	Latino	African Am	Asian Am	Women	X Open to all
College Level	Pre College	1st Yr.	2nd Yr.	3rd Yr.	4th Yr.	X Graduate Studies

Area Served: National
Citizenship requirements: Doesn't matter

BASIS FOR AWARD

			Extracurricular Activities
Financial Need	Grades	Interviews	Community Involvement
Essays	Minimum G.P.A.	SAT ACT	Letters of Recommendation

MAJOR SCHOLARSHIPS

RESEARCH TRAINING & FELLOWSHIPS PROGRAM

ORGANIZATION | GOVERNMENT | FELLOWSHIP

Organization **The National Institute of Mental Health**
Department Division of Services and Intervention Research
Address 6001 Executive Blvd., Room 8184, MSC 9663
Bethesda State MD Zip code 20892

WEBSITES | Where to apply: Online

Organization
Scholarship www.nimh.nih.gov/grants

ANNUAL OPPORTUNITIES (ESTIMATED)

Scholarships Offered Annually	100-499
Average per Scholarship	$35,000

FIELD OF STUDY MEDICINE — Mental Health and Illness

TARGET AUDIENCES

					Tribe	Overall Diverse
Aimed At	Am. Indian	Latino	African Am	Asian Am	Women	X Open to all
College Level	Pre College	1st Yr.	2nd Yr.	3rd Yr.	4th Yr.	X Graduate Studies

Area Served: National
Citizenship requirements: Doesn't matter

BASIS FOR AWARD

			Extracurricular Activities
Financial Need	Grades	Interviews	Community Involvement
Essays	Minimum G.P.A.	SAT ACT	Letters of Recommendation

ROCKEFELLER BROTHERS FUND FELLOWSHIP PROGRAM

ORGANIZATION | FOUNDATION | FELLOWSHIP

Organization **Rockefeller Brothers Fund**
Department
Address 437 Madison Ave. 37th Floor
New York State NY Zip code 10022-7001

WEBSITES | Where to apply: Online

Organization
Scholarship http://www.rbf.org

ANNUAL OPPORTUNITIES (ESTIMATED)

Scholarships Offered Annually	20-49
Average per Scholarship	$22,100

FIELD OF STUDY EDUCATION — Teaching Profession

TARGET AUDIENCES

					Tribe	X Overall Diverse
Aimed At	Am. Indian	Latino	African Am	Asian Am	Women	Open to all
College Level	Pre College	1st Yr.	2nd Yr.	3rd Yr.	X 4th Yr.	X Graduate Studies

Area Served: National
Citizenship requirements: Doesn't matter

BASIS FOR AWARD

			X Extracurricular Activities
X Financial Need	X Grades	Interviews	X Community Involvement
Essays	Minimum G.P.A.	SAT ACT	Letters of Recommendation

More scholarships are added every month: Go to **www.EmpoweringStudents.com**

SACNAS National Conference Travel & Lodging

Organization	Non-Profit	Award

Organization **SACNAS - Society for Advancement of Chicanos and Native Americans in**
Department Student Programs
Address P.O. Box 8526
Santa Cruz State CA Zip code 95061-8526

Websites — Where to apply: Online

Organization www.sacnas.org
Scholarship

Annual Opportunities (estimated)

Scholarships Offered Annually	500-999
Average per Scholarship	$1,000

Field of Study: STEM — All Sciences

Target Audiences

				Tribe	X	Overall Diverse
Aimed At	X Am. Indian	X Latino	African Am	Asian Am	Women	Open to all
College Level	Pre College	X 1st Yr.	X 2nd Yr.	X 3rd Yr.	X 4th Yr.	X Graduate Studies

Area Served: National
Citizenship requirements: Must be permanent resident or citizen

Basis For Award

			Extracurricular Activities
Financial Need	X Grades	X Interviews	X Community Involvement
X Essays	Minimum G.P.A.	SAT ACT	X Letters of Recommendation

Scholarships

Organization	College Program	Scholarship

Organization **University of Colorado School of Law**
Department Admissions Office
Address 403 UCB
Boulder State CO Zip code 80309-0403

Websites — Where to apply: Online

Organization
Scholarship http://www.colorado.edu/law

Annual Opportunities (estimated)

Scholarships Offered Annually	100-499
Average per Scholarship	$2,526

Field of Study: Various — Law

Target Audiences

				Tribe		Overall Diverse
Aimed At	Am. Indian	Latino	African Am	Asian Am	Women	X Open to all
College Level	Pre College	1st Yr.	2nd Yr.	3rd Yr.	4th Yr.	X Graduate Studies

Area Served: Regional
Citizenship requirements: U.S. Citizenship required

Basis For Award

			Extracurricular Activities
Financial Need	Grades	Interviews	Community Involvement
Essays	Minimum G.P.A.	SAT ACT	Letters of Recommendation

More scholarships are added every month: Go to **www.EmpoweringStudents.com**

Seattle University Regent's Award

Organization | College Program | Award

Organization **Seattle University**
Department Financial Aid Office
Address 900 Broadway
Seattle State WA Zip code 98122-4340

Websites — Where to apply: Online

Organization
Scholarship http://www.seattleu.edu.

Annual Opportunities (estimated)

Scholarships Offered Annually	100-499
Average per Scholarship	$6,000

Field of Study: GENERAL — All Fields of Study

Target Audiences

Aimed At	X	Am. Indian	X	Latino	X	African Am		Asian Am		Women		Open to all
										Tribe		Overall Diverse
College Level		Pre College	X	1st Yr.	X	2nd Yr.	X	3rd Yr.	X	4th Yr.		Graduate Studies

Area Served: Regional
Citizenship requirements: Must be permanent resident or citizen

Basis For Award

X	Financial Need	X	Grades		Interviews
	Essays	2.7	Minimum G.P.A.	X	SAT ACT
	Extracurricular Activities	X	Community Involvement	X	Letters of Recommendation

Stokes Educational Scholarship Program

Organization | Government | Scholarship

Organization **National Security Agency**
Department Stokes
Address 9800 Savage Rd, Suite 6779
Fort George G. Meade State MD Zip code 20755-6779

Websites — Where to apply: Either by mail or online

Organization
Scholarship http://www.nsa.gov/careers/opportunities_4_u/students/stokes.shtml

Annual Opportunities (estimated)

Scholarships Offered Annually	100-499
Average per Scholarship	$12,500

Field of Study: STEM — Computer science or computer/electrical engineering

Target Audiences

Aimed At		Am. Indian		Latino		African Am		Asian Am		Women		Open to all
										Tribe	X	Overall Diverse
College Level		Pre College	X	1st Yr.	X	2nd Yr.	X	3rd Yr.	X	4th Yr.		Graduate Studies

Area Served: National
Citizenship requirements: U.S. Citizenship required

Basis For Award

	Financial Need	X	Grades		Interviews
X	Essays	3.0	Minimum G.P.A.	X	SAT ACT
	Extracurricular Activities		Community Involvement		Letters of Recommendation

More scholarships are added every month: Go to ***www.EmpoweringStudents.com***

SUMMER RESEARCH PROGRAM FOR MINORITIES & WOMEN

ORGANIZATION	BUSINESS	PROGRAM

Organization **Lucent Technologies**
Department Bell Laboratories
Address 600 Mountain Ave. Rm 3-D -302
Murray Hill State NJ Zip code 07974-0636

WEBSITES Where to apply: Online
Organization www.alcatel-lucent.com
Scholarship

ANNUAL OPPORTUNITIES (ESTIMATED)

Scholarships Offered Annually	50-99
Average per Scholarship	$6,552

FIELD OF STUDY Engineering, Science
STEM

TARGET AUDIENCES

				Tribe	X	Overall Diverse
Aimed At	Am. Indian	Latino	African Am	Asian Am	X Women	Open to all
College Level	Pre College	1st Yr.	2nd Yr.	X 3rd Yr.	X 4th Yr.	Graduate Studies

Area Served: National
Citizenship requirements: Must be permanent resident or citizen

BASIS FOR AWARD

			Extracurricular Activities
Financial Need	Grades	Interviews	Community Involvement
Essays	Minimum G.P.A.	SAT ACT	Letters of Recommendation

TECHNOLOGY SCHOLAR PROGRAM

ORGANIZATION	COLLEGE PROGRAM	PROGRAM

Organization **Connecticut Innovations**
Department
Address 999 West St.
Rocky Hill State CT Zip code 06067

WEBSITES Where to apply: Online
Organization
Scholarship http://www.ctinnovations.com

ANNUAL OPPORTUNITIES (ESTIMATED)

Scholarships Offered Annually	Over 1,000
Average per Scholarship	$2,000

FIELD OF STUDY Science or Technology
STEM

TARGET AUDIENCES

				Tribe		Overall Diverse
Aimed At	Am. Indian	Latino	African Am	Asian Am	Women	X Open to all
College Level	Pre College	X 1st Yr.	2nd Yr.	3rd Yr.	4th Yr.	Graduate Studies

Area Served: Regional
Citizenship requirements: Must be permanent resident or citizen

BASIS FOR AWARD

			Extracurricular Activities
Financial Need	X Grades	Interviews	Community Involvement
Essays	3.0 Minimum G.P.A.	SAT ACT	Letters of Recommendation

MAJOR SCHOLARSHIPS

Terry Foundation Scholarship

Organization | College Program | Scholarship

Organization **University of Texas at Austin**
Department Office of Student Financial Services
Address P. O. Box 7758, U. T. Station
Austin State TX Zip code 78713-7758

Websites Where to apply: Online

Organization
Scholarship http://www.utexas.edu/

Annual Opportunities (estimated)

Scholarships Offered Annually	100-499
Average per Scholarship	$9,000

Field of Study Open — General

Target Audiences

Aimed At	Am. Indian	Latino	African Am	Asian Am	Tribe / Women	Overall Diverse	X Open to all
College Level	Pre College	X 1st Yr.	X 2nd Yr.	X 3rd Yr.	X 4th Yr.	Graduate Studies	

Area Served: Regional
Citizenship requirements: U.S. Citizenship required

Basis For Award

- [X] Financial Need
- [X] Grades
- [ ] Interviews
- [X] Extracurricular Activities
- [X] Community Involvement
- [ ] Essays
- [ ] Minimum G.P.A.
- [X] SAT ACT
- [X] Letters of Recommendation

Texas General Nursing Scholarship Program

Organization | Government | Scholarship

Organization **Texas Higher Education Coordinating Board**
Department Student Services Division
Address P.O. Box 12788
Austin State TX Zip code 78711-2788

Websites Where to apply: Online

Organization
Scholarship www.collegefortexans.com

Annual Opportunities (estimated)

Scholarships Offered Annually	100-499
Average per Scholarship	$3,000

Field of Study Professional Nursing — Medicine

Target Audiences

Aimed At	Am. Indian	Latino	African Am	Asian Am	Tribe / Women	Overall Diverse	X Open to all
College Level	Pre College	X 1st Yr.	X 2nd Yr.	X 3rd Yr.	X 4th Yr.	X Graduate Studies	

Area Served: Regional
Citizenship requirements: Doesn't matter

Basis For Award

- [ ] Financial Need
- [X] Grades
- [X] Interviews
- [ ] Extracurricular Activities
- [ ] Community Involvement
- [ ] Essays
- [ ] Minimum G.P.A.
- [X] SAT ACT
- [ ] Letters of Recommendation

Texas Health Service Corps Scholarship

Organization | Government | Scholarship

Organization **Texas Higher Education Coordinating Board**
Department Student Services Division
Address PO Box 12877
Austin State TX Zip code 78711-2788

Websites — Where to apply: Online

Organization
Scholarship www.orca.state.tx.us

Annual Opportunities (estimated)

Scholarships Offered Annually	50-99
Average per Scholarship	$20,000

Field of Study: Medicine — Health professions

Target Audiences

									Tribe			Overall Diverse
Aimed At		Am. Indian	X	Latino		African Am		Asian Am		Women	X	Open to all
College Level		Pre College	X	1st Yr.	X	2nd Yr.	X	3rd Yr.	X	4th Yr.	X	Graduate Studies

Area Served: Regional
Citizenship requirements: Non-citizens only

Basis For Award

							Extracurricular Activities
	Financial Need	X	Grades	X	Interviews		Community Involvement
	Essays		Minimum G.P.A.	X	SAT ACT		Letters of Recommendation

Texas State Student Incentive Grant for Students

Organization | Government | Grant

Organization **Texas Higher Education Coordinating Board**
Department Student Services Division
Address P.O. Box 12788
Austin State TX Zip code 78711-2788

Websites — Where to apply: Online

Organization
Scholarship www.collegefortexans.com

Annual Opportunities (estimated)

Scholarships Offered Annually	Over 1,000
Average per Scholarship	$2,500

Field of Study: General — All Fields of Study

Target Audiences

									Tribe			Overall Diverse
Aimed At		Am. Indian		Latino		African Am		Asian Am		Women	X	Open to all
College Level		Pre College	X	1st Yr.	X	2nd Yr.	X	3rd Yr.	X	4th Yr.		Graduate Studies

Area Served: Regional
Citizenship requirements: Must be permanent resident or citizen

Basis For Award

							Extracurricular Activities
X	Financial Need	X	Grades	X	Interviews		Community Involvement
	Essays		Minimum G.P.A.	X	SAT ACT		Letters of Recommendation

Texas Tuition Equalization Grant

Organization	Government	Grant

Organization: **Texas Higher Education Coordinating Board**
Department: Student Services Division
Address: P.O. Box 12788
Austin   State TX   Zip code 78711-2788

Websites — Where to apply: Online
Organization:
Scholarship: www.collegefortexans.com

Annual Opportunities (estimated)
Scholarships Offered Annually: Over 1,000
Average per Scholarship: $3,644

Field of Study: General — All Fields of Study

Target Audiences

Aimed At	Am. Indian	Latino	African Am	Asian Am	Women	X Open to all
					Tribe	Overall Diverse
College Level	Pre College	X 1st Yr.	X 2nd Yr.	X 3rd Yr.	X 4th Yr.	X Graduate Studies

Area Served: Regional
Citizenship requirements: U.S. Citizenship required

Basis For Award

X Financial Need	X Grades	X Interviews	Extracurricular Activities
Essays	Minimum G.P.A.	X SAT ACT	Community Involvement
			Letters of Recommendation

The Air Force College Fund Program

Organization	Government	Program

Organization: **United States Department of the Air Force**
Department:
Address:
Washington   State DC   Zip code

Websites — Where to apply: Online
Organization:
Scholarship: www.airforce.com, www.afreserve.com

Annual Opportunities (estimated)
Scholarships Offered Annually: 50-99
Average per Scholarship: $10,000

Field of Study: General — Open

Target Audiences

Aimed At	Am. Indian	Latino	African Am	Asian Am	Women	X Open to all
					Tribe	Overall Diverse
College Level	Pre College	X 1st Yr.	X 2nd Yr.	X 3rd Yr.	X 4th Yr.	Graduate Studies

Area Served: National
Citizenship requirements: U.S. Citizenship required

Basis For Award

Financial Need	X Grades	Interviews	Extracurricular Activities
Essays	Minimum G.P.A.	X SAT ACT	X Community Involvement
			Letters of Recommendation

The Army College Fund Program

Organization	Government	Program

Organization **United States Department of the Army**

Department

Address

Washington — State DC — Zip code

Websites — Where to apply: Online

Organization

Scholarship http://www.goarmy.com

Annual Opportunities (estimated)	
Scholarships Offered Annually	50-99
Average per Scholarship	$30,000

Field of Study: General — Open

Target Audiences

					Tribe	Overall Diverse
Aimed At	Am. Indian	Latino	African Am	Asian Am	Women	X Open to all
College Level	Pre College	X 1st Yr.	X 2nd Yr.	X 3rd Yr.	X 4th Yr.	Graduate Studies

Area Served: National

Citizenship requirements: U.S. Citizenship required

Basis For Award

			Extracurricular Activities
Financial Need	Grades	Interviews	Community Involvement
Essays	Minimum G.P.A.	SAT ACT	Letters of Recommendation

The AXA Achievement Scholarship

Organization	Foundation	Scholarship

Organization **AXA Foundation**

Department

Address 1290 Avenue of the the Americas

New York — State NY — Zip code 10104

Websites — Where to apply: Online

Organization www.axa-equitable.com

Scholarship http://www.axa-equitable.com/axa-foundation/AXA-achievement-scholarship.html

Annual Opportunities (estimated)	
Scholarships Offered Annually	50-99
Average per Scholarship	$12,885

Field of Study: STEM — Chemistry

Target Audiences

					Tribe	Overall Diverse
Aimed At	X Am. Indian	X Latino	African Am	Asian Am	Women	X Open to all
College Level	X Pre College	1st Yr.	2nd Yr.	3rd Yr.	4th Yr.	Graduate Studies

Area Served: National

Citizenship requirements: Must be permanent resident or citizen

Basis For Award

			X Extracurricular Activities
Financial Need	X Grades	Interviews	X Community Involvement
Essays	Minimum G.P.A.	SAT ACT	Letters of Recommendation

Major Scholarships

More scholarships are added every month: Go to **www.EmpoweringStudents.com**

The Bayliss Radio Scholarship

Organization — Non-Profit — Scholarship

Organization **The John Bayliss Broadcast Foundation**
Department
Address P.O. Box 51126
Pacific Grove State CA Zip code 93950

Websites — Where to apply: Online

Organization
Scholarship www.baylissfoundation.org

Annual Opportunities (estimated)

Scholarships Offered Annually	10-19
Average per Scholarship	$50,000

Field of Study: Radio Broadcasting/Journalism — JOURNALISM

Target Audiences

Aimed At	Am. Indian	Latino	African Am	Asian Am	Women	Tribe	Overall Diverse
							X Open to all
College Level	Pre College	1st Yr.	2nd Yr.	X 3rd Yr.	X 4th Yr.		X Graduate Studies

Area Served: National
Citizenship requirements: Must be permanent resident or citizen

Basis For Award

Financial Need	X Grades	Interviews	Extracurricular Activities
Essays	3.0 Minimum G.P.A.	SAT ACT	Community Involvement
			Letters of Recommendation

The College Assistance Migrant Program (CAMP)

Organization — College Program — Program

Organization **St. Edwards University**
Department
Address 3001 S. Congress Ave.
Austin State TX Zip code 78704

Websites — Where to apply: Online

Organization
Scholarship www.stedwards.edu/camp

Annual Opportunities (estimated)

Scholarships Offered Annually	20-49
Average per Scholarship	$22,724

Field of Study: Open — GENERAL

Target Audiences

Aimed At	Am. Indian	Latino	African Am	Asian Am	Women	Tribe	X Overall Diverse
							X Open to all
College Level	Pre College	X 1st Yr.	2nd Yr.	3rd Yr.	4th Yr.		Graduate Studies

Area Served: Regional
Citizenship requirements: Must be permanent resident or citizen

Basis For Award

X Financial Need	Grades	Interviews	Extracurricular Activities
Essays	Minimum G.P.A.	SAT ACT	Community Involvement
			Letters of Recommendation

More scholarships are added every month: Go to **www.EmpoweringStudents.com**

THE CONSORTIUM FOR GRADUATE STUDY IN

ORGANIZATION	NON-PROFIT	PROGRAM

Organization **The Consortium for Graduate Study in Management**
Department
Address 5585 Pershing Ave., Suite 240
St. Louis State MO Zip code 63112-1795

WEBSITES Where to apply: Online
Organization www.cgsm.org
Scholarship

ANNUAL OPPORTUNITIES (ESTIMATED)

Scholarships Offered Annually	100-499
Average per Scholarship	$61,538

FIELD OF STUDY Management — BUSINESS

TARGET AUDIENCES

										Tribe	X	Overall Diverse
Aimed At		Am. Indian		Latino		African Am		Asian Am		Women		Open to all
College Level		Pre College		1st Yr.		2nd Yr.		3rd Yr.		4th Yr.	X	Graduate Studies

Area Served: Regional
Citizenship requirements: Must be permanent resident or citizen

BASIS FOR AWARD

							Extracurricular Activities
	Financial Need	X	Grades	X	Interviews		Community Involvement
	Essays		Minimum G.P.A.		SAT ACT		Letters of Recommendation

THE DISTINGUISHED ACHIEVEMENT AWARD

ORGANIZATION	COLLEGE PROGRAM	AWARD

Organization **Prairie View A & M University**
Department Office of Student Affairs - Scholarship Division
Address Box 337
Prairie View State TX Zip code 77446

WEBSITES Where to apply: Online
Organization www.pvamu.edu
Scholarship

ANNUAL OPPORTUNITIES (ESTIMATED)

Scholarships Offered Annually	
Average per Scholarship	?

FIELD OF STUDY Open — GENERAL

TARGET AUDIENCES

										Tribe		Overall Diverse
Aimed At		Am. Indian		Latino		African Am		Asian Am		Women	X	Open to all
College Level		Pre College	X	1st Yr.	X	2nd Yr.	X	3rd Yr.	X	4th Yr.		Graduate Studies

Area Served: Regional
Citizenship requirements: Doesn't matter

BASIS FOR AWARD

						X	Extracurricular Activities
	Financial Need	X	Grades	X	Interviews	X	Community Involvement
	Essays	3.5	Minimum G.P.A.	X	SAT ACT	X	Letters of Recommendation

MAJOR SCHOLARSHIPS

More scholarships are added every month: Go to **www.EmpoweringStudents.com**

The National Merit Scholarship Program

Organization | Foundation | **Scholarship**

Organization **National Merit Scholarship Corporation**

Department

Address 1560 Sherman Ave., Suite 200

Evanston State IL Zip code 60201

Websites Where to apply: Online

Organization

Scholarship www.nationalmerit.org

Annual Opportunities (estimated)

Scholarships Offered Annually	Over 1,000
Average per Scholarship	$2,500

Field of Study: GENERAL — All Fields of Study

Target Audiences

Aimed At	[ ] Am. Indian	[ ] Latino	[ ] African Am	[ ] Asian Am	[ ] Women	[X] Overall Diverse / Open to all
College Level	[ ] Pre College	[ ] 1st Yr.	[ ] 2nd Yr.	[ ] 3rd Yr.	[ ] 4th Yr.	[ ] Graduate Studies

Tribe

Area Served: International

Citizenship requirements: U.S. Citizenship required

Basis For Award

[ ] Financial Need	[ ] Grades	[ ] Interviews	[ ] Extracurricular Activities
[ ] Essays	[ ] Minimum G.P.A.	[ ] SAT ACT	[ ] Community Involvement
			[ ] Letters of Recommendation

The Navy College Fund Program

Organization | Government | **Program**

Organization **United States Department of the Navy**

Department

Address

Washington State DC Zip code

Websites Where to apply: Online

Organization www.public.navy.mil // www.navy.mil

Scholarship

Annual Opportunities (estimated)

Scholarships Offered Annually	50-99
Average per Scholarship	$25,000

Field of Study: GENERAL — Open

Target Audiences

Aimed At	[ ] Am. Indian	[X] Latino	[ ] African Am	[ ] Asian Am	[ ] Women	[ ] Overall Diverse / Open to all
College Level	[ ] Pre College	[X] 1st Yr.	[X] 2nd Yr.	[X] 3rd Yr.	[X] 4th Yr.	[ ] Graduate Studies

Tribe

Area Served: National

Citizenship requirements: U.S. Citizenship required

Basis For Award

[ ] Financial Need	[ ] Grades	[ ] Interviews	[ ] Extracurricular Activities
[ ] Essays	[ ] Minimum G.P.A.	[ ] SAT ACT	[ ] Community Involvement
			[ ] Letters of Recommendation

More scholarships are added every month: Go to ***www.EmpoweringStudents.com***

The Presidential Award

Organization	College Program	Award

Organization **Prairie View A & M University**
Department Office of Student Affairs - Scholarship Division
Address Box 337
Prairie View State TX Zip code 77446

Websites — Where to apply: Online

Organization www.pvamu.edu
Scholarship

Annual Opportunities (estimated)

Scholarships Offered Annually	50-99
Average per Scholarship	$7,442

Field of Study Open — GENERAL

Target Audiences

								Tribe				Overall Diverse
Aimed At		Am. Indian		Latino		African Am		Asian Am		Women	X	Open to all
College Level		Pre College	X	1st Yr.	X	2nd Yr.	X	3rd Yr.	X	4th Yr.		Graduate Studies

Area Served: Regional
Citizenship requirements: Doesn't matter

Basis For Award

						X	Extracurricular Activities
	Financial Need	X	Grades	X	Interviews	X	Community Involvement
	Essays	3.5	Minimum G.P.A.	X	SAT ACT	X	Letters of Recommendation

The Presidential Scholars Program

Organization	College Program	Program

Organization **University of New Mexico**
Department Scholarship Office
Address Mesa Vista Hall Rm 3020
Albuquerque State NM Zip code 87131-2001

Websites — Where to apply: Online

Organization
Scholarship www.unm.edu/chol/schol.html

Annual Opportunities (estimated)

Scholarships Offered Annually	100-499
Average per Scholarship	$4,500

Field of Study All Fields of Study — GENERAL

Target Audiences

								Tribe				Overall Diverse
Aimed At		Am. Indian	X	Latino		African Am		Asian Am		Women	X	Open to all
College Level		Pre College	X	1st Yr.	X	2nd Yr.	X	3rd Yr.	X	4th Yr.		Graduate Studies

Area Served: Regional
Citizenship requirements: Must be permanent resident or citizen

Basis For Award

						X	Extracurricular Activities
	Financial Need	X	Grades	X	Interviews	X	Community Involvement
	Essays	3.75	Minimum G.P.A.	X	SAT ACT	X	Letters of Recommendation

More scholarships are added every month: Go to ***www.EmpoweringStudents.com***

The Prudential Spirit of Community Awards

Organization	Non-Profit	Award

Organization **Prudential Financial, National Association of Secundary School Principals**

Department

Address 751 Broad St., 16th Floor

Newark State NJ Zip code 07102

Websites — Where to apply: Online

Organization

Scholarship www.prudential.com/spirit

Annual Opportunities (estimated)

Scholarships Offered Annually	Over 1,000
Average per Scholarship	$1,000

Field of Study: GENERAL — All Fields of Study

Target Audiences

									Tribe				Overall Diverse
Aimed At		Am. Indian		Latino		African Am		Asian Am		Women	X	Open to all	
College Level	X	Pre College		1st Yr.		2nd Yr.		3rd Yr.		4th Yr.		Graduate Studies	

Area Served: National

Citizenship requirements: Must be permanent resident or citizen

Basis For Award

						X	Extracurricular Activities
	Financial Need		Grades		Interviews	X	Community Involvement
	Essays		Minimum G.P.A.		SAT ACT		Letters of Recommendation

The Sallie Mae Fund "Unmet Need" Scholarship

Organization	Foundation	Scholarship

Organization **The Sallie Mae Fund**

Department

Address 12061 Bluemont Way

Reston State VA Zip code 20190

Websites — Where to apply: Online

Organization

Scholarship www.thesalliemaefund.org/smfnew/scholarship/

Annual Opportunities (estimated)

Scholarships Offered Annually	500-999
Average per Scholarship	$1,333

Field of Study: GENERAL — All Fields of Study

Target Audiences

									Tribe	X	Overall Diverse		
Aimed At		Am. Indian		Latino		African Am		Asian Am		Women		Open to all	
College Level		Pre College	X	1st Yr.	X	2nd Yr.	X	3rd Yr.	X	4th Yr.		Graduate Studies	

Area Served: National

Citizenship requirements: Must be permanent resident or citizen

Basis For Award

							Extracurricular Activities
X	Financial Need	X	Grades		Interviews		Community Involvement
	Essays	2.5	Minimum G.P.A.		SAT ACT		Letters of Recommendation

More scholarships are added every month: Go to **www.EmpoweringStudents.com**

THE TARGET ALL-AROUND SCHOLARSHIP

ORGANIZATION | **BUSINESS** | **SCHOLARSHIP**

Organization **Target**
Department Target All - Around Scholarship
Address 1505 Riverview Rd.
St. Peter State MN Zip code

WEBSITES Where to apply: Online

Organization
Scholarship www.target.com

ANNUAL OPPORTUNITIES (ESTIMATED)

Scholarships Offered Annually	Over 1,000
Average per Scholarship	$1,017

FIELD OF STUDY: GENERAL — All Fields of Study

TARGET AUDIENCES

									Tribe	X	Overall Diverse
Aimed At		Am. Indian		Latino		African Am		Asian Am		Women		Open to all
College Level		Pre College	X	1st Yr.	X	2nd Yr.	X	3rd Yr.	X	4th Yr.		Graduate Studies

Area Served: National
Citizenship requirements: Must be permanent resident or citizen

BASIS FOR AWARD

							Extracurricular Activities
X	Financial Need	X	Grades		Interviews	X	Community Involvement
	Essays	2.0	Minimum G.P.A.		SAT ACT		Letters of Recommendation

TOYOTA COMMUNITY SCHOLARS PROGRAM

ORGANIZATION | **BUSINESS** | **PROGRAM**

Organization **Toyota MotorSales, U.S.A., Inc.**
Department
Address 19001 South Western Ave.
Torrance State CA Zip code 90509-2991

WEBSITES Where to apply: Online

Organization www.davidsongifted.org
Scholarship www.davidsongifted.org/db/Resources_id_14847

ANNUAL OPPORTUNITIES (ESTIMATED)

Scholarships Offered Annually	100-499
Average per Scholarship	$150,000

FIELD OF STUDY: GENERAL

TARGET AUDIENCES

									Tribe		Overall Diverse
Aimed At		Am. Indian		Latino		African Am		Asian Am		Women	X	Open to all
College Level		Pre College		1st Yr.		2nd Yr.		3rd Yr.		4th Yr.		Graduate Studies

Area Served: National
Citizenship requirements: U.S. Citizenship required

BASIS FOR AWARD

							Extracurricular Activities
	Financial Need	X	Grades		Interviews	X	Community Involvement
	Essays	3.0	Minimum G.P.A.		SAT ACT		Letters of Recommendation

MAJOR SCHOLARSHIPS

More scholarships are added every month: Go to ***www.EmpoweringStudents.com***

TRUSTEE SCHOLARSHIP

ORGANIZATION | COLLEGE PROGRAM | SCHOLARSHIP

Organization **Loyola Marymount University**
Department Financial Aid
Address Xavier Hall, One Lmu Drive, Ste. 200
Los Angeles State CA Zip code 90045

WEBSITES Where to apply: Online

Organization
Scholarship www.lmu.edu/financialaid

ANNUAL OPPORTUNITIES (ESTIMATED)

Scholarships Offered Annually: 10-19
Average per Scholarship: $50,000

FIELD OF STUDY Open: GENERAL

TARGET AUDIENCES

Aimed At	Am. Indian	Latino	African Am	Asian Am	Women	X Open to all (Tribe / Overall Diverse)
College Level	Pre College	X 1st Yr.	X 2nd Yr.	X 3rd Yr.	X 4th Yr.	Graduate Studies

Area Served: Regional
Citizenship requirements: Must be permanent resident or citizen

BASIS FOR AWARD

X Financial Need	X Grades	X Interviews	X Extracurricular Activities
Essays	3.7 Minimum G.P.A.	X SAT ACT	X Community Involvement
			X Letters of Recommendation

TUITION EQUALIZATION SCHOLARSHIP PROGRAM

ORGANIZATION | COLLEGE PROGRAM | SCHOLARSHIP

Organization **Bluffton University**
Department Office of Admissions
Address Unversity Dr.
Bluffton State OH Zip code 45817-2104

WEBSITES Where to apply: Online

Organization
Scholarship www.bluffton.edu

ANNUAL OPPORTUNITIES (ESTIMATED)

Scholarships Offered Annually: 100-499
Average per Scholarship: $10,000

FIELD OF STUDY Open: GENERAL

TARGET AUDIENCES

Aimed At	Am. Indian	Latino	African Am	Asian Am	Women	X Open to all (Tribe / Overall Diverse)
College Level	Pre College	X 1st Yr.	X 2nd Yr.	X 3rd Yr.	X 4th Yr.	Graduate Studies

Area Served: Regional
Citizenship requirements: Must be permanent resident or citizen

BASIS FOR AWARD

X Financial Need	X Grades	Interviews	Extracurricular Activities
Essays	3.0 Minimum G.P.A.	X SAT ACT	Community Involvement
			Letters of Recommendation

More scholarships are added every month: Go to ***www.EmpoweringStudents.com***

UNITED STATES AIR FORCE ACADEMY

ORGANIZATION | COLLEGE PROGRAM | SCHOLARSHIP

Organization **United States Air Force Academy**
Department HQ USA-RRS
Address 2304 Cadet Dr. Ste. 200
USAF Academy State CO Zip code 80840-5025

WEBSITES Where to apply: Online

Organization
Scholarship http://www.usafa.edu/rr

ANNUAL OPPORTUNITIES (ESTIMATED)

Scholarships Offered Annually: 100-499
Average per Scholarship: $28,767

FIELD OF STUDY Open: GENERAL

TARGET AUDIENCES

					Tribe	Overall Diverse
Aimed At	Am. Indian	Latino	African Am	Asian Am	Women	X Open to all
College Level	Pre College	X 1st Yr.	X 2nd Yr.	X 3rd Yr.	X 4th Yr.	Graduate Studies

Area Served: National
Citizenship requirements: Must be permanent resident or citizen

BASIS FOR AWARD

			X Extracurricular Activities
Financial Need	X Grades	X Interviews	X Community Involvement
Essays	3.5 Minimum G.P.A.	X SAT ACT	X Letters of Recommendation

UNITED STATES ARMY

ORGANIZATION | COLLEGE PROGRAM | SCHOLARSHIP

Organization **United States Military Academy**
Department
Address 606 Thayer Rd.
West Point State NY Zip code 10996-1797

WEBSITES Where to apply: Online

Organization
Scholarship http://www.usma.edu

ANNUAL OPPORTUNITIES (ESTIMATED)

Scholarships Offered Annually: 500-999
Average per Scholarship: $60,000

FIELD OF STUDY Open: GENERAL

TARGET AUDIENCES

					Tribe	Overall Diverse
Aimed At	Am. Indian	Latino	African Am	Asian Am	Women	X Open to all
College Level	Pre College	X 1st Yr.	X 2nd Yr.	X 3rd Yr.	X 4th Yr.	Graduate Studies

Area Served: National
Citizenship requirements: U.S. Citizenship required

BASIS FOR AWARD

			X Extracurricular Activities
Financial Need	X Grades	X Interviews	X Community Involvement
Essays	Minimum G.P.A.	X SAT ACT	X Letters of Recommendation

MAJOR SCHOLARSHIPS

More scholarships are added every month: Go to **www.EmpoweringStudents.com**

University of Delaware Academic Scholarships

Organization | College Program | **Scholarship**

Organization **University of Delaware**
Department Office of Scholarships and Financial Aid
Address 224 Hullihen hall
Newark State DE Zip code 19716

Websites Where to apply: Online

Organization
Scholarship http://www.udel.edu

Annual Opportunities (estimated)

Scholarships Offered Annually	500-999
Average per Scholarship	$4,225

Field of Study Open: GENERAL

Target Audiences

Aimed At	Am. Indian	Latino	African Am	Asian Am	Women	Tribe	X Overall Diverse Open to all
College Level	Pre College	X 1st Yr.	X 2nd Yr.	X 3rd Yr.	X 4th Yr.		Graduate Studies

Area Served: Regional
Citizenship requirements: Must be permanent resident or citizen

Basis For Award

X Financial Need	X Grades	X Interviews	X Extracurricular Activities
Essays	Minimum G.P.A.	X SAT ACT	X Community Involvement
			X Letters of Recommendation

University of Idaho Presidential Scholarship

Organization | College Program | **Scholarship**

Organization **University of Idaho**
Department Student Financial Aid Services
Address
Moscow State ID Zip code 83844-2431

Websites Where to apply: Online

Organization
Scholarship http://www.uidaho.edu

Annual Opportunities (estimated)

Scholarships Offered Annually	Over 1,000
Average per Scholarship	$662

Field of Study Open: GENERAL

Target Audiences

Aimed At	Am. Indian	Latino	African Am	Asian Am	Women	Tribe	X Overall Diverse Open to all
College Level	Pre College	X 1st Yr.	2nd Yr.	3rd Yr.	4th Yr.		Graduate Studies

Area Served: Regional
Citizenship requirements: Must be permanent resident or citizen

Basis For Award

Financial Need	X Grades	X Interviews	X Extracurricular Activities
Essays	3.6 Minimum G.P.A.	X SAT ACT	X Community Involvement
			X Letters of Recommendation

USC National Hispanic Scholarship

Organization	College Program	Scholarship

Organization **University of Southern California**
Department Financial Aid
Address University Park Campus, 700 Childs Way, JHH 325
Los Angeles State CA Zip code 90089-0914

Websites — Where to apply: Online

Organization http://www.usc.edu
Scholarship http://www.usc.edu/admission/undergraduate/apply/scholarship.html

Annual Opportunities (estimated)

Scholarships Offered Annually	50-99
Average per Scholarship	$13,000

Field of Study: Open — GENERAL

Target Audiences

Aimed At	Am. Indian	X Latino	African Am	Asian Am	Women	Tribe	Overall Diverse / Open to all
College Level	Pre College	X 1st Yr.	X 2nd Yr.	X 3rd Yr.	X 4th Yr.		Graduate Studies

Area Served: Regional
Citizenship requirements: Must be permanent resident or citizen

Basis For Award

			X Extracurricular Activities
Financial Need	X Grades	X Interviews	X Community Involvement
Essays	Minimum G.P.A.	X SAT ACT	X Letters of Recommendation

USC Presidential Scholarship

Organization	College Program	Scholarship

Organization **University of Southern California**
Department Financial Aid
Address University Park Campus, 700 Childs Way, JHH 325
Los Angeles State CA Zip code 90089-0914

Websites — Where to apply: Online

Organization http://www.usc.edu
Scholarship http://www.usc.edu/admission/undergraduate/apply/scholarship.html

Annual Opportunities (estimated)

Scholarships Offered Annually	100-499
Average per Scholarship	$22,000

Field of Study: Open — GENERAL

Target Audiences

Aimed At	Am. Indian	Latino	African Am	Asian Am	Women	Tribe	Overall Diverse / X Open to all
College Level	Pre College	X 1st Yr.	X 2nd Yr.	X 3rd Yr.	X 4th Yr.		Graduate Studies

Area Served: Regional
Citizenship requirements: Must be permanent resident or citizen

Basis For Award

			X Extracurricular Activities
Financial Need	X Grades	X Interviews	X Community Involvement
Essays	3.75 Minimum G.P.A.	X SAT ACT	X Letters of Recommendation

USC TRUSTEE SCHOLARSHIP

ORGANIZATION	COLLEGE PROGRAM	SCHOLARSHIP

Organization **University of Southern California**

Department Financial Aid

Address University Park Campus, 700 Childs Way, JHH 325

Los Angeles State CA Zip code 90089-0914

WEBSITES
Where to apply Online

Organization http://www.usc.edu

Scholarship http://www.usc.edu/admission/undergraduate/apply/scholarship.html

ANNUAL OPPORTUNITIES (ESTIMATED)

		FIELD OF STUDY	Open
Scholarships Offered Annually	100-499	GENERAL	
Average per Scholarship	$44,000		

TARGET AUDIENCES

Aimed At		Am. Indian		Latino		African Am		Asian Am		Women	X	Tribe		Overall Diverse
														Open to all

College Level		Pre College	X	1st Yr.	X	2nd Yr.	X	3rd Yr.	X	4th Yr.		Graduate Studies

Area Served Regional

Citizenship requirements Must be permanent resident or citizen

BASIS FOR AWARD

	Financial Need	X	Grades	X	Interviews	X	Extracurricular Activities
						X	Community Involvement
	Essays		Minimum G.P.A.	X	SAT ACT	X	Letters of Recommendation

---

UW DIVERSITY SCHOLARSHIP AWARD

ORGANIZATION	BUSINESS	SCHOLARSHIP

Organization **Costco /University of Washington**

Department Office of Student Financial Services

Address 178 Schmitz Hall, Box 355880

Seattle State WA Zip code 98195-5831

WEBSITES
Where to apply Online

Organization

Scholarship http://costcoscholarshipfund.org

ANNUAL OPPORTUNITIES (ESTIMATED)

		FIELD OF STUDY	All Fields of Study
Scholarships Offered Annually	50-99	GENERAL	
Average per Scholarship	$10,000		

TARGET AUDIENCES

Aimed At		Am. Indian		Latino		African Am		Asian Am		Women		Tribe	X	Overall Diverse
														Open to all

College Level		Pre College	X	1st Yr.		2nd Yr.		3rd Yr.		4th Yr.		Graduate Studies

Area Served Regional

Citizenship requirements U.S. Citizenship required

BASIS FOR AWARD

X	Financial Need	X	Grades	X	Interviews		Extracurricular Activities
						X	Community Involvement
	Essays	3.0	Minimum G.P.A.	X	SAT ACT	X	Letters of Recommendation

---

More scholarships are added every month: Go to **www.EmpoweringStudents.com**

W. W. Smith Charitable Trust

Organization	Foundation	Program

Organization **W. W. Smith Charitable Trust**
Department Financial Aid Programs for College Students
Address 200 Four Falls Corporate Center, Suite 300
West Conshohocken State PA Zip code 19428

Websites — Where to apply: Online

Organization www.wwsmithcharitabletrust.org
Scholarship

Annual Opportunities (estimated)

Scholarships Offered Annually	50-99
Average per Scholarship	$10,870

Field of Study: Open — GENERAL

Target Audiences

							Tribe
Aimed At	Am. Indian	Latino	African Am	Asian Am	Women	Overall Diverse	X Open to all
College Level	Pre College	X 1st Yr.	X 2nd Yr.	X 3rd Yr.	X 4th Yr.	Graduate Studies	

Area Served: Regional
Citizenship requirements: Doesn't matter

Basis For Award

			X Extracurricular Activities
X Financial Need	X Grades	Interviews	X Community Involvement
Essays	Minimum G.P.A.	SAT ACT	X Letters of Recommendation

Washington University Hispanic Scholarship

Organization	College Program	Scholarship

Organization **Washington University**
Department Undergraduate Admissions
Address Campus Box 1089
St. Louis State MO Zip code 63130-4899

Websites — Where to apply: Online

Organization
Scholarship http://www.wustl.edu

Annual Opportunities (estimated)

Scholarships Offered Annually	5-9
Average per Scholarship	$100,000

Field of Study: All Fields of Study — GENERAL

Target Audiences

							Tribe
Aimed At	Am. Indian	X Latino	African Am	Asian Am	Women	Overall Diverse	Open to all
College Level	Pre College	X 1st Yr.	2nd Yr.	3rd Yr.	4th Yr.	Graduate Studies	

Area Served: Regional
Citizenship requirements: Doesn't matter

Basis For Award

			X Extracurricular Activities
Financial Need	X Grades	X Interviews	X Community Involvement
Essays	Minimum G.P.A.	SAT ACT	X Letters of Recommendation

MAJOR SCHOLARSHIPS

More scholarships are added every month: Go to ***www.EmpoweringStudents.com***

Add Your Scholarship To Those Listed In This Directory

Want to add your scholarship to those that are listed or update an existing listing? Please email Listings@EmpoweringStudents.com and put "Listings" in the subject field. We will send you a simple form and we'll get you into the Directory.

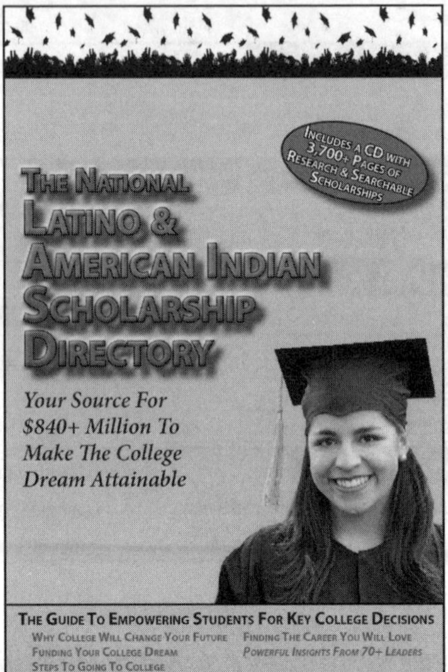

Section Seven
Indexes

Insights
"It's A Cultural Clash"

"Going to college is the cultural shock of going off the reservation. I went from a community of 5,500 people and all of my family to a community of millions of people. It's a cultural clash. You're in a rural community where you don't see that many Anglos and you're going to a community that predominantly Anglo and African Americans. I got my degree in Construction Management from Northern Arizona University and the experience from Syntex Homes here in Las Vegas. I've now taken all that education and experience that I got off the reservation back to the Kayenta Township."

***Gabriel Yazzie**, Department Manager, Kayenta Township, Navajo*

All Scholarships By State & Name

On the enclosed CD you will find detailed searchable profiles on each of the following awards (A), fellowships (F), grants (G), internships (I), programs (P), and scholarships (S).

Type & Name of the Scholarship

Alabama

- S Air Force ROTC 4-YEAR Scholarship
- S Alabama Commission on Higher Education
- G Alabama Space Grant Consortium Undergraduate Scholarship
- S America's Junior Miss Scholarship Program
- P America's Junior Miss Scholarship Program
- S American Indian Nurse Scholarship Award
- S Junior & Community College Performing Arts Scholarship
- S Two-Year College Academic Scholarship

Alaska

- S CIRI Foundation Scholarships

Arizona

- P Adelante Program
- S Agustina Valdez Scholarship
- S Amelia M. Maldonado Scholarship in Elementary Education
- S American Indian/Alaska Native Association for NCRS Scholarship
- S Arizona Association of Chicanos for Higher Education Scholarships
- F Arizona State University Library Training Fellowship
- S BigSun Scholarships
- S CALGON - Take Me Away To College Scholarship
- S Carlos C. & Alex G. Jacome Memorial Scholarship
- S Cesar E. Chavez Leadership Scholarship
- S Chaparales/Rotary Club of Tucson Graduate Scholarship
- S Chief Ellis Scholarship
- S Chief Manuelito Scholarship Program
- S Colorado River Indian Scholarship
- S Concerned Media Professionals Scholarship
- S Dale E. Fridell Memorial Scholarship
- A Diversity Award
- S Don Carson CMP Scholarship
- S Donald G. Shropshire Scholarship
- S Dr. Manuel T. & Karen Pacheco Scholarship
- S Farmilant Scholarships
- S Gila River Indian Community Division of Student Services Scholarships
- S Grand Canyon University Scholarships
- S Hopi Scholarship
- S IBM Scholarship
- S J.C. Penney Co. Scholarship
- S Jose Franco & Francisco Ocampo Quesada Research Scholarship
- S Los Diablos Scholarship
- S Los Endowment Scholarship
- S Maria Urquides Scholarship
- I Morris K. Udall Foundation Internships
- S Morris K. Udall Scholarship
- S NAFOA Scholarship
- S National Center for American Indian Enterprise Development Scholarships
- I Native American Congressional Internships
- P NAU Educational Talent Search
- S Navajo Generating Station Navajo Scholarship
- S Navajo Nation Scholarship & Financial Assistance Program
- S Pima Scholarship Program
- S Reforma Scholarship
- S Rigulo Cuesta Memorial Scholarships for Hispanics
- S Rose Trevino Memorial Scholarship
- S Rosita Cota Scholarship
- S Shandiin Scholarship Fund
- S The AzPC of AISES Scholarship
- S Tostitos Cesar Chavez Latino Scholarship
- S UA Hispanic Alumni Scholarship Program
- S United States Hispanic Leadership Institute Scholarship

- **S** Cisco Diversity Scholarship
- **P** Citi/TELACU Scholars Program
- **F** CLCI Polanco Fellowship
- **S** Club Música Latina Scholarship Program
- **S** Coalition for Nursing Careers in California Scholarship Program
- **S** COCA-COLA Live Positivity and Hispanic Scholarship Fund Essay Contest
- **S** College Retention/General Scholarship Program
- **A** College Television Awards
- **S** Communications Scholarship Fund
- **S** Community College Scholarship Program
- **S** Community College Transfer Scholarship Program
- **S** Community Service Scholarship
- **S** Connie Hernandez Scholarship Fund
- **S** CRAEF Scholarship
- **S** Cruzando Fronteras/Ayudando a la Comunidad
- **I** CSRC Getty Undergraduate Summer Arts Internship
- **I** CSRC Getty Undergraduate Summer Arts Internship
- **S** CSU Fresno Scholarship Fund
- **S** CSU Minority Business Graduate Scholarship
- **S** CSU Minority Engineering Program Scholarship
- **G** CSU National Action Council for Minorities in Engineering (NACME) Grants
- **S** CSU Scholarships for Future Scholars
- **S** CSUB Hispanic Excellence Scholarship Fund Program
- **S** CSUF TELACU Scholarship Program
- **S** CSULB Scholarship Program
- **S** CTA Martin Luther King, Jr. Memorial Scholarship Fund
- **S** CTA Scholarship Program for Dependent Children
- **S** CTA Scholarship Program for Members
- **S** Cuban American Scholarship Fund (CASF)
- **S** Cuban American Teachers' Association Scholarship
- **S** Daddy Longlegs Scholarship
- **F** David C. Lizarraga Graduate Fellowship
- **S** Dean's Scholarship for Ethnic & Cultural Diversity
- **S** Deans' Scholarship
- **S** Domingo Garcia Scholarship
- **S** Don Diego Scholarship
- **S** Dr. Amanda Perez Scholarship
- **S** Dr. Bertha O. Pendelton Scholarship Fund
- **S** Dr. Carreon Foundation
- **S** Dr. Karin Duran Memorial Youth Scholarship Fund
- **S** Dr. Karin Duran Scholarship
- **S** Earth Science Scholarship
- **P** Edison Scholars Program
- **S** EDSF Board of Directors Scholarships
- **S** El Centro's Gloria Delaney Scholarship Fund
- **S** Elizabeth Martinez Scholarship
- **S** Esther Renteria Community Service Scholarship
- **S** Estrada Scholarship Fund
- **F** Eugene Cota Robles Fellowship
- **A** Excellence in 3D Animation Award
- **A** Exito Escolar Media Award
- **P** Extended Opportunity Programs & Services
- **P** Fellowship Program on Health and Environmental Health for California Ethnic Media Journalists
- **S** Ford Salute to Education
- **S** Ford/EEOC Endowed Scholarship Program
- **P** Fountainhead Essay Contest
- **S** Frank del Olmo Memorial Scholarship
- **S** Friends of University of California Irvine Scholarship
- **S** "Full filling Our Dreams" Scholarship Fund
- **P** Future Scholars Program
- **A** Governor's Math & Science Award
- **A** Governor's Scholars Award
- **S** GOYA Foods Culinary Arts & Food Sciences Scholarship Program
- **S** Gracia Molina Enriquez de Pick Endowed Undergraduate Scholarship
- **F** Graduate Equity Fellowship Award
- **S** Graham-Fancher Scholarship
- **P** Great Minds in STEM HENAAC Scholars Program
- **S** Great Minds in STEM HENAAC Student Leadership Award
- **S** Greater Houston Retailers Association and Coca-Cola Live Positively Scholarship Program
- **S** Half-Century Trojans Scholarship
- **S** High School Annual Scholarship Award
- **S** Hispanic Bar Association of Orange County High School Juniors Scholarship Program
- **S** Hispanic Community Affairs Council Scholarship Fund

- S J.W. Van Dyke Memorial Scholarships
- F Jack R. Howard Science Reporting Institute at Caltech Fellowships
- S JACL National Scholarship Program
- S James S. Bosco Minority Incentive Graduate Scholarship
- S Janine Gonzalez Scholarship
- S Jeremy Gabriel Mancilla Memorial Scholarship
- S Jesse Arias Scholarship Fund
- S Jesuit / Marymount High School Scholarship
- S Jesuit Community Scholarship
- S Joseph Shinoda Memorial Scholarship
- S Juan Cisneros Scholarship Fund
- S Jules H. Strauss Photography Scholarship
- I Kaiser Media Internships in Urban Health Reporting
- S La Raza Lawyers of Santa Clara County Scholarship
- S Latina Leadership Network (LLN) - Scholarship Program
- S Latino Association of Faculty & Staff Scholarships at California State University San Marcos
- S Latino Faculty/Staff & Student Association Scholarship
- S LEAD Cash for College Workshops
- S Leadership for Diversity Scholarship
- S Leadership Scholarship
- S Letty Zanchez Memorial Scholarship
- S Lillian S. Sherman Scholarship
- S Lincoln Forum Scholarship
- S LMU Mexican-American Alumni Association Scholarship
- S Lowrider Magazine Scholarship Fund
- S Loyola Presidential Scholarship
- S LSAT Scholarship
- S LULAC National Scholarship Fund
- A MAES Local Chapter Awards
- S Mahatma Gandhi Memorial Scholarship
- S MALDEF Law School Scholarship Program
- S Marin Education Fund
- S Mary Moy Quon Ing Memorial Scholarship Award
- P MassMutual Multicultural Scholars Program
- S MECHA de UC Riverside Alumni Scholarship
- P MEDI-CORPS
- P Mentorships & Opportunities for Research in Engineering (MORE)
- S Meritus Scholarship
- S Mexican American Bar Foundation Scholarship
- S Mexican American Business & Professional Scholarship
- S Mexican American Grocers Association
- S Minority Media Scholarship
- P Minority Science Programs
- S Minoru Yasui Memorial Scholarship Award
- S MiraCosta College Foundation Scholarship Program
- S Mister Rogers Memorial Scholarship
- P Modesto Junior College - Pre-College/TRIO Programs
- S MTS & Coca Cola Laptop Scholarship
- S MTS/Coca Cola High School Scholarship
- S National Hispanic University Scholarships
- S National Merit Finalist Presidential Scholarship
- F National Physical Science Consortium
- S NHFA Entertainment Industry Scholarship Program
- S Nissan Scholarship Program
- S North County Building Industry Association Scholarship
- S Pac-West Telecomm, Inc. Scholarship
- S Pacific Life Holiday Bowl Memorial Scholarship Award
- P PacifiCare's Latino Health Scholars Program
- A Pass-It-On Awards Program
- A PennySaver YES Award
- P Post-Baccalaureate Program
- S President Obama/HSF STEM Teacher Scholarship Program
- S Project GRAD Los Angeles
- S Que Llueva Cafe Scholarship
- S QuestBridge Scholarship
- S Ralph J. Flynn Memorial Fund
- S Ramona's Mexican Food Products Scholarships
- S Ray Uribe / Associated Students Memorial Scholarship for EOP Students
- F Research Fellowships in the Department of Pharmacology
- S Robert A. Hine Memorial Scholarship
- F Robert Toigo MBA Fellowship
- S Rodney T. Mathews, Jr. Memorial Scholarship for California Indians
- S Rudy Acuña Scholarship Fund
- S Russell Caldwell Neighborhood Scholarship

- P Toyota Community Scholars Program
- S Toyota/TELACU Scholarship Program
- A Trujillo Chemistry Award
- S Trustee Scholarship
- S UAL/UABT Scholarship Program
- P UCI Women & Minority Engineering Program
- F UCLA Graduate Opportunity Fellowship Program
- P UCLA Premedical/Predental Enrichment Program
- P UCLA Re-Application Program
- S UCSD Black Alumni Scholarship
- P United States Senate Youth Program
- S University Annual Scholarship Award
- S USC Associates Scholarship
- S USC National Hispanic Scholarship
- S USC Presidential Scholarship
- S USC Trustee Scholarship
- S Vikki Carr Scholarship Foundation for California
- P We the Living Essay Contest
- S Wilbur Family Fund Hispanic Scholarship
- S William & Marcella Powell Scholarship Award
- S William Hernandez Memorial Scholarship
- S William Randolph Hearst Endowment Scholarship
- S Women's Environmental Council Scholarship
- S Xyplor Canada Scholarship
- S Youth Opportunities Foundation Scholarships
- A Zala Art Muralist Award
- S Zinch Super Student Stimulus Scholarship

COLORADO

- P Adams State College
- A Advocacy Diversity Award
- S American Indian College Fund
- S Anthem Blue Cross & Blue Shield - West Region Diversity Council
- S AORN Foundation Scholarship
- P Arizona Public Service Navajo Scholars Program
- S Arnold Scholarship
- S Austin Family Scholarship Endowment
- S AWG Minority Scholarship for Women
- S Cargill Scholarship Program
- S Citi Foundation Scholarship Program
- S Coca-Cola First Generation Scholarship
- S Colorado Foundation Scholarship
- S Community College Transfer Scholarship
- S Council of Energy Resource Tribes (CERT) Scholarships
- P Crow Canyon High School Archaeology Camp
- S CSAP & Academic Scholarship Program
- S Dorothy E. & Ray Malone Scholarship
- S Ecotrust Native American Scholarship Program
- S Ediger Scholarship for Ouray High School
- G First Generation Grant
- S First Nations Scholarship
- S Ford Motor Company Tribal College Scholarship
- P Fort Lewis College Free Tuition Waiver
- S Foundation Scholarship
- S Frank & Gina Day Scholarship
- S General Mills Foundation
- S Gochman Fund Scholarship
- P GRMAD
- S Hiram C. Gardener Scholarship
- S Hispanic Alumni Scholarship Fund
- S HORISONS (Hispanic Out-Reach In Search Of New Scholarships)/GRAD
- S Joe Francomano Scholarship
- S Latin American Educational Foundation (LAEF)
- A Lilly Endowment, Inc: Woksape Oyate: "Wisdom of the People" Distinguished Scholar Award
- A Lilly Endowment, Inc: Woksape Oyate: "Wisdom of the People" Keepers of the Next Generation Award
- S Louis F. & Jean H. Bein Memorial Scholarship
- S Malcom Erickson Scholarship
- S Midge Korczak Scholarship
- S Miramontes Arts and Sciences Program (MASP) Scholarship
- P Morgan Stanley Tribal Scholars Program
- S Multicultural Engineering Program (MEP) Scholarship
- P Newmont Mining Corporation Tribal Scholars Program
- S Nissan North America, Inc. Scholarship
- S NSCA Minority Scholarship
- S Scholarships
- S Seven Stars Graduate Scholarship

Connecticut

Delaware

Florida

- **S** Mas Family Scholarships
- **S** Miami Herald South Florida Scholarship
- **P** Minority Scholars Program
- **S** NAMPEA Beginning Freshman Engineering Student Award
- **S** National Merit & Achievement, National Hispanic Scholars
- **S** New York Times Scholarships
- **S** Orlando Sentinel / South Florida Sun-Sentinel Scholarships
- **S** Pablo J. Lopez Memorial Scholarship
- **S** Pearce-Deyo Scholarship
- **S** Peter C. Barr Advertising Scholarship
- **S** Presidential-International Baccalaureate Scholarship
- **S** Red Barber Radio Scholarship
- **S** Rollins College Presidential Scholarship
- **S** Special Honors Scholarship
- **S** St. Petersburg Times Scholarship
- **S** Stovall Minority Scholarship
- **A** The Centennial Award
- **S** The Dyzco Essay Contest
- **S** The Freedom Forum Scholarships
- **S** The Mass Family Scholarship
- **S** The Palm Beach Post/Cox Foundation Scholarship
- **S** Tomas Garcia Fuste Scholarship
- **S** Transfer Engineering Student Award
- **S** UNF Minority Community College Transfer Scholarships
- **P** UNF/QUEST Program
- **S** University of Florida College of Journalism Florida Times-Union Scholarship
- **S** University of Florida College of Journalism Minority Scholarships
- **S** University of Florida College of Journalism Ocala Star-Banner Minority Scholarship
- **S** University of Florida College of Journalism Philip L. Graham Minority Scholarship
- **S** USF Latino Scholarship

Georgia

- **G** Atlanta Ronald McDonald House Charities Grant
- **S** Celia & Marcos Scholarship Fund
- **P** Coca-Cola Scholars Program
- **S** Goizueta Scholarships
- **S** Hope Scholarship
- **S** Jeanette Rankin Women's Scholarship Fund
- **S** KFC Colonel's Scholars Program
- **S** LULAC National Scholarship Fund
- **S** Ola M. Brown Scholarship
- **S** Possible Woman Foundation International Scholarship
- **F** Rosalynn Carter Fellowships for Mental Health Journalism
- **S** Sal Diaz-Verson Scholarship
- **S** The Coca-Cola Two-Year Colleges Scholarship Program
- **S** United Parcel Service Scholarship for Minority Students

Hawaii

- **S** Asia General Hospital Association Scholarship
- **G** Bruce T. and Jakie Mahi Erickson Grant
- **S** Charles Cockett `Ohana Scholarship
- **S** Choy-Kee O'hana Scholarship
- **S** Cora Aguda Manayan Fund
- **S** Dr. Hans & Clara Zimmerman Foundation Health Scholarships
- **S** George Hi'ilani Mills Scholarship
- **S** Jalene Kanani Bell 'Ohana Scholarship
- **S** Joseph A. Sowa Scholarship
- **S** Joseph Nawahi Scholarship
- **S** Kamehameha Schools Class of 1952 "Nä Hoaloha O Kamehameha" Scholarship
- **S** Kamehameha Schools Class of 1956 Scholarship
- **S** Kamehameha Schools Class of 1968 "Ka Poli O Kaiona" Scholarship
- **S** Kamehameha Schools Class of 1970 Scholarship
- **S** Kamehameha Schools Class of 1972 Scholarship
- **S** Minority Student Scholarships
- **S** Tauati 'Ohana Scholarship
- **S** Tesoro Corporation Scholarship
- **S** Ula Baker Sheecha Scholarship
- **S** William S. Richardson Commemorative Scholarship

Idaho

- **S** Avista Corporation Scholarship
- **S** CAMP Scholarship
- **S** Diversity Out-of-State Tuition Waiver
- **S** Diversity Scholarship
- **S** Diversity Scholarship Program
- **S** Hispanic Business Association Richard G. Cortez Scholarship

- **S** Government Finance Officers Association Scholarship
- **S** Graduate Scholarship
- **A** GRI / Giacomo Bologna Scholarship
- **S** HACE Collegiate Challenge Scholarship
- **P** HACE Leadership Development Program
- **I** HACE Student Development Internship Program
- **S** HACE Student Development Scholarship Program
- **S** Hallie Q. Brown Scholarships For Women
- **S** HBCU Study Abroad Scholarships
- **S** Hispanic Designers Inc. Scholarships
- **S** Honeywell International Inc. Scholarships
- **S** Incoming Freshman Scholarship
- **S** Institute of Real Estate Management (IREM) Foundation
- **S** Ivy M. Parker Memorial Scholarship
- **S** James F. Schumar Scholarship
- **S** James R. Vogt Scholarship
- **S** John Culver Woody Scholarship
- **S** John R. Lamarsh Scholarship
- **S** John Randall Scholarship
- **S** Johnetta Haley Scholarship
- **S** Joseph R. Dietrich Scholarship
- **S** Judith Resnik Memorial Scholarship
- **S** Karen O'Neil Endowed Advanced Nursing Practice Scholarship
- **S** Kellogg Scholarship
- **S** Latino Medical Student Association (LMSA) MCAT Scholarship
- **S** Lillian Moller Gilbreth Memorial Scholarship
- **A** Living Faith Award
- **S** LMSA Scholarship for U.S. Medical Students
- **S** Lockheed Martin Freshman Scholarship
- **S** LULAC National Educational Service Center
- **S** Mel Larson Scholarships
- **I** MillerCoors Scholars Summer Internship Program
- **S** Minorities in Government Finance Scholarship
- **S** Minority Teachers of Illinois Scholarship Program
- **S** MLA Scholarship for Minority Students
- **S** Music Scholarships
- **S** National Achievement Scholarship Program
- **S** NEED - Delayed Education Scholarship for Women
- **S** NEED - John & Muriel Landis Scholarship
- **P** New Futuro Summit
- **S** New York State ENA September 11 Scholarship
- **S** NRAEF Scholarships
- **S** Operations & Power Division Scholarship
- **S** Pittsburgh Local Section Scholarship
- **S** Presidential Scholarship for Minority Students
- **S** Procter & Gamble Professional Oral Health / HDA Foundation Scholarship
- **S** Raymond DiSalvo Scholarship
- **S** Robert A. Dannels Scholarship
- **S** Robert G. Lacy Scholarship
- **S** Robert T. Liner Scholarship
- **S** Ross Essay Contest
- **S** Rotary Foundation Academic-Year Ambassadorial Scholarships
- **S** Society of Actuaries Minority Student Scholarships
- **S** Society of Women Engineers
- **S** The Alumni Scholarships
- **A** The Curt Tech Award
- **A** The Diane Hauser-Grell Award
- **A** The Marshall Award
- **S** The National Merit Scholarship Program
- **S** The Papercheck.com Essay Contest
- **P** The Ruth & Jesse Owens Scholars Program
- **A** The Ruth Kantzer Award
- **P** The Society of Actuaries James C. Hickman Scholar Doctoral Stipend Program
- **S** The T.E.A.C.H. Early Childhood® Illinois Scholarship & Compensation Project
- **S** Trinity Int. University Presidential Scholarship
- **S** Trinity International University Athletic Scholarships
- **S** Underrepresented Minority Dental Student Scholarship
- **S** Vern R. Dapp Scholarship
- **S** Walter Meyer Scholarship
- **S** William R & Mila Kimel Nuclear Engineering Scholarship
- **S** Young Women in Public Affairs Fund

INDIANA

- **S** American Legion Auxiliary Children of Warriors National Presidents' Scholarship
- **S** American Legion Auxiliary Non-Traditional Student Scholarship

- **S** Allison E. Fisher Scholarship
- **S** APS Minority Scholarship
- **S** APS Scholarship for Minority Undergraduate Physics Majors
- **S** Bolivar San Martin Scholarship
- **S** Center for Student Opportunity Scholarship
- **S** David Risling Emergency Aid Scholarships
- **S** Displaced Homemaker Scholarships
- **S** Elizabeth and Sherman Asche Memorial Scholarship Fund
- **S** Emilie Hesemeyer Memorial Scholarship
- **S** Emilie Hesemeyer Memorial Scholarship
- **S** Florence Young Memorial Scholarships
- **S** Forum for Concerns of Minorities Scholarship
- **S** Health Professions Pre-Graduate Scholarship
- **S** Health Professions Preparatory Scholarship
- **S** Health Professions Scholarship
- **G** Howard Hughes Medical Institute Fellowships & Grants
- **S** IHS Scholarship Program
- **S** Maryland State Delegate Scholarship
- **P** Minority Research Infrastructure Support Program
- **S** NABA National Scholarship Program
- **S** National Association of Black Journalists Scholarship Awards Program
- **I** NIDDK/OMHRC Summer Internship Program (SIP) for Underrepresented Minorities
- **S** NOAA Educational Partnership Program Program Undergraduate Scholarships
- **F** Phillips Foundation Journalism Fellowships
- **P** Research Training & Career Development Program
- **F** Research Training & Fellowships Program
- **A** Scholar Athlete Milk Mustache of the Year (SAMMY)
- **S** Scholastic Achievement Fellows
- **A** Scholastic Achievement Scholars Award
- **S** Sequoya Graduate Scholarships
- **S** Sequoyah Graduate Scholarships
- **S** Sherry R. Arnstein Minority Student Scholarship
- **S** Sodexho Foundation
- **S** Stokes Educational Scholarship Program
- **I** T. Howard Foundation Internships
- **S** The Allogan Slagle Memorial Scholarship
- **F** The Charles Bannerman Memorial Fellowship Program
- **P** The Meyerhoff Scholars Program
- **F** The National Institute of Mental Health Fellowships
- **F** The Stan Beck Fellowship
- **S** The Undergraduate Scholarship Program
- **P** United States Navy

Mass.

- **S** AMS Freshman Undergraduate Scholarship
- **F** AMS Graduate Fellowship in the History of Science
- **S** AMS Undergraduate Named Scholarship
- **S** AMS/Industry Minority Scholarships
- **F** AMS/Industry/Government Graduate Fellowships
- **S** Arturo Schomburg Scholarship
- **S** Bentley Undergraduate Scholarships
- **S** City of Boston Scholarship
- **A** City Year & AmeriCorps
- **F** Dr. Pedro Grau
- **S** Emmanuel College Dean's Scholarship
- **S** Emmanuel College Presidential Scholarship
- **F** Five College Fellowship Program for Minority Students
- **S** Friends of Emmanuel Scholarship
- **P** Goldsmith Awards Program
- **P** Hispanic Office of Planning & Evaluation (Talent Search)
- **S** HOPE Scholarship Fund
- **S** Mark J. Schroeder Scholarship in Meteorology
- **S** Marshall / Chavez / Means Scholarship
- **S** Middlesex Community College Scholarship Programs
- **S** Minority Engineering Education Effort
- **F** National Teaching Fellowship
- **F** Nieman Fellowships for Journalists at Harvard University
- **S** Scholarships for the Arts & Sciences
- **S** Sisters of Notre Dame Scholarship
- **S** The American Academy of Underwater Sciences Scholarship
- **A** The Father James B. Macelwane Award

Michigan

- **S** Adrian College Trustee Scholarship
- **S** Automotive Hall of Fame Scholarship
- **S** Bodman-Longley Scholarship
- **S** Buick Achievers Scholarship Program

Minnesota

Mississippi

Missouri

- A Stephen Bufton Memorial Education Award
- P The Consortium for Graduate Study in Management
- A Transfer Multicultural Scholastic Leadership Award
- S Washington University Hispanic Scholarship Program

Montana

- S Crow Tribal Higher Education Program
- S Crow Tribe Adult Vocational Training Program
- P Crow Tribe Johnson O'Malley Program
- S Hearst Scholarship
- S Hispanic Scholarships
- P Native American Fee Waivers
- S Presidential Leadership Scholarships
- S The Dailey Study Abroad Scholarship
- S The Jane Buttrey Memorial Scholarship
- S The Watkins Scholarship
- A Undergraduate Student/Faculty Research Awards

Nebraska

- S Catalan Latino Endowed Scholarship
- S Dana College Honor Scholarship
- S DAR American Indian Scholarship
- S Davis Scholarship
- S Frances Crawford Marvin American Indian Scholarship
- S Mutual of Omaha Actuarial Scholarship for Minority Students
- S N.P.P.F. Television News Scholarship
- G Native American Tuition Assistance Grant
- S St. Paul Companies Scholarship For Minority Students
- S The Davis Scholarship
- S UNK Multicultural Community Service Scholarship
- S Vietnam Veterans Endowed Scholarship

Nevada

- S Davidson Fellows Scholarship
- S Hispanic Heritage Day Scholarship
- S N.S.G.C. Undergraduate Scholarship Program
- S Nevada Millennium Scholarship (AKA Gov. Guinn Millennium Scholarship)
- S University of Nevada Scholarships
- S Washoe Tribe Higher Education Scholarship

New Hampshire

- F Cesar E. Chavez Dissertation Fellowship for U.S. Latino

New Jersey

- P ASPIRA Programs
- F Cooperative Research Fellowship Program
- S Create-A-Greeting-Card Scholarship Contest
- P Doctoral Programs in Accounting
- S Hispanic Business & Professional Association Scholarship
- S Hispanic Theological Initiative Doctoral Scholarship
- S James Dickson Carr Minority Merit Scholarships
- P Minority Business Reporting Program
- P Minority Editing Intern Program for College Seniors
- G Minority High School Journalism Workshop
- P Minority Medical Education Program
- S Miss America Scholarship
- G New Jersey Educational Opportunity Fund Grants
- S Organic Way To Grow Essay Contest
- S Seton Hall University Scholarship Program
- S Siemens Foundation
- P Summer Research Program for Minorities & Women
- S The ARC Salon & Scholarship Competition
- S The Helen L. Haber Scholarship
- A The Prudential Spirit of Community Awards
- F Thomas R. Pickering Graduate & Undergraduate Foreign Affairs Fellowship Program

New Mexico

- S A.T. Anderson Memorial Scholarship
- S Accenture American Indian Scholarship Program
- A AIGC Graduate Fellowship
- S AISES Google Scholarship
- S AISES Intel Scholarship
- S Alamogordo Excalibur Scholarship
- S All Indian Pueblo Council Scholarship Program
- S All Native American High School Academic Team
- S American Copy Editors Society Scholarship
- S American Indian Graduate Center/Undergraduate Scholarships
- P Amigo Scholars Program
- S Amigo Transfer Scholarship Program
- S Burlington Northern Santa Fe Foundation Scholarship
- S Catching The Dream
- P Catching The Dream - The MESBEC Program

New York

INDEXES

- S Five Towns College Music Program Scholarship
- S Frank Kazmierczak Memorial Migrant Scholarship
- A Franklin C. McLean Award
- S Friends of Senator Jack Perry Migrant Scholarship
- S Girls Going Places Entreprenuership Awards
- S Glamour's Top Ten College Women Competition
- S Gloria & Joseph Mattera National Scholarship Fund For Migrant Children
- F Graduate Newspaper Fellowship & Apprenticeship for Minorities
- A Hall of Fame Award
- S Health Facility Planning & Design
- S Hispanic Cultural Heritage Scholarship
- S Hispanic Health Professional Student Scholarship
- A International Student Award
- S Jackie Robinson Foundation Scholarship Program
- S James Beard Scholarship
- S Joseph Ehrenreich-National Press Photographers Foundation Scholarships
- F Journalism Fellowships in Science & Religion
- S Juanita Crippen Memorial Scholarship
- A Kodak Minority Academic Awards
- S La Unidad Latina Scholarships
- S Le Moyne College Native American Scholarships
- S Loyola Scholarships
- F Magnet/Humana Foundation Doctoral Fellowships
- S Max Kade Scholarships
- S Mayor's Graduate Scholarship Program
- S Migrant Farmworker Baccalaureate Scholarship
- P Minority Editorial Training Program
- S Minority Graduate Accounting Scholarships
- F Minority Postdoctoral Fellowship Program
- S Minority Student Scholarship
- S NACME Pre-Engineering Student Scholarships
- S National Sculpture Society Scholarship
- F National Urban Fellowship Award
- S Native American Cultural Heritage Scholarship
- A New York Life Award
- P New York State for Part-time Study
- A New York State Higher Education Opportunity Award
- I Newhouse Newspaper Graduate Fellowship/Internship for Minorities
- S Newsday Scholarship In Communications
- S NSF Scholarship
- S One Person Can Make A Difference
- S Operation JumpStart
- S Overseas Press Club Foundation Scholarships
- F Rockefeller Brothers Fund Fellowship Program
- F Rome Prize Fellowship
- S Seneca Nation Higher Education Scholarship
- F SSRC-Mellon Minority Fellowship Program
- S Stephen D. Pisinski Memorial Scholarship
- S The AXA Achievement Scholarship
- S The CosmoGIRL! of the Year/Maybelline Scholarship
- P The Elie Wiesel Prize in Ethics Essay Contest
- S The Geneseo Migrant Center
- S The Latino College Expo, Inc. Scholarship
- S The New York Times College Scholarship Program
- F The Paul & Daisy Soros Fellowships for New Americans
- A The Paul Zindel First Novel Award
- A The Queens Gallery Service Award
- S The Roothbert Fund Scholarship
- S Third Wave Scholarships for Young Women
- P Time Inc. Summer Editorial Intern Program
- P United Nations Correspondents Association Ranan Lurie Political Cartoon Prize
- S United States Army
- S University Scholarship Program to Study in Israel
- S Vaughan/NAHWW Home Workshop Writers Scholarship
- S W. Eugene Smith Memorial Fund
- S World Studio Foundation Scholarship
- S Xerox Technical Minority Scholarship

North Carolina

- S A.W. Huckle Memorial Scholarship
- S Ameel Fisher Scholarship
- S Beatrice Cobb Scholarship
- S Bob Quincy Scholarship
- S C. A. "Pete" McKnight Scholarship
- S Carl C. Council Scholarship
- S Carolinas Healthcare Scholarship

S David Julian Whichard Scholarship
S Deborah Brotherton Sykes Scholarship
S Dick Taylor Scholarship
S Donald S. Maurer Advertising Scholarship
S Edward Heywood Megson Scholarship
S Elkin Tribune-Thomas J. Fleming Scholarship
S Elton Casey Scholarship
S Erwin Potts Scholarship
S Floyd S. Alford Jr. Scholarship
S Freedom Newspapers Scholarship
S Gene Jackson Scholarship
S Gerald Johnson Scholarship
S Glenn Keever Scholarship
S Hal Tanner Sr. Scholarship
S Harvey Laffoon Memorial Scholarship
S Henry A. Dennis & William B. Dennis Scholarship
S Henry Lockwood Phillips Scholarship
S Hispanic League of The Piedmont Triad Scholarship
S Holt McPherson Scholarship
S Isabella Carvalho Health Scholarship
S James Davis Scholarship
S James F. Hurley III Bicentennial Merit Scholarship
A James M. Johnson Awards
S John Boy & Billy Scholarship
S John W. Harden Scholarship
S John W. Hartman Scholarship
S Jonathan Daniels Scholarship
S Joseph E. Pogue Scholarships
S Julius C. Hubbard Scholarship
S Knight Foundation Distinguished Journalism Scholarship
S L. C. Gifford Distinguished Journalism Scholarship
P Landmark Scholars Program
A Latino Diamante Awards-Youth Accomplishment
S Louis Graves Scholarship
S Louis M. Connor Jr. Scholarship
S Marjorie Usher Ragan Scholarship
S Mark Ethridge Scholarship
S Michael Ubmgardner Scholarship
S Mildred Gifford Scholarship
G Minority Presence Grants (General Program II)
S Molly McKay Scholarship
S N. C. Black Publishers Association Scholarship
F National Humanities Center Fellowship
S North Carolina Press Association-North Carolina Press Services Scholarship
S North Carolina Working Press Scholarship
S O.J. Coffin Scholarship
S OP Loftbed Scholarship
S Paul Green Houston Scholarship
S Pete Ivey Scholarship
S Quincy Sharpe Mills Scholarship
S R.C. Rivers Memorial Scholarship
S Reese Felts Scholarship
S Rick Brewer Scholarship
I Robert Pittman Scholarship - Internship
S Robert Winchester Dodson Scholarship
S Roy Rabon Scholarship
S Roy Wilkins Scholarship
S Steed Rollins Scholarship
S The 2006 Thomas Wolfe Student Essay Prize
S Tom Bost Scholarship
S Triangle Advertising Federation Scholarship
S University of North Carolina at Chapel Hill School of Journalism & Mass Communication Scholarships
S Victoria M. Gardner Scholarship
S Walter Spearman Scholarship
S William McWhorter Cochrane Scholarship
S WTVD Scholarship

North Dakota

S Dr. David M. Gipp Scholarship Fellows
S HEROS Scholarship Program
S North Dakota Indian Scholarship
S North Dakota Indian Scholarship Program
P North Dakota Scholars Program
P Northern Plains Tribal Technical Assistance Program (NPTTAP)
S Opportunities in the Making Scholarship Fund

Ohio

- **S** AES Engineers Scholarship
- **S** AGC of Ohio Education Foundation Scholarships
- **S** Bexley Women's Club College/University Scholarship
- **S** Bexley Women's Club High School Scholarship
- **S** Colombus Rotary Phoenix Scholarship
- **S** Community Enrichment Scholarship Program
- **S** CSOHIMSS Jane A. Blank Scholarship Program
- **S** Darwin T. Turner Scholarship
- **S** Denison University HLA Scholarship
- **S** Denison University Multicultural Achievement Scholarship
- **S** Duck Brand Stuck at Prom Scholarship
- **S** Esperanza Scholarship Program
- **S** Gustavo A. Parajon Scholarship
- **S** HBCU Minority Student Scholarships
- **S** Image Latino Scholarship
- **A** Incentive Award
- **A** King-Chavez-Parks Award
- **S** Lancelot C. A. Thompson Minority Scholarship
- **S** Latin Ladies Scholarship
- **A** National Hispanic Honorable Mention Supplement Award
- **S** Nationwide Children's Hospital Scholarship
- **S** Ohio State Distinction Scholarship
- **S** Perennial Plant Association Scholarship Program
- **S** Prestigious Scholarship
- **P** Templeton Scholars Program
- **S** The Collegiate Inventors Competition
- **S** The Columbus Chapter Scholarships
- **S** The Willis Knapp Jones Scholarship
- **S** Tower Scholarship
- **S** Tuition Equalization Scholarship Program
- **S** University of Toledo MECHA Scholarship
- **S** University of Toledo Student Achievement Scholarship
- **S** UT National Hispanic Scholarship

Oklahoma

- **S** 180 Medical College Scholarship Program
- **S** Amoco Accounting Scholarships
- **S** Anna Belle Mitchell Memorial Scholarship
- **A** At-Large Tribal Council Award
- **S** Bill Rabbit Legacy Art Scholarship
- **S** Blackwell Scholarships
- **S** Cherokee Nation Businesses Scholarship
- **S** Cherokee Nation Pell Scholarship
- **S** Cherokee Nation Undergraduate and Graduate Scholarships
- **S** Cherokee Promise Scholarship
- **S** Cheyenne-Arapaho Tribes of Oklahoma Scholarships
- **P** Chickasaw Nation Concurrent Enrollment
- **P** Chickasaw Nation Education Foundation Program
- **S** Chickasaw Nation General Scholarship Program
- **S** Chickasaw Nation Governor's Scholarship
- **G** Chickasaw Nation Higher Education Grant
- **S** Chickasaw Nation Legislators' Scholarship
- **S** Chickasaw Nation Lt. Governor's Scholarship
- **S** Chief Pushmataha College Scholarship Fund
- **S** Choctaw Language Teacher Education Scholarship
- **G** Choctaw Nation of Oklahoma Higher Education Grants
- **S** Citizen Potawatomi Nation Tribal Rolls Scholarship
- **S** Comanche Nation Scholarship Program
- **S** Creek Nation Higher Education Program
- **S** Daughters of Indian Wars Scholarship
- **S** F. Browning Pipestem Memorial Scholarship
- **S** Flintco Scholarship
- **S** Heinz College - Choctaw Nation Scholarship Program
- **S** Inter-Tribal Council of the Five Civilized Tribes - Johnson O'Malley Scholarship
- **S** John C. Smith Scholarship
- **A** John Shurr Journalism Award
- **S** Langston's Non-Black Scholarship
- **S** Leading With Diligence Scholarship
- **S** Louie LeFlore/Grant Foreman Scholarship
- **S** Louie LeFlore/Grant Foreman Scholarship
- **S** MEFUSA Scholarships for Native Americans
- **S** NAJA Scholarships
- **S** Oklahoma Christian MBA Scholarship Opportunity
- **S** Oklahoma City University Choctaw Student Award (undergraduate)
- **P** Oklahoma State Regents Academic Scholars Program

- S Scholarship for Student Leaders
- S The Lori Rhett Memorial Scholarship
- S The Markley Scholarship
- S The Tese Caldarelli Memorial Scholarship
- S The Zagunis Student Leader Scholarship

South Dakota

- S AIEF Graduate Scholarships
- S AIEF Undergraduate Scholarships
- S American Indian Education Foundation Scholarship Program
- S Crazy Horse Memorial (Book)
- S Crazy Horse Memorial (Jonas)
- S Crazy Horse Memorial Scholarship Program
- G Dakota Indian Foundation Grant
- S Dakota Indian Foundation Scholarship
- S Golden West Scholarship Program
- S Honorary Leonard Peltier Scholarship
- S John E. Hess Scholarship
- S Johnson Entrepreneurship Scholarship
- S Joseph and Mary Cacioppo Foundation Scholarship
- S Josephine Nipper Memorial Scholarship
- S Max Pell Book Scholarship
- S Oglala Lakota College Scholarships
- S Paul Francis Memorial Scholarship
- S The Big Sky Foundation Scholarship

Tennessee

- S Chancellor's Scholarships for Outstanding Minority Students
- S College of Agricultural Science & Natural Resources Scholarship for Minorities
- S Dean's Scholarships
- S Estes Kefauver Memorial Endowment Scholarship
- A Golden Key Service Award
- A H. W. Durham Senior Scholars Award
- F Judith L. Weidman Racial Ethnic Minority Fellowship
- S Lanier Family Scholarships
- S Leonard M. Perryman Communications Scholarship
- S Minority Scholarship
- S National Achievement Scholarships
- F Stoody-West Fellowship for Graduate Study
- S The Charles S. Watson Minority Scholarship
- S The J. Douglass & Dorothy K. Wood Scholarship
- S The RMHC/HACER Scholarship Program
- S The Sonat Foundation Diversity Engineering Scholarship Program
- S United Methodist Ethnic Minority Scholarships
- S United South & Eastern Tribes, Inc. Scholarships
- S William A. & Nancy F. McMinn Honor Scholarships in the Natural Sciences

Texas

- S Abercrombie & Fitch Future Leaders Scholarship
- S Academic Achievement Scholarship
- S ACCD Endowed Scholarship
- S ¡Adelante! US Education Leadership Fund
- P African American/Hispanic Architectural Education Work/Study Program
- S African-American Endowed Scholarship
- S Alamo Colleges Foundation Scholarships
- S Alliance for Minority Participation Scholarship
- S American Association of Hispanic CPAs Scholarship
- P American Economic Association Summer Program
- S Annie Byrd Memorial Scholarship
- S Asociación Boricua de Dallas, Inc. Scholarship
- S Benjamin A. Gilman International Scholarship
- S Centennial Scholarship
- S Coastal Bend College
- S College Essay Contest
- P Communities in School of San Antonio
- S Community College Scholarships
- S Dallas Area Community College Scholarships
- S Dawson Endowed Scholarships
- A Dean's Scholar Awards
- S Dedman Distinguished Scholars
- P Dell Scholars Program
- P Deloitte Scholars Program
- S Distinguished Achievement Academic Scholarship
- S East Texas Baptist University Scholarship Level 1
- G Established Investigator Grant
- S ETBU College Transfer Level 1
- S Ethnic Recruitment Scholarships

S Fifth Year Accounting Student Scholarship
A Foundation Excellence Awards
S Freshman Achievement Scholarship
S Freshman Honors Scholarship
S Good Neighbor Scholarship Program
F Graduate Diversity Fellowships
G Grant-in-Aid
S H-E-B/Adelante Future Leaders Scholarship
S H. D. Bruce National Merit Achievement Scholarship
S Hana Scholars Program
S Hispanic Association of Colleges & Universities (HACU) Scholarship Program
P Hispanic Deaf Teacher Training Program
S Honor Transfer Scholarships
S HOPE Scholarship (CPS Energy Dependents ONLY)
S Improve Your Life Scholarship
S John Philip Goudge Memorial Scholarship
S Kappa Delta Chi Foundation - High School Scholar
S Kappa Delta Chi National Foundation
S Kristen A. Sanchez Deloitte Student of the Year Scholarship
P LANZATE! Travel Award Program - Giving Flight to Your Success/Dandole Alas a Tu Exito
A Leadership Award
S Learn, Inc.
S License Plate Insignia Schoarship
S LULAC National Educational Service Center
S LULAC/ACCD Parent/Child Scholarship Program
S MAES Founders Scholarships
S MAES General Scholarships
S MAES Presidential Scholarship
S MAES Presidential Scholarships
S MAES Scholarship Program
S McMurray University Presidential Scholarships
P Mexican Citizens with Financial Need-Border County Waiver
P Mexican Citizens with Financial Need-Border Nations Waiver
S MillerCoors Chicago
S MillerCoors Engineering & Sciences
S MillerCoors National Scholarship
F NASA/Texas Space Fellowship
S NASA/Texas Space Scholarship
A Nascar/Wendell Scott Sr. Award
S National Black Police Association Scholarships
A National Merit Scholars
S Nemo Herrera Scholarship
A Opportunity Award
S Outstanding Freshman Scholarship
S Outstanding Transfer Scholarship
S Paul Douglas Teacher Scholarships
S Phi Theta Kappa Scholarship
S President's Charter Scholarship
S President's Endowed Scholarship
P President's Endowed University Scholars Program
A President's Scholar Awards
S Presidential Endowed Scholarship
S Presidents Achievement Scholarship
S Rayburn/Mayo Housing Scholarship
S Rice University Presidential Scholarships
S Ritchie-Jennings Memorial Scholarship
P Robert Schreck Memorial Fund
S Rural Emergency Medical Services Scholarship
G Scientist Development Grant
S SMU Scholars
S South Texas Scholarship Program
S Spare Funds Scholarships
S STMU Undergraduate Scholarships
P Sul Ross State University Honors Program
S Terry Foundation Scholarship
S Texas A & M Presidential Scholarship
P Texas Aid for Students whose Parents Received TANF
F Texas Association of Chicanos in Higher Education (TACHE)-Gradute Fellowship
A Texas Excellence Awards
S Texas General Nursing Scholarship Program
S Texas Health Service Corps Scholarship
G Texas State Student Incentive Grant for Students at Public Institutions
S Texas Tennis Foundation Scholarships
G Texas Tuition Equalization Grant

- **S** The Amoco Foundation Scholarship
- **S** The Boy Scouts of America National College
- **A** The Carnation Incentive Award
- **P** The College Assistance Migrant Program (CAMP)
- **P** The Deloitte Tax Scholars Program
- **A** The Distinguished Achievement Award
- **S** The Dow Chemical Company Scholarship
- **S** The Nancy Ann & Ray L. Hunt Leadership Scholars
- **A** The Presidential Award
- **S** The Shell Incentive Scholarship
- **S** Transfer Achievement Scholarship
- **S** Tri Delta Foundation Scholarships
- **I** United Health Foundation/Hispanic Association of Colleges and Universities Scholarship
- **S** United Health Foundation/HWNT Scholarship
- **S** University of Texas Scholarship Program
- **P** University of Texas-Brownsville (Talent Search)
- **S** University of Texas-Pan American Excellence Scholarships
- **A** University Scholars
- **S** University Scholars Partnership
- **S** Urban Scholarship Fund
- **S** UTA Hispanic Endowed Scholarship
- **S** UTA Transfer Honors Scholarship
- **S** Vikki Carr Scholarship Foundation
- **S** Vocational Nursing Scholarships
- **P** Waiver for Students from Mexico Enrolled in Graduate Degree Programs in Public Health
- **S** Wayne Duke Student Leadership Scholarship
- **S** William Marsh Rice Scholarships

Utah

- **S** American Indian Services Scholarships
- **S** AT&T - WGU Native American Scholarship
- **S** Chicano Scholarship Fund
- **P** Discover Scholarship Program
- **S** Diversity Scholarships
- **F** Graduate Research Fellowships
- **S** Pete Suazo Memorial Scholarship - "Commitment to Community"
- **S** WGU Scholarship in Business & Information Technology

Vermont

- **P** English Teaching Fellows Program

Virginia

- **S** 9/11 Memorial Scholarship
- **S** AAAE Foundation Scholarship for Native Americans
- **S** AFAS General Henry H. Arnold Education Grant Program
- **S** AFCEA General John A. Wickham Scholarship
- **S** AFCEA/ORINCON IT Scholarship
- **S** AGC Undergraduate Scholarships
- **S** AGI Minority Geoscience Graduate Scholarship
- **S** AGI Minority Geoscience Undergraduate Scholarship
- **S** American Express Travel Scholarship
- **S** ASAV Scholarship
- **I** Ashoka Internship
- **S** ATCA Scholarship Program
- **G** Augusta Grant
- **S** Bailey Scholarship
- **S** Baldwin Scholarship
- **S** Barry M. Goldwater Scholarship
- **S** CAS Trust Scholarship
- **P** Cigna Scholars Program
- **S** Computer Graphic Design Scholarship
- **S** Datatel Scholars Foundation Scholarship
- **A** Fernando R. Ayuso Award
- **S** Film & Fiction Scholarship
- **S** Food Service Scholarship
- **F** GEM Fellowship
- **S** Idea of America Essay Contest
- **P** IIPP Fellows Program
- **S** ILUMINA Bolivian Scholarship Program
- **S** Jack Kent Cooke Foundation Scholarship
- **S** James F. Powell Scholarships
- **S** Jimi Hendrix Endowment Fund Scholarship
- **S** Kirsten Lorentzen Award
- **F** McCormick Fellowship
- **F** Minority Clinical/Research Fellowship
- **F** Minority Journalism Educators Fellowship
- **F** NAA Minority Fellowship Program

F NAA Minority Fellowships - "Escalating to Newspaper Management Success"
F NAA Minority Fellowships in New Media
S National Association of Hispanic Federal Executives (NAHFE) Scholarship Program
S National Health Service Corps Scholarship Program
S Physician Assistants for Latino Health Scholarships
S Presidential Classroom Scholars
S Randolph Macon Minority Scholarships
F Rollan D. Melton Fellowship
P Ron Brown Scholar Program
S Stanley E. Jackson Scholarship for the Handicapped
S Student CEC Ethnic Diversity Scholarship
S Surflant Scholarship
S The Applegate-Jackson-Parks Future Teacher Scholarship
S The Chrome Scholarships
S The Environmental Essay Contest
P The Gates Millennium Scholars Program
S The Holland Dunston Ellis, Jr. Memorial Scholarship
F The Institute for Humane Studies Fellowships
S The Maureen and Howard Blitman, P.E., Scholarship To Promote Diversity In Engineering
S The Minority Scholarship Fund
P The National Hispanic Scholar Recognition Program
S The Sallie Mae Fund "Unmet Need" Scholarship Program
S The Vice Admiral Samuel L. Gravely Scholarship
F Walter Everett Fellowship
S Washington & Lee Honor Scholarships Program
S William B. Ruggles Journalist Scholarship

Washington

S Academic Achievement Diversity Scholarship
S American Indian Endowed Scholarship
S Bannan Scholarship
S Cultural Diversity Scholarships
S First People's Scholarship
S Graduate Diversity Scholarship
S Kit C. King Graduate Scholarship
F Martinez Foundation Fellowships
S Martinez Foundation Scholarships
S Master's in Social Work Minority Scholarship
S Microsoft Scholarship Program
S National Foster Parent Association (NFPA) College Scholarship
S Nellie Martin Carman Scholarship Committee
S Northwest Indian Housing Association Scholarship
S Paralegal Scholarships
S Reid Blackburn Scholarship
A Seattle University Regents Award
A Sullivan Leadership Awards
S The Mary M. Fraijo Scholarships
S UW Diversity Scholarship Award
S Washington Indian Gaming Association Scholarships
G Washington State Need Grant
S Yakama Nation Tribal Scholarship

Washington DC

S AARP Foundation Women's Scholarship Program
G AAUW Educational Foundation Career Development Grants
S ABC News - Joanna Bistany Memorial Scholarship
S Abe Schechter Graduate Scholarship
G Academic Competitiveness Grants (ACG)
S ACS Scholars Program
S ACS-Hach Land Grant Undergraduate Scholarship
S ACS-Hach Second Career Teacher Scholarship
S Advanced Summer Course on Spanish Language & Culture
S AIA/AAF Minority Disadvantaged Scholarship
S American Architectural Foundation Minority Scholarship
S American Chemical Society (ACS) Scholars Program
P American Chemistry Society Scholars Program
S American Hotel & Lodging Educational Foundation
S American Indian Scholarship
S American Indian Scholarships
P American Political Science Association
F American Psychological Association-Minority Fellowship
G AmeriCorps VISTA
S Anna Maria Arias Scholarship
G Annual Grant Competition
S Antonio M. Marinelli Founders' Scholarship
S APIASF Scholarship Program

S APSA Fund for Latino Scholarship
F APSA Minority Graduate Fellowship Program
S Art Scholarship
F ASM Minority Undergraduate Research Fellowship
S Assurant Scholarship Program
S AVON Products Foundation Scholarship for Women in Business Studies
S BEA National Scholarships in Broadcasting
S Beta Zeta Boule Foundation Scholarship
S BIA Higher Education Grant
S Boren Scholarships
S BPW Career Advancement Scholarship Program
S BPW Foundation Career Advancement Scholarships
G Bureau of Indian Education Higher Education Grant Program
S CareFirst BlueCross BlueShield Scholarship Program
S Carmen E. Turner Scholarship
S Caroline E. Holt Nursing Scholarship
S Center for Native American Youth Scholarship
S CHCI Scholarship Award
P CIA Undergraduate Scholarship Program
S Civil Engineering Corps (CEC)
P College Board National Hispanic Scholar Recognition Program
F Community Builders Fellowship Program
S Computer Packages, Inc. Scholarship Program
P Core Fulbright Scholar Program
S Cristina Saralegui Scholarship Program
I CSIS Intern Program
I CSIS Minority Internship in International Affairs
F Curso de Lengua y Cultura Españolas - Universidad de Salamanca
F Curso de Literatura Infantil y Juvenil Universidad Complutense Madrid
S Daimler Chrysler/HACU Scholarship Fund
S David E. Lumley Young Scientist Scholarship
S David S. Liederman Scholarship Program
S Development Fund for Black Students in Science and Technology
A Diversity Leaders Award
S Donna Jamison Lago Memorial Scholarship
S Ed Bradley Scholarship
S Ellen Masin Persina Scholarship
S Embassy of Spain Scholarships
A Eugene Katz Award for Excellence in the Coverage of Immigration
P Federal Student Financial Assistance Programs
F Feldman Fellowship for Graduate Studies in Journalism
F Fellowships at the Wilson Center
S Financial Literacy Scholarship
S Ford Blue Oval Nationwide Scholarship
S Ford Blue Oval Puerto Rico Scholarship
F Ford Foundation Dissertation Fellowships for Minorities
F Ford Foundation Postdoctoral Fellowships for Minorities
F Ford Foundation Predoctoral & Dissertation Fellowships for Minorities
G Fulbright Grant
A Fulbright Occassional Lecturer Fund
S Future Leaders Scholarship
F G. Richard Tucker Summer Fellowship
S Gannett Foundation/NAHJ Scholarships
S Google Hispanic College Fund Scholarship Program
I HACU National Internship Program (HNIP)
S Harry S. Truman Scholarship
A Heywood Broun Award
S Hispanic College Fund
A Hispanic Heritage Youth Awards
F Hispanic Link Journalism Foundation Reporting Fellowship
F HLJF Journalism Fellowship
F Howard Hughes Medical Institute Pre doctoral Fellowships - Biological Sciences
F Humanities Fellowship in Latino Cultural Research in a National Museum Context
P Hyatt Hotels Fund for Minority Lodging Management Students
S IAHI Scholarship Program
G Indian Employment Assistance Grants
S Ingram-White Castle Foundation Scholarship
S Intel Scholarship Program
S J.J. Barr Scholarship
F Jacob K. Javits Fellowships Program
F Jacque Minnotte Health Reporting Fellowship

F James Madison Memorial Fellowship Program

S Javits-Frasier Teacher Scholarship Fund for Diverse Talent Development

S Jay Charles Levine Scholarship

S Juan Eugene Ramos Scholarship

S Juanita Robles-Lopez Scholarship

G Kellogg Leadership Grant

A Knight International Journalism Award

P Latino Student Fund Scholars Program

S League of United Latin American Citizens

S Lou & Carole Prato Sports Reporting Scholarship

S Louise Moritz Molitoris Leadership Scholarship for Undergraduates

S Lowes Fall ACCESS Scholarship

S M & T Bank Scholarship Program

F M F P Mental Health & Substance Abuse Services

S Mana National Scholarship Endowment

P Marriott Scholars Program

S MasterCard Worldwide Scholarship Program

S McDonald's Scholarship Program: Me Encanta

F Michele Clarke Fellowship

S Mike Reynolds Scholarship

F Minority Fellowship Program

F N.S. Bienstock Fellowship

S NAHJ Ford Motor Company Fund Scholarships

S NAHJ General Scholarships - Ruben Salazar Fund

S NAHJ Geraldo Rivera Scholarship

S NAHJ Maggie Rodriguez Scholarship Program

S NAHJ Maria Elena Salinas Scholarship

S NAHJ PepsiCo Scholarships

S NAHJ Soledad O'Brien Scholarship

F NAHJ/NBC Fellowships

I NAHJ/NHPF Ford Blue Oval Journalism Internships

S NAHN Nursing Scholarships

S National Association of Hispanic Nurses

F National Congress of American Indians Fellowships

I National Congress of American Indians Internships

F National Congress of American Indians Native Graduate Health Fellowship

S National Essay Contest for Native American High School Students

I National Gallery of Art Internships

S National Hispanic Foundation for the Arts

S National Hispanic Press Foundation

P National Research Council Research Associateship Programs

F National Security Education Program's David L. Boren Graduate Fellowships

I Native American Political Leadership Program Ongoing Internship

S New York Life Foundation Scholarships for Women in the Health Professions

S Newhouse Scholarship Program

S NIEA John C. Rouillard and Alice Tonemah Memorial Scholarship

S NROTC Immediate Selection Decision (ISD)

F NSF Graduate Research Fellowship Program (GRFP)

S Nuclear Propulsion Officer (NUPOC)

G Oracle Community Impact Grant

S Patricia V. Asip Scholarship

S Persina Scholarship for Minorities in Journalism

S PFLAG National Scholarship Program

S Police Corps Scholarship

F Predoctoral Training in The Neurosciences

G Priority Grant Competition

S Project SEED Scholarships

I Public Health for Hispanic Women Scholarship & Internship Programs

S René Matos Scholarship

F Research Training Fellowship

F Robert D. Watkins Minority Graduate Research Fellowship

A Robert F. Kennedy Journalism Awards

S Ronald Reagan College Leaders Scholarship

S Rosa L. Parks Scholarship

S RTNDA Scholarship

S RTNDF President's 2500 Scholarships

S SAA Arthur C. Parker Scholarship or NSF Scholarship for Archaeological Training

S SAA Native American Graduate Archaeology Scholarship

S SAA Native American Undergraduate Archaeology Scholarship

S Sam's Club Hispanic-serving institution (HSI) Scholarship Competition

S Scholarship for Journalism Diversity

F Spanish Cultural & Language Fellowships

I Summer in Washington Internship

P Summer Medical and Dental Education Program

F Teaching Ambassador Fellowship Program

P The Air Force College Fund Program

A The Anne Armstrong Leadership Awards

P The Army College Fund Program

S The ASPIRA Association

F The Congressional Hispanic Caucus Institute Graduate & Young Professional Fellowship

S The Congressional Hispanic Caucus Institute Scholarship

S The Esperanza Scholarship for GED Holders

S The Esperanza Scholarship for High School Seniors

S The General Electric/LULAC Scholarship Program

S The George Foreman Tribute to Lyndon B. Johnson Scholarship

S The LULAC National Scholarship Fund

P The Navy Baccalaureate Degree Completion Program (BDCP)

P The Navy College Assistance Student Headstart Program (NAVY CASH)

P The Navy College Fund Program

S Trailblazer Scholarship

P United Health Foundation Latino Health Scholars Program

I United States Department of State Internships

P United Water Corporate Scholars Program

F Universidad Pompeu Fabra Barcelona

F Universidad Santiago de Compostela

I USDA Summer Internship Program

S USDA/1994 Tribal Scholarship Program

S USHCC Scholarship Fund

F Vada & Barney Oldfield National Security Reporting Fellowship

F Vilar institute for Arts Management - Fellowships

I Vilar institute for Arts Management - Internships

I Washington Internships for Native Students (WINS)

S William Randolph Hearst Endowed Scholarship for Minority Students

F WWC-Washington Post Fellowship for Latin American Journalists

S Wyeth-Ayerst Labs Scholarship for Women in Graduate Medical/Health

Wisconsin

S Agriculture Scholarship

S Alverno College Scholarships

S Ebbie and Peggy Neese Scholarship

G Madison Minority Retention Grant

S Menominee Adult Vocational Training Scholarship

S Mount Mary College President's Scholarship

S Ripon College Valedictorian Scholarship

S Roma Hoff Scholarship for Excellence

P Something Good From the Hood

S Tona Diebels Scholarship

S WHSF/Mexican Fiesta Scholarships

S Wisconsin Future Teachers Scholarship

Wyoming

S Multicultural Pride Scholarship

S University of Wyoming Chicano Studies Scholarship

S University of Wyoming Scholarship Program

X Argentina

S CIE Scholarship

X Canada

S CGarchitect.com/ART VPS Scholarship

S Mosaic Scholarship

X Spain

S Spain Scholarship Program

X United Kingdom

S De Montford University Scholarship

X México

S Mexico Scholarship Program

Insights

"College Broadened My Scope"

"College broadened my scope of the world and myself. It inspired me to take on fields I wouldn't have taken on before. I was brought up in a family that cut timber for a living and college got me out of that life."

Tim Ryan,
EthnoTech, LLC, Confederated Salish & Kootenai Tribes of the Flathead Reservation, Montana

20 OR MORE SCHOLARSHIPS

BY STATE & NAME

On the enclosed CD you will find detailed searchable profiles on each of the following awards (A), fellowships (F), grants (G), internships (I), programs (P), and scholarships (S).

Type & Name of the Scholarship

ALABAMA

- S Air Force ROTC 4-YEAR Scholarship
- S Alabama Commission on Higher Education
- S America's Junior Miss Scholarship Program
- S American Indian Nurse Scholarship Award
- S Junior & Community College Performing Arts Scholarship
- S Two-Year College Academic Scholarship

ALASKA

- S CIRI Foundation Scholarships

ARIZONA

- S Carlos C. & Alex G. Jacome Memorial Scholarship
- S Chief Manuelito Scholarship Program
- S Colorado River Indian Scholarship
- S Gila River Indian Community Division of Student Services Scholarships
- S Hopi Scholarship
- S Los Diablos Scholarship
- I Morris K. Udall Foundation Internships
- S Morris K. Udall Scholarship
- S Navajo Generating Station Navajo Scholarship
- S Navajo Nation Scholarship & Financial Assistance Program
- S Pima Scholarship Program
- S Reforma Scholarship
- S Shandiin Scholarship Fund
- S UA Hispanic Alumni Scholarship Program

ARKANSAS

- S Arkansas Academic Challenge Scholarship
- S National Dental Association/Colgate Palmolive Pre-Doctoral Scholarship
- P Wal-mart Competitive Edge Program

CALIFORNIA

- S (AAHCPA) Scholarship Program
- S Academic Scholarship
- A Achievement Awards
- S Alice Newell Joslyn Medical Fund
- S Alumnae Scholarship Program
- S Anthem Essay Contest
- S Association of Latino Professionals in Finance and Accounting
- P Atlas Shrugged Essay Contest
- S Beca Foundation Scholarships
- S Black Alumni Association / Ebonics Support Group Scholarship
- S C.A.R. Scholarships
- G Cal Grant Undergraduate Scholarship Program
- S California Chicano News Media Association (CCNMA)
- S California Congress of Parents and Teachers, Teacher Education Scholarships
- S California State University-Monterey Bay General Scholarships
- S California State University, Los Angeles Scholarships
- S Chicana/Latina Foundation Scholarship Program
- S Cien Amigos - IME Becas Scholarship Fund
- S Coalition for Nursing Careers in California Scholarship Program
- S COCA-COLA Live Positivity and Hispanic Scholarship Fund Essay Contest
- S College Retention/General Scholarship Program
- S Community College Scholarship Program
- S Community College Transfer Scholarship Program
- S Community Service Scholarship
- S CRAEF Scholarship
- I CSRC Getty Undergraduate Summer Arts Internship
- I CSRC Getty Undergraduate Summer Arts Internship
- S CSU Fresno Scholarship Fund
- S CSU Minority Engineering Program Scholarship
- S CSU Scholarships for Future Scholars

- S CSUB Hispanic Excellence Scholarship Fund Program
- S CSUF TELACU Scholarship Program
- S CSULB Scholarship Program
- S CTA Martin Luther King, Jr. Memorial Scholarship Fund
- S CTA Scholarship Program for Dependent Children
- S Cuban American Teachers' Association Scholarship
- S Daddy Longlegs Scholarship
- S Deans' Scholarship
- S Dr. Bertha O. Pendelton Scholarship Fund
- S Dr. Carreon Foundation
- S EDSF Board of Directors Scholarships
- P Extended Opportunity Programs & Services
- S Ford Salute to Education
- P Fountainhead Essay Contest
- S "Full filling Our Dreams" Scholarship Fund
- P Great Minds in STEM HENAAC Scholars Program
- S Greater Houston Retailers Association and Coca-Cola Live Positively Scholarship Program
- S Hispanic Bar Association of Orange County High School Juniors Scholarship Program
- S Hispanic Community Affairs Council Scholarship Fund
- S Hispanic Scholarship Fund
- S Hon. Mario G. Olmos Memorial Scholarship
- S HSF / Coca-Cola Live Positively Publix Supermarkets Scholarship Program
- S HSF / Macy's Scholarship Program
- S HSF / USHCC-Wells Fargo Scholarship
- S HSF/ Achievement Scholarship Program
- S HSF/ General College Scholarships
- S HSF/ALPFA Scholarship Program
- S HSF/Budweiser Cup Tournament Scholarship Program
- S HSF/Budweiser World Cup Scholarship Program
- S HSF/Coca-Cola Refreshments West Region Scholarship Program
- S HSF/Cummins Scholarship Program
- S HSF/ExxonMobil Scholarship Program
- S HSF/General Scholarships
- A HSF/Goldman Sachs 10,000 Women Business Leadership Award
- S HSF/HACEMOS Scholarship
- S HSF/HSBC-North America Scholarship Program
- S HSF/Morgan Stanley Foundation Scholarship Program
- S HSF/Nissan North America, Inc. Scholarship Program
- S HSF/Telemundo Scholarship
- S HSF/Toyota Scholarship Program
- S HSF/Travelers Scholarship
- S HSF/Verizon Foundation Scholarship
- S HSF/Verizon Wireless Tu Mandas Scholarship
- S HSF/Wal-Mart Stores, Inc. High School Scholarship Program
- S Imperial Valley College
- S Inland Empire Scholarship
- F Jack R. Howard Science Reporting Institute at Caltech Fellowships
- S JACL National Scholarship Program
- S Jesuit Community Scholarship
- S Latino Association of Faculty & Staff Scholarships at California State University San Marcos
- S Leadership Scholarship
- S Lowrider Magazine Scholarship Fund
- S Loyola Presidential Scholarship
- S LSAT Scholarship
- S Mahatma Gandhi Memorial Scholarship
- S MALDEF Law School Scholarship Program
- S Marin Education Fund
- P MEDI-CORPS
- S Meritus Scholarship
- S MiraCosta College Foundation Scholarship Program
- S MTS & Coca Cola Laptop Scholarship
- S National Hispanic University Scholarships
- F National Physical Science Consortium
- S NHFA Entertainment Industry Scholarship Program
- S Nissan Scholarship Program
- P PacifiCare's Latino Health Scholars Program
- S President Obama/HSF STEM Teacher Scholarship Program
- S Que Llueva Cafe Scholarship
- F Robert Toigo MBA Fellowship
- A SACNAS National Conference Travel & Lodging Awards
- S Salvadoran-American Leadership & Educational Fund
- S San Diego County Citizen's Scholarship Foundation
- S San Jose G.I. Forum Scholarship

S SCions Scholarship
S Sears Craftman Scholarship
S Sheldon "Shelly" Fay Videography
I Shell Legislative Internship Program
S Society of Hispanic Professional Engineers (SHPE) Scholarships
S Student Leader Scholarship
I Summer Academic Research Internship (SARI)
P Summer Engineering/Architecture Student Trainee Program
P Summer Program for Undergraduate Research Students
P Summer Research Opportunities Program
P Summer Training Academy for Research in the Sciences (S.T.A.R.S.)
S Summer Undergraduate Research in Chemistry
S TELACU Education Foundation Scholarships
S The Beca Scholarship Foundation
S The CareerFitter.com Scholarship
S The Education and Leadership Foundation's Merit Scholarship
S The Google Anita Borg Memorial Scholarship: USA
P The Howard Hughes Undergraduate Science Enrichment Program (HHUSEP)
P The Howard Hughes Undergraduate Science Enrichment Program (HHUSEP)
S The Lagrant Foundation
S The National Hispanic Foundation for the Arts
S The Orange County Hispanic Education Endowment Fund (HEEF)
S The Padres Scholar
P The UCSF Summer Research Training Program
S The Valerie Kantor Memorial Scholarship
P Toyota Community Scholars Program
S UAL/UABT Scholarship Program
P UCI Women & Minority Engineering Program
P UCLA Premedical/Predental Enrichment Program
P UCLA Re-Application Program
P United States Senate Youth Program
S USC National Hispanic Scholarship
S USC Presidential Scholarship
S USC Trustee Scholarship
P We the Living Essay Contest
S Wilbur Family Fund Hispanic Scholarship
S Youth Opportunities Foundation Scholarships

Colorado

P Adams State College
S American Indian College Fund
P Arizona Public Service Navajo Scholars Program
S Community College Transfer Scholarship
S Council of Energy Resource Tribes (CERT) Scholarships
S General Mills Foundation
S Hispanic Alumni Scholarship Fund
S Latin American Educational Foundation (LAEF)
S Multicultural Engineering Program (MEP) Scholarship
S Scholarships
S Success in Engineering Through Excellence & Diversity
S United States Air Force Academy
S University of Colorado at Boulder Diversity Scholarships
S University of Northern Colorado Universal Scholarships

Connecticut

P Technology Scholar Program
S The James Beard Foundation Scholarship Program

Delaware

S Inspire Scholarship
S University of Delaware Academic Scholarships

Florida

SS American Dream Scholarship
S Arts Recognition & Talent Search (ARTS)
S Florida A&M University School of Journalism
A High School Achievement
S John S. & James L. Knight Foundation Scholarship
S Marta Elena Rodriguez - Fundora Scholarship
S University of Florida College of Journalism Minority Scholarships

Georgia

G Atlanta Ronald McDonald House Charities Grant
P Coca-Cola Scholars Program
S Hope Scholarship
S Jeanette Rankin Women's Scholarship Fund
S KFC Colonel's Scholars Program
S LULAC National Scholarship Fund
S Possible Woman Foundation International Scholarship

S The Coca-Cola Two-Year Colleges Scholarship Program

Hawaii

S Minority Student Scholarships

Idaho

S CAMP Scholarship

S Diversity Out-of-State Tuition Waiver

S Diversity Scholarship

S Diversity Scholarship Program

S Minority Student Scholarships

P UI Scholars Program

S University of Idaho Presidential Scholarship

Illinois

F ABF Summer Research Fellowship in Law & Social Studies for Minorities

G Academic Incentive Grants

S Academic Scholarship for Undergraduate Students

S Actuarial Diversity Scholarship

S AHBAI Scholarships

S Alpha Kappa Educational Advancement Foundation Financial Need Scholarship

S Alpha Kappa Educational Advancement Foundation Merit Scholarship

S Alpha Kappa Educational Advancement Foundation Youth Partners Accessing Capital (P.A.C.) Scholarship

S American GI Forum Hispanic Education Foundation Scholarship

S Barat College Presidential Scholarships

S Colgate Bright Smiles, Bright Futures Minority Scholarship

S Dr. Juan Andrade Jr. Scholarship for Young Hispanic Leaders

A Elks Most Valuable Student Awards

S Graduate Scholarship

S Minorities in Government Finance Scholarship

S Minority Teachers of Illinois Scholarship Program

S MLA Scholarship for Minority Students

S National Achievement Scholarship Program

S NRAEF Scholarships

S Procter & Gamble Professional Oral Health / HDA Foundation Scholarship

S Society of Women Engineers

S The National Merit Scholarship Program

S The T.E.A.C.H. Early Childhood® Illinois Scholarship & Compensation Project

S Trinity International University Athletic Scholarships

S Underrepresented Minority Dental Student Scholarship

S Young Women in Public Affairs Fund

Indiana

S Departmental Scholarship

S Global Leadership Program in Prague Scholarship

S National High School Oratorical Contest Scholarship

S Samsung American Legion Scholarship

Iowa

F AAUW International Fellowship

S Central College Distinguished Scholarships

S George Washington Carver Scholarship

S Hy-Vee Foundation Scholarship

Kentucky

S Children of Missionaries Scholarship

A Minority Leadership Award

S Native American Education Grant

Louisiana

S General Scholarship Fund

Maryland

F AGA Student Research Fellowships

S APS Minority Scholarship

S Center for Student Opportunity Scholarship

S David Risling Emergency Aid Scholarships

S Health Professions Pre-Graduate Scholarship

S Health Professions Preparatory Scholarship

S Health Professions Scholarship

G Howard Hughes Medical Institute Fellowships & Grants

S IHS Scholarship Program

S Maryland State Delegate Scholarship

P Minority Research Infrastructure Support Program

S NABA National Scholarship Program

P Research Training & Career Development Program

F Research Training & Fellowships Program

A Scholar Athlete Milk Mustache of the Year (SAMMY)

S Sequoya Graduate Scholarships

S Sherry R. Arnstein Minority Student Scholarship

S Sodexho Foundation

S Stokes Educational Scholarship Program

- **S** Breakthrough To Nursing Scholarships For Ethnic People of Color
- **A** Elmira College Key Award
- **S** ESA Foundation Computer & Video Game Scholarship Program
- **S** Gloria & Joseph Mattera National Scholarship Fund For Migrant Children
- **S** Jackie Robinson Foundation Scholarship Program
- **A** Kodak Minority Academic Awards
- **S** La Unidad Latina Scholarships
- **S** Le Moyne College Native American Scholarships
- **S** Mayor's Graduate Scholarship Program
- **S** Migrant Farmworker Baccalaureate Scholarship
- **S** Minority Graduate Accounting Scholarships
- **S** NACME Pre-Engineering Student Scholarships
- **F** National Urban Fellowship Award
- **F** Rockefeller Brothers Fund Fellowship Program
- **F** Rome Prize Fellowship
- **S** Seneca Nation Higher Education Scholarship
- **S** The AXA Achievement Scholarship
- **F** The Paul & Daisy Soros Fellowships for New Americans
- **S** The Roothbert Fund Scholarship
- **S** United States Army
- **S** Xerox Technical Minority Scholarship

North Carolina

- **S** Isabella Carvalho Health Scholarship
- **A** James M. Johnson Awards
- **S** John W. Hartman Scholarship
- **S** Joseph E. Pogue Scholarships
- **S** OP Loftbed Scholarship
- **S** University of North Carolina at Chapel Hill School of Journalism & Mass Communication Scholarships

North Dakota

- **S** North Dakota Indian Scholarship
- **S** Opportunities in the Making Scholarship Fund

Ohio

- **S** Darwin T. Turner Scholarship
- **S** Duck Brand Stuck at Prom Scholarship
- **S** Esperanza Scholarship Program
- **S** Ohio State Distinction Scholarship
- **S** Prestigious Scholarship
- **S** Tuition Equalization Scholarship Program

Oklahoma

- **S** Cheyenne-Arapaho Tribes of Oklahoma Scholarships
- **S** Chickasaw Nation General Scholarship Program
- **S** Citizen Potawatomi Nation Tribal Rolls Scholarship
- **S** Comanche Nation Scholarship Program
- **S** Creek Nation Higher Education Program
- **S** F. Browning Pipestem Memorial Scholarship
- **S** Langston's Non-Black Scholarship
- **S** Louie LeFlore/Grant Foreman Scholarship
- **S** MEFUSA Scholarships for Native Americans
- **S** Oklahoma Christian MBA Scholarship Opportunity
- **S** ORU Freshman Academic Scholarships
- **S** Osage Tribal Education Committee Scholarships
- **P** Patty Iron Cloud National Native American Youth Initiative Scholarship

Oregon

- **S** Connect2 High Tech Talent Scholarship
- **S** Dick French Memorial Scholarship
- **A** George Fox University Multi Ethnic Student Awards
- **S** Helen Fe Jones Scholarship
- **S** The Truman D. Picard Scholarship Program

Pennsylvania

- **S** Big 33 Scholarships
- **S** Ethnic Minority Bachelor's Scholarship
- **S** International Baptist Seminary Scholarship Fund
- **S** The Gain Scholarship
- **S** The Kor Memorial Scholarship
- **P** W. W. Smith Charitable Trust Financial Aid Programs for College Students
- **S** Women's Opportunity Awards Program

Puerto Rico

- **P** ASPIRA, Inc. of Puerto Rico
- **P** Becapel
- **S** Inter-American University of Puerto Rico-San German
- **S** UMET Scholarships
- **S** Universidad of Puerto Rico-Rio Piedras

South Carolina

- **P** Coca-Cola Clemson Scholars Program

Utah

- **S** American Indian Services Scholarships
- **S** WGU Scholarship in Business & Information Technology

Vermont

- **P** English Teaching Fellows Program

Virginia

- **S** 9/11 Memorial Scholarship
- **S** AFCEA General John A. Wickham Scholarship
- **S** AFCEA/ORINCON IT Scholarship
- **S** AGC Undergraduate Scholarships
- **S** AGI Minority Geoscience Undergraduate Scholarship
- **S** American Express Travel Scholarship
- **S** Bailey Scholarship
- **S** Barry M. Goldwater Scholarship
- **S** Jack Kent Cooke Foundation Scholarship
- **S** James F. Powell Scholarships
- **F** NAA Minority Fellowships - "Escalating to Newspaper Management Success"
- **F** NAA Minority Fellowships in New Media
- **S** National Association of Hispanic Federal Executives (NAHFE) Scholarship Program
- **S** National Health Service Corps Scholarship Program
- **S** Presidential Classroom Scholars
- **S** Randolph Macon Minority Scholarships
- **P** The Gates Millennium Scholars Program
- **F** The Institute for Humane Studies Fellowships
- **S** The Minority Scholarship Fund
- **P** The National Hispanic Scholar Recognition Program
- **S** The Sallie Mae Fund "Unmet Need" Scholarship Program
- **S** Washington & Lee Honor Scholarships Program

Washington

- **S** Academic Achievement Diversity Scholarship
- **S** Bannan Scholarship
- **S** Cultural Diversity Scholarships
- **S** Graduate Diversity Scholarship
- **S** Microsoft Scholarship Program
- **S** Nellie Martin Carman Scholarship Committee
- **A** Seattle University Regents Award
- **S** UW Diversity Scholarship Award
- **S** Washington Indian Gaming Association Scholarships
- **S** Yakama Nation Tribal Scholarship

Washington DC

- **S** AARP Foundation Women's Scholarship Program
- **G** AAUW Educational Foundation Career Development Grants
- **G** Academic Competitiveness Grants (ACG)
- **S** ACS Scholars Program
- **S** Advanced Summer Course on Spanish Language & Culture
- **S** American Architectural Foundation Minority Scholarship
- **S** American Hotel & Lodging Educational Foundation
- **S** American Indian Scholarship
- **S** American Indian Scholarships
- **P** American Political Science Association
- **G** AmeriCorps VISTA
- **G** Annual Grant Competition
- **S** AVON Products Foundation Scholarship for Women in Business Studies
- **S** BEA National Scholarships in Broadcasting
- **S** BIA Higher Education Grant
- **S** Boren Scholarships
- **S** BPW Career Advancement Scholarship Program
- **G** Bureau of Indian Education Higher Education Grant Program
- **S** CHCI Scholarship Award
- **S** Civil Engineering Corps (CEC)
- **P** College Board National Hispanic Scholar Recognition Program
- **F** Community Builders Fellowship Program
- **F** Curso de Lengua y Cultura Españolas - Universidad de Salamanca
- **F** Curso de Literatura Infantil y Juvenil Universidad Complutense Madrid
- **A** Diversity Leaders Award
- **S** Embassy of Spain Scholarships
- **F** Ford Foundation Dissertation Fellowships for Minorities
- **F** Ford Foundation Postdoctoral Fellowships for Minorities
- **F** Ford Foundation Predoctoral & Dissertation Fellowships for Minorities
- **G** Fulbright Grant
- **I** HACU National Internship Program (HNIP)
- **S** Harry S. Truman Scholarship
- **S** Hispanic College Fund

F Howard Hughes Medical Institute Pre doctoral Fellowships - Biological Sciences

G Indian Employment Assistance Grants

F Jacob K. Javits Fellowships Program

S Javits-Frasier Teacher Scholarship Fund for Diverse Talent Development

P Latino Student Fund Scholars Program

S League of United Latin American Citizens

S Mana National Scholarship Endowment

S McDonald's Scholarship Program: Me Encanta

S NAHJ Ford Motor Company Fund Scholarships

S NAHJ General Scholarships - Ruben Salazar Fund

S National Association of Hispanic Nurses

F National Congress of American Indians Fellowships

I National Congress of American Indians Internships

S National Hispanic Foundation for the Arts

F National Security Education Program's David L. Boren Graduate Fellowships

S New York Life Foundation Scholarships for Women in the Health Professions

S NROTC Immediate Selection Decision (ISD)

F NSF Graduate Research Fellowship Program (GRFP)

S Nuclear Propulsion Officer (NUPOC)

S PFLAG National Scholarship Program

S Police Corps Scholarship

G Priority Grant Competition

I Public Health for Hispanic Women Scholarship & Internship Programs

S Ronald Reagan College Leaders Scholarship

P The Air Force College Fund Program

P The Army College Fund Program

S The ASPIRA Association

S The Congressional Hispanic Caucus Institute Scholarship

S The LULAC National Scholarship Fund

P The Navy College Fund Program

P United Health Foundation Latino Health Scholars Program

I Vilar institute for Arts Management - Internships

S Wyeth-Ayerst Labs Scholarship for Women in Graduate Medical/Health

Wisconsin

S Agriculture Scholarship

S Menominee Adult Vocational Training Scholarship

S WHSF/Mexican Fiesta Scholarships

X Canada

S Mosaic Scholarship

X Spain

S Spain Scholarship Program

Insights

"A Life Saving and Life Afirming Experience"

"College did more than just change my life, college was a life saving and life affirming experience. During the four years of my college education, I learned more than what was taught in textbooks; I discovered my own intellect, grew as a person and a woman, and developed my life's mission. Living the life I have now is due to my college education."

Nancy De Los Santos Reza.
Writer, Producer, Director

Insights

"College Changed My Life 100%

"College changed my life 100% - I would not be here if I hadn't gone to college. It's one of the best alternatives a person has for growth and success in life. Life is too competitive for us not to be prepared—and if we don't have education, we're not prepared to compete."

Roy Jasso,
Wells Fargo Bank

Latino Scholarships

By State & Name

On the enclosed CD you will find detailed searchable profiles on each of the following awards (A), fellowships (F), grants (G), internships (I), programs (P), and scholarships (S).

Type & Name of the Scholarship

Arizona

- P Adelante Program
- S Agustina Valdez Scholarship
- S Amelia M. Maldonado Scholarship in Elementary Education
- S Arizona Association of Chicanos for Higher Education Scholarships
- S Carlos C. & Alex G. Jacome Memorial Scholarship
- S Cesar E. Chavez Leadership Scholarship
- S Chaparales/Rotary Club of Tucson Graduate Scholarship
- S Concerned Media Professionals Scholarship
- S Don Carson CMP Scholarship
- S Donald G. Shropshire Scholarship
- S Dr. Manuel T. & Karen Pacheco Scholarship
- S Farmilant Scholarships
- S IBM Scholarship
- S J.C. Penney Co. Scholarship
- S Jose Franco & Francisco Ocampo Quesada Research Scholarship
- S Los Diablos Scholarship
- S Los Endowment Scholarship
- S Maria Urquides Scholarship
- S Reforma Scholarship
- S Rigulo Cuesta Memorial Scholarships for Hispanics
- S Rosita Cota Scholarship
- S Tostitos Cesar Chavez Latino Scholarship

California

- S A.W. Bodine - Sunkist Memorial Scholarship
- S (AAHCPA) Scholarship Program
- S AHPE Corporate Scholarship
- S Alice Newell Joslyn Medical Fund
- S AMAE Scholarship
- S Architecture & Engineering Scholarship Program
- S Art Scholarship Program
- S Association of Latino Professionals in Finance and Accounting
- S Association of Raza Educators Scholarship
- S Aztec Scholarship Fund Academic Awards
- S Beca Foundation Scholarships
- P BYU Marriott School/TELACU MBA Program
- S California Broadcasters Association Scholarship
- S California Chicano News Media Association (CCNMA)
- S California Congress of Parents and Teachers, Teacher Education Scholarships
- A Cesar Chavez Award
- F Chicana Dissertation Fellowships
- S Chicana/Latina Foundation Scholarship Program
- S Chicano Latino Education
- S Chicano Latino Faculty & Staff Association Scholarship
- S Chicano News Media Scholarship
- S Cien Amigos - IME Becas Scholarship Fund
- S Cisco Diversity Scholarship
- P Citi/TELACU Scholars Program
- S Club Música Latina Scholarship Program
- S COCA-COLA Live Positivity and Hispanic Scholarship Fund Essay Contest
- S College Retention/General Scholarship Program
- S Communications Scholarship Fund
- S Community College Scholarship Program
- S Community College Transfer Scholarship Program
- S Community Service Scholarship
- S Connie Hernandez Scholarship Fund
- S Cruzando Fronteras/Ayudando a la Comunidad
- S CSUB Hispanic Excellence Scholarship Fund Program
- S CSUF TELACU Scholarship Program
- S Cuban American Scholarship Fund (CASF)

INDEXES

- S HSF/Morgan Stanley Foundation Scholarship Program
- S HSF/Nissan North America, Inc. Scholarship Program
- S HSF/Peierls Rising Star Scholarship
- S HSF/Qualcomm Q Awards Scholarship
- S HSF/Sendero al Futuro Scholarship Program
- S HSF/Telemundo Scholarship
- S HSF/Toyota Scholarship Program
- S HSF/Travelers Scholarship
- S HSF/Verizon Foundation Scholarship
- S HSF/Wal-Mart Stores, Inc. High School Scholarship Program
- S HSF/Winchell's & Yum Yum Donuts Scholarship
- S Imperial Valley College
- S Independent Colleges of Southern California (ICSC) Scholarships
- S Inland Empire Scholarship
- S International Health Elective Scholarship
- S Janine Gonzalez Scholarship
- S Jeremy Gabriel Mancilla Memorial Scholarship
- S Juan Cisneros Scholarship Fund
- S La Raza Lawyers of Santa Clara County Scholarship
- S Latina Leadership Network (LLN) - Scholarship Program
- S Latino Association of Faculty & Staff Scholarships at California State University San Marcos
- S Latino Faculty/Staff & Student Association Scholarship
- S LEAD Cash for College Workshops
- S Leadership for Diversity Scholarship
- S LMU Mexican-American Alumni Association Scholarship
- S Lowrider Magazine Scholarship Fund
- S LULAC National Scholarship Fund
- A MAES Local Chapter Awards
- S MALDEF Law School Scholarship Program
- P MassMutual Multicultural Scholars Program
- S MECHA de UC Riverside Alumni Scholarship
- P MEDI-CORPS
- S Mexican American Bar Foundation Scholarship
- S Mexican American Business & Professional Scholarship
- S Mexican American Grocers Association
- S National Hispanic University Scholarships
- S National Merit Finalist Presidential Scholarship
- S NHFA Entertainment Industry Scholarship Program
- P PacifiCare's Latino Health Scholars Program
- S President Obama/HSF STEM Teacher Scholarship Program
- S Que Llueva Cafe Scholarship
- S QuestBridge Scholarship
- S Ramona's Mexican Food Products Scholarships
- S Robert A. Hine Memorial Scholarship
- S Saber es Poder Scholarship Program
- A SACNAS National Conference Travel & Lodging Awards
- S Salvadoran-American Leadership & Educational Fund
- S San Jose G.I. Forum Scholarship
- S Saul Ibarra Scholarship
- I Shell Legislative Internship Program
- S "Si Se Puede" AMCAS/AACOMAS Scholarship
- S Sigma Lambda Beta Fraternity: Tau Chapter Scholarship
- S Silicon Valley Latina Scholarship Fund
- S Society of Hispanic Professional Engineers (SHPE) Scholarships
- S Soka University of America Scholarship Fund
- S Southern California G. I. Forum Scholarships
- S Spanish American Institute Scholarship
- P Summer Associates Program
- S TELACU Education Foundation Scholarships
- P TELACU Health Careers Program
- S The Beca Scholarship Foundation
- S The Davis Family
- P The Greenlining Institute Work Study Program
- S The Helena Rubenstein Endowment Scholarship
- S The Lagrant Foundation
- S The Matt Garcia Memorial Scholarship
- S The Mike Carona Foundation Law Enforcement Scholarship
- S The National Hispanic Foundation for the Arts
- S The Orange County Hispanic Education Endowment Fund (HEEF)
- S The Valerie Kantor Memorial Scholarship
- S Toyota/TELACU Scholarship Program
- A Trujillo Chemistry Award
- S UAL/UABT Scholarship Program
- S USC National Hispanic Scholarship

- S Vikki Carr Scholarship Foundation for California
- S Wilbur Family Fund Hispanic Scholarship
- S William Randolph Hearst Endowment Scholarship
- S Youth Opportunities Foundation Scholarships
- A Zala Art Muralist Award
- S Zinch Super Student Stimulus Scholarship

Colorado

- S Anthem Blue Cross & Blue Shield - West Region Diversity Council
- P GRMAD
- S Hispanic Alumni Scholarship Fund
- S HORISONS (Hispanic Out-Reach In Search Of New Scholarships)/GRAD
- S Latin American Educational Foundation (LAEF)
- S Miramontes Arts and Sciences Program (MASP) Scholarship
- S Success in Engineering Through Excellence & Diversity
- S The BOLD Center Program Participation Scholarships
- S University of Colorado at Boulder Diversity Scholarships
- S William J. Elliot Scholarship

Connecticut

- S Fleming/Blaszcak Scholarship
- S Maria Borrero Scholarship
- S NSCA Minority Scholarship and Training Program

Delaware

- F American Society of Criminal Fellowships for Ethnic Minorities

Florida

- P ASPIRA of Florida, Inc.
- S Association of Cuban Engineers Scholarship Foundation Scholarships
- S Association of Cuban University Women
- S Association of Cuban University Women
- S Florida Nicaraguan & Haitian Scholarship
- S Hispanic Heritage Scholarship Fund
- G Jose Marti Scholarship Challenge Grant Fund
- S Jose Martinez Scholarship Challenge Grant Fund
- S Latino Transfer Student Scholarship
- S LULAC National Educational Service Center
- S Marta Elena Rodriguez - Fundora Scholarship
- S NAMPEA Beginning Freshman Engineering Student Award
- S National Merit & Achievement, National Hispanic Scholars
- S Special Honors Scholarship
- S The Mass Family Scholarship
- S Tomas Garcia Fuste Scholarship
- S Transfer Engineering Student Award
- S USF Latino Scholarship

Georgia

- G Atlanta Ronald McDonald House Charities Grant
- S Celia & Marcos Scholarship Fund
- S Goizueta Scholarships
- S LULAC National Scholarship Fund
- S Sal Diaz-Verson Scholarship

Idaho

- S CAMP Scholarship
- S Hispanic Business Association Richard G. Cortez Scholarship
- S Image de Idaho del Sudeste Leadership Scholarships
- S Image de Idaho Scholarship
- S Ruth & Royal B. Irving Scholarships

Illinois

- S Actuarial Diversity Scholarship
- S American GI Forum Hispanic Education Foundation Scholarship
- P ASPIRA Inc. of Illinois
- S Colgate-Palmolive / HDA Foundation Scholarship
- S Diageo - Celebrate The Future Hispanic Scholarship Fund
- S Dr. Juan Andrade Jr. Scholarship for Young Hispanic Leaders
- S Dr. Juan D. Villarreal / HDA Foundation Scholarship
- S Government Finance Officers Association Scholarship
- S HACE Collegiate Challenge Scholarship
- P HACE Leadership Development Program
- I HACE Student Development Internship Program
- S HACE Student Development Scholarship Program
- S Hispanic Designers Inc. Scholarships
- S Latino Medical Student Association (LMSA) MCAT Scholarship
- S LMSA Scholarship for U.S. Medical Students
- S LULAC National Educational Service Center
- I MillerCoors Scholars Summer Internship Program
- S Minorities in Government Finance Scholarship

- **S** MLA Scholarship for Minority Students
- **P** New Futuro Summit
- **S** Procter & Gamble Professional Oral Health / HDA Foundation Scholarship

Indiana

- **S** Booker T. Washington Scholarship
- **F** GEM Fellowship Program

Kansas

- **S** Kansas Ethnic Minority Scholarship
- **S** LULAC National Educational Service Center
- **S** Warren E. Bottenberg Memorial Scholarship

Kentucky

- **S** Hallmark Scholarship

Maryland

- **S** APS Minority Scholarship
- **S** APS Scholarship for Minority Undergraduate Physics Majors
- **S** Bolivar San Martin Scholarship
- **S** Center for Student Opportunity Scholarship
- **I** NIDDK/OMHRC Summer Internship Program (SIP) for Underrepresented Minorities
- **S** Sherry R. Arnstein Minority Student Scholarship
- **F** The Charles Bannerman Memorial Fellowship Program

Mass.

- **P** Hispanic Office of Planning & Evaluation (Talent Search)
- **S** HOPE Scholarship Fund
- **S** Marshall / Chavez / Means Scholarship

Michigan

- **S** Cesar E. Chavez Scholarship
- **S** Gannett Foundation Hispanics in Journalism Scholarship
- **S** La Sed Scholarship
- **S** Latina Smart Scholarship Program
- **S** Michigan Hispanic Scholarship Fund
- **S** Saginaw LULAC Scholarship Council #11055
- **G** WMU Presidentís Grant for Study Abroad

Minnesota

- **S** Accenture Scholarship Program for Minorities
- **S** Andersen Consulting Scholarship Program for Minorities
- **S** National Society of Hispanic MBA's Scholarship Program

Mississippi

- **S** United Methodists Ethnic Minority Scholarships

Missouri

- **S** Annika Rodriguez Scholarship for Hispanic Students
- **S** Greater Kansas City Hispanic Scholarship Fund
- **S** Heartland's Alliance for Minority Participation
- **S** Hispanic Student Scholarship
- **S** Martin Luther King Jr. Scholarship (NMSU)
- **S** Missouri Minority Teacher Education Scholarship
- **S** Washington University Hispanic Scholarship Program

Montana

- **S** Hispanic Scholarships

Nebraska

- **S** Catalan Latino Endowed Scholarship
- **S** Davis Scholarship

Nevada

- **S** Hispanic Heritage Day Scholarship

New Hampshire

- **F** Cesar E. Chavez Dissertation Fellowship for U.S. Latino Scholars

New Jersey

- **P** ASPIRA Programs
- **S** Hispanic Business & Professional Association Scholarship
- **S** Hispanic Theological Initiative Doctoral Scholarship
- **S** James Dickson Carr Minority Merit Scholarships

New Mexico

- **S** Alamogordo Excalibur Scholarship
- **S** Coronado-Remides Scholarship
- **S** General Motors Endowed Scholarship
- **S** LULAC National Educational Service Center
- **S** Martha Guerra-Arteaga Scholarship
- **S** Matching Scholarship Fund
- **S** Minority Presidential Scholarship
- **A** New Mexico Alliance for Minority Participation
- **S** New Mexico Manufactured Housing Scholarship Program
- **S** NMAMA Scholarship Fund.
- **S** NOPHNRCSE Scholarships
- **S** Public Service Company of New Mexico (PNM) LLAVE Scholarship
- **S** Ray T. Margo Scholarship
- **P** State Government Intern Program

New York

North Carolina

Ohio

Oklahoma

Oregon

Pennsylvania

Puerto Rico

South Carolina

- **S** Multicultural Scholarship Program
- **S** The Markley Scholarship

Tennessee

- **S** The RMHC/HACER Scholarship Program

Texas

- **S** ¡Adelante! US Education Leadership Fund
- **P** African American/Hispanic Architectural Education Work/Study Program
- **S** American Association of Hispanic CPAs Scholarship
- **P** American Economic Association Summer Program
- **S** Asociación Boricua de Dallas, Inc. Scholarship
- **S** College Essay Contest
- **P** Communities in School of San Antonio
- **P** Deloitte Scholars Program
- **S** Good Neighbor Scholarship Program
- **S** Hana Scholars Program
- **S** Hispanic Association of Colleges & Universities (HACU) Scholarship Program
- **P** Hispanic Deaf Teacher Training Program
- **S** HOPE Scholarship (CPS Energy Dependents ONLY)
- **S** Kristen A. Sanchez Deloitte Student of the Year Scholarship
- **P** LANZATE! Travel Award Program - Giving Flight to Your Success/Dandole Alas a Tu Exito
- **S** LULAC National Educational Service Center
- **S** LULAC/ACCD Parent/Child Scholarship Program
- **S** MAES Founders Scholarships
- **S** MAES General Scholarships
- **S** MAES Presidential Scholarship
- **S** MAES Presidential Scholarships
- **S** MAES Scholarship Program
- **P** Mexican Citizens with Financial Need-Border County Waiver
- **P** Mexican Citizens with Financial Need-Border Nations Waiver
- **S** MillerCoors Chicago
- **S** MillerCoors Engineering & Sciences
- **S** MillerCoors National Scholarship
- **S** South Texas Scholarship Program
- **F** Texas Association of Chicanos in Higher Education (TACHE)-Gradute Fellowship
- **S** Texas Health Service Corps Scholarship
- **S** The Boy Scouts of America National College
- **I** United Health Foundation/Hispanic Association of Colleges and Universities Scholarship
- **S** United Health Foundation/HWNT Scholarship
- **S** Urban Scholarship Fund
- **S** UTA Hispanic Endowed Scholarship
- **S** Vikki Carr Scholarship Foundation
- **P** Waiver for Students from Mexico Enrolled in Graduate Degree Programs in Public Health

Utah

- **S** Chicano Scholarship Fund
- **S** Pete Suazo Memorial Scholarship - "Commitment to Community"

Virginia

- **S** AGI Minority Geoscience Undergraduate Scholarship
- **S** ASAV Scholarship
- **A** Fernando R. Ayuso Award
- **F** GEM Fellowship
- **S** ILUMINA Bolivian Scholarship Program
- **S** Jimi Hendrix Endowment Fund Scholarship
- **S** National Association of Hispanic Federal Executives (NAHFE) Scholarship Program
- **P** The Gates Millennium Scholars Program
- **S** The Maureen and Howard Blitman, P.E., Scholarship To Promote Diversity In Engineering
- **P** The National Hispanic Scholar Recognition Program

Washington

- **S** First People's Scholarship
- **S** Martinez Foundation Scholarships
- **S** Master's in Social Work Minority Scholarship
- **S** Microsoft Scholarship Program
- **A** Seattle University Regents Award

Washington DC

- **G** AAUW Educational Foundation Career Development Grants
- **S** ACS Scholars Program
- **S** American Chemical Society (ACS) Scholars Program
- **P** American Chemistry Society Scholars Program
- **S** Anna Maria Arias Scholarship
- **S** APSA Fund for Latino Scholarship
- **S** CareFirst BlueCross BlueShield Scholarship Program
- **S** Carmen E. Turner Scholarship
- **S** CHCI Scholarship Award

- **P** College Board National Hispanic Scholar Recognition Program
- **S** Computer Packages, Inc. Scholarship Program
- **S** Daimler Chrysler/HACU Scholarship Fund
- **S** Ford Blue Oval Nationwide Scholarship
- **S** Ford Blue Oval Puerto Rico Scholarship
- **A** Fulbright Occassional Lecturer Fund
- **S** Future Leaders Scholarship
- **S** Gannett Foundation/NAHJ Scholarships
- **S** Google Hispanic College Fund Scholarship Program
- **I** HACU National Internship Program (HNIP)
- **A** Heywood Broun Award
- **S** Hispanic College Fund
- **A** Hispanic Heritage Youth Awards
- **F** Hispanic Link Journalism Foundation Reporting Fellowship
- **F** HLJF Journalism Fellowship
- **F** Humanities Fellowship in Latino Cultural Research in a National Museum Context
- **S** Ingram-White Castle Foundation Scholarship
- **S** Intel Scholarship Program
- **S** Juan Eugene Ramos Scholarship
- **P** Latino Student Fund Scholars Program
- **S** League of United Latin American Citizens
- **S** M & T Bank Scholarship Program
- **S** Mana National Scholarship Endowment
- **P** Marriott Scholars Program
- **S** MasterCard Worldwide Scholarship Program
- **S** McDonald's Scholarship Program: Me Encanta
- **S** NAHJ Ford Motor Company Fund Scholarships
- **S** NAHJ General Scholarships - Ruben Salazar Fund
- **S** NAHJ Geraldo Rivera Scholarship
- **S** NAHJ Maggie Rodriguez Scholarship Program
- **S** NAHJ Maria Elena Salinas Scholarship
- **S** NAHJ PepsiCo Scholarships
- **S** NAHJ Soledad O'Brien Scholarship
- **F** NAHJ/NBC Fellowships
- **I** NAHJ/NHPF Ford Blue Oval Journalism Internships
- **S** NAHN Nursing Scholarships
- **S** National Association of Hispanic Nurses
- **S** National Hispanic Foundation for the Arts
- **S** National Hispanic Press Foundation
- **S** Newhouse Scholarship Program
- **F** NSF Graduate Research Fellowship Program (GRFP)
- **S** Patricia V. Asip Scholarship
- **S** Project SEED Scholarships
- **I** Public Health for Hispanic Women Scholarship & Internship Programs
- **S** René Matos Scholarship
- **F** Robert D. Watkins Minority Graduate Research Fellowship
- **S** Sam's Club Hispanic-serving institution (HSI) Scholarship Competition
- **I** Summer in Washington Internship
- **S** The ASPIRA Association
- **F** The Congressional Hispanic Caucus Institute Graduate & Young Professional Fellowship
- **S** The Congressional Hispanic Caucus Institute Scholarship
- **S** The LULAC National Scholarship Fund
- **P** The Navy College Fund Program
- **P** United Health Foundation Latino Health Scholars Program
- **S** USHCC Scholarship Fund
- **F** WWC-Washington Post Fellowship for Latin American Journalists

Wisconsin

- **S** Roma Hoff Scholarship for Excellence
- **P** Something Good From the Hood
- **S** WHSF/Mexican Fiesta Scholarships

Wyoming

- **S** University of Wyoming Chicano Studies Scholarship

X México

- **S** Mexico Scholarship Program

Insights

"The Support of My Tribe"

"I funded going to college with getting good grades and the support of my tribe."
Selena Brown,
Graphic Artist,
Yavapai-Prescott Tribe

INDEXES

Perfect Books For Various College Courses

Some of the books that we publish have been used by various up division college courses. Please call us at 760-434-1223 if you are interested in using any of these books at your college.

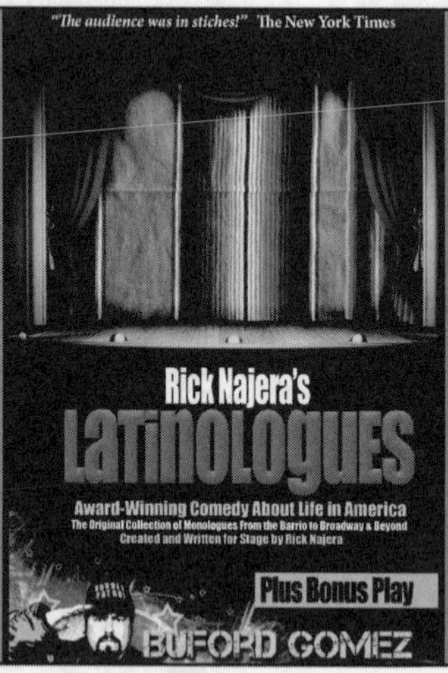

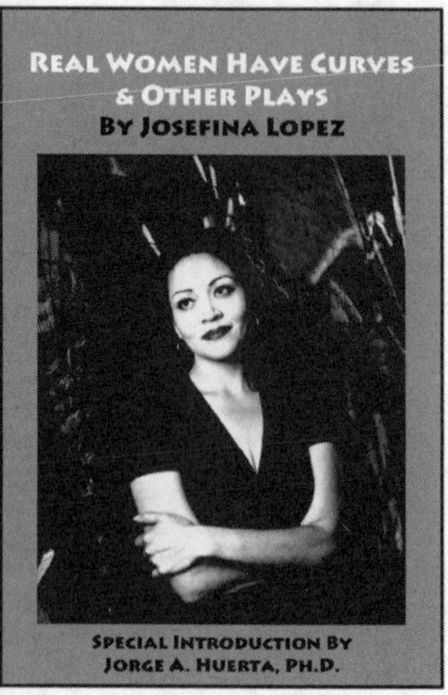

These two award winning authors have seen their works turned into movies – and used by colleges across the USA.

These two books are appropriate for a variety of college courses and are by well known Ph.D's Ambassador Nava was the first Latino to serve as U.S. Ambassador to Mexico.

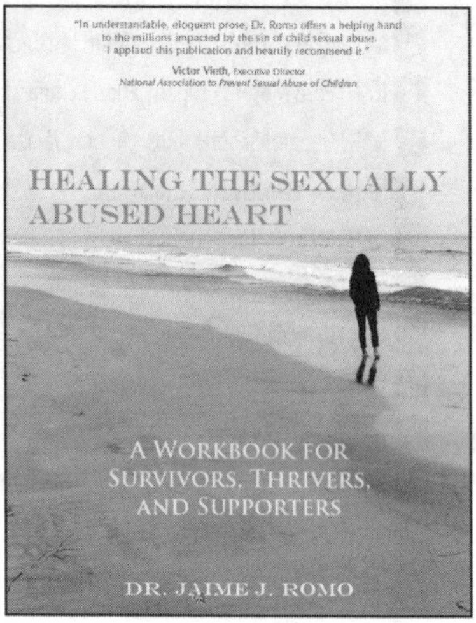

American Indian Scholarships By State & Name

On the enclosed CD you will find detailed searchable profiles on each of the following awards (A), fellowships (F), grants (G), internships (I), programs (P), and scholarships (S).

Type & Name of the Scholarship

Alabama

- S American Indian Nurse Scholarship Award

Alaska

- S CIRI Foundation Scholarships

Arizona

- S American Indian/Alaska Native Association for NCRS Scholarship
- F Arizona State University Library Training Fellowship
- S Chief Ellis Scholarship
- S Chief Manuelito Scholarship Program
- S Colorado River Indian Scholarship
- S Gila River Indian Community Division of Student Services Scholarships
- S Grand Canyon University Scholarships
- S Hopi Scholarship
- S Los Endowment Scholarship
- S NAFOA Scholarship
- S National Center for American Indian Enterprise Development Scholarships
- I Native American Congressional Internships
- S Navajo Generating Station Navajo Scholarship
- S Navajo Nation Scholarship & Financial Assistance Program
- S Shandiin Scholarship Fund

California

- P American Indian Chamber Education Fund
- S ASI American Indian in honor of Lee Dixon Scholarship
- S Dean's Scholarship for Ethnic & Cultural Diversity
- P Great Minds in STEM HENAAC Scholars Program
- A HP Scholar Award
- S Independent Colleges of Southern California (ICSC) Scholarships
- S Leadership for Diversity Scholarship
- S Lillian S. Sherman Scholarship
- S Robert A. Hine Memorial Scholarship
- S Rodney T. Mathews, Jr. Memorial Scholarship for California Indians
- A SACNAS National Conference Travel & Lodging Awards
- P Summer Associates Program
- P The Greenlining Institute Work Study Program
- S The Lagrant Foundation
- S The National Hispanic Foundation for the Arts
- S Zinch Super Student Stimulus Scholarship

Colorado

- S American Indian College Fund
- P Arizona Public Service Navajo Scholars Program
- S Austin Family Scholarship Endowment
- S Cargill Scholarship Program
- S Citi Foundation Scholarship Program
- S Coca-Cola First Generation Scholarship
- S Colorado Foundation Scholarship
- S Council of Energy Resource Tribes (CERT) Scholarships
- P Crow Canyon High School Archaeology Camp
- S Ecotrust Native American Scholarship Program
- S First Nations Scholarship
- S Ford Motor Company Tribal College Scholarship
- P Fort Lewis College Free Tuition Waiver
- S Foundation Scholarship
- S General Mills Foundation
- A Lilly Endowment, Inc: Woksape Oyate: "Wisdom of the People" Distinguished Scholar Award
- A Lilly Endowment, Inc: Woksape Oyate: "Wisdom of the People" Keepers of the Next Generation Award
- P Morgan Stanley Tribal Scholars Program
- P Newmont Mining Corporation Tribal Scholars Program
- S Nissan North America, Inc. Scholarship
- S Seven Stars Graduate Scholarship
- S Sovereign Nations Scholarship Fund
- S Spirit of Sovereignty Foundation (NIGA) Tribal College

- **S** Traveler's Foundation Scholarship
- **S** United Health Foundation Scholarship
- **S** University of Colorado at Boulder Diversity Scholarships
- **S** Vine Deloria Jr. Memorial Scholarship
- **S** White Antelope Memorial Scholarship (WAMS)

DELAWARE

- **F** American Society of Criminal Fellowships for Ethnic Minorities

FLORIDA

- **S** IAPA Scholarship Fund
- **S** NAMPEA Beginning Freshman Engineering Student Award
- **S** Transfer Engineering Student Award

HAWAII

- **G** Bruce T. and Jakie Mahi Erickson Grant
- **S** Charles Cockett `Ohana Scholarship
- **S** Choy-Kee O'hana Scholarship
- **S** George Hi'ilani Mills Scholarship
- **S** Jalene Kanani Bell 'Ohana Scholarship
- **S** Joseph A. Sowa Scholarship
- **S** Joseph Nawahi Scholarship
- **S** Kamehameha Schools Class of 1956 Scholarship
- **S** Kamehameha Schools Class of 1970 Scholarship
- **S** Kamehameha Schools Class of 1972 Scholarship
- **S** Tauati 'Ohana Scholarship
- **S** Tesoro Corporation Scholarship
- **S** Ula Baker Sheecha Scholarship
- **S** William S. Richardson Commemorative Scholarship

ILLINOIS

- **S** Actuarial Diversity Scholarship
- **F** Francis C. Allen Fellowships
- **S** Government Finance Officers Association Scholarship
- **S** Minorities in Government Finance Scholarship
- **S** MLA Scholarship for Minority Students

INDIANA

- **S** Booker T. Washington Scholarship
- **F** GEM Fellowship Program

IOWA

- **S** Crazy Horse Scholarship

KANSAS

- **P** National Center for Cooperative Education (NCCE) in Natural Resources
- **S** Warren E. Bottenberg Memorial Scholarship
- **A** Wells Award

KENTUCKY

- **S** Native American Education Grant

MARYLAND

- **S** Adolph Van Pelt Special Fund for Indian Scholarships
- **I** Alaska Native Undergraduate Summer Internship Program (ANUSIP)
- **S** APS Minority Scholarship
- **S** APS Scholarship for Minority Undergraduate Physics Majors
- **S** David Risling Emergency Aid Scholarships
- **S** Displaced Homemaker Scholarships
- **S** Elizabeth and Sherman Asche Memorial Scholarship Fund
- **S** Emilie Hesemeyer Memorial Scholarship
- **S** Emilie Hesemeyer Memorial Scholarship
- **S** Florence Young Memorial Scholarships
- **S** Forum for Concerns of Minorities Scholarship
- **S** Health Professions Pre-Graduate Scholarship
- **S** Health Professions Preparatory Scholarship
- **S** Health Professions Scholarship
- **S** IHS Scholarship Program
- **I** NIDDK/OMHRC Summer Internship Program (SIP) for Underrepresented Minorities
- **S** Sequoya Graduate Scholarships
- **S** Sequoyah Graduate Scholarships
- **S** Sherry R. Arnstein Minority Student Scholarship
- **S** The Allogan Slagle Memorial Scholarship
- **F** The Charles Bannerman Memorial Fellowship Program

MASS.

- **S** Marshall / Chavez / Means Scholarship

MINNESOTA

- **S** 2012 Talbots Scholarship Program
- **S** Accenture Scholarship Program for Minorities
- **S** Andersen Consulting Scholarship Program for Minorities
- **S** CSB Ratelle Endowed Scholarship for Native American Students
- **S** Marvin Rull Memorial Scholarship
- **S** Minnesota Bois Forte Scholarship

- P Chickasaw Nation Concurrent Enrollment
- P Chickasaw Nation Education Foundation Program
- S Chickasaw Nation General Scholarship Program
- S Chickasaw Nation Governor's Scholarship
- G Chickasaw Nation Higher Education Grant
- S Chickasaw Nation Legislators' Scholarship
- S Chickasaw Nation Lt. Governor's Scholarship
- S Chief Pushmataha College Scholarship Fund
- G Choctaw Nation of Oklahoma Higher Education Grants
- S Citizen Potawatomi Nation Tribal Rolls Scholarship
- S Comanche Nation Scholarship Program
- S Creek Nation Higher Education Program
- S Daughters of Indian Wars Scholarship
- S F. Browning Pipestem Memorial Scholarship
- S Flintco Scholarship
- S Heinz College - Choctaw Nation Scholarship Program
- S Inter-Tribal Council of the Five Civilized Tribes - Johnson O'Malley Scholarship
- S John C. Smith Scholarship
- A John Shurr Journalism Award
- S Leading With Diligence Scholarship
- S Louie LeFlore/Grant Foreman Scholarship
- S Louie LeFlore/Grant Foreman Scholarship
- S MEFUSA Scholarships for Native Americans
- S NAJA Scholarships
- S Oklahoma Christian MBA Scholarship Opportunity
- S Oklahoma City University Choctaw Student Award (undergraduate)
- S Osage Tribal Education Committee Scholarships
- P Patty Iron Cloud National Native American Youth Initiative Scholarship
- S Phil and Cathy Busey - Oklahoma City University Choctaw Student Scholarship
- S The Eliphalet Nott Wright Scholarship
- S The O.J. and Mary Christine Harvey Foundation Scholarship
- P The Wake Forest University Schools of Business
- S Tvshka Chunkash (Heart of a Warrior) Scholarship

Oregon

- S Dick French Memorial Scholarship
- S Diversity Recognition Scholarship
- S Oregon Native American Chamber Scholarships
- S The Truman D. Picard Scholarship Program

Pennsylvania

- S Ethnic Minority Bachelor's Scholarship
- S Racial-Ethnic Education Scholarship

South Carolina

- S Multicultural Scholarship Program
- S North American Indian Department Scholarship

South Dakota

- S AIEF Graduate Scholarships
- S AIEF Undergraduate Scholarships
- S American Indian Education Foundation Scholarship Program
- S Crazy Horse Memorial (Book)
- S Crazy Horse Memorial (Jonas)
- S Crazy Horse Memorial Scholarship Program
- G Dakota Indian Foundation Grant
- S Dakota Indian Foundation Scholarship
- S Honorary Leonard Peltier Scholarship
- S John E. Hess Scholarship
- S Johnson Entrepreneurship Scholarship
- S Joseph and Mary Cacioppo Foundation Scholarship
- S Josephine Nipper Memorial Scholarship
- S Max Pell Book Scholarship
- S Oglala Lakota College Scholarships
- S Paul Francis Memorial Scholarship
- S The Big Sky Foundation Scholarship

Tennessee

- S National Achievement Scholarships
- S United South & Eastern Tribes, Inc. Scholarships

Texas

- P American Economic Association Summer Program
- S Hana Scholars Program
- S President's Endowed Scholarship
- S The Boy Scouts of America National College

Utah

- S American Indian Services Scholarships
- S AT&T - WGU Native American Scholarship

Virginia

- S AAAE Foundation Scholarship for Native Americans
- S AGI Minority Geoscience Undergraduate Scholarship

F GEM Fellowship

S The Maureen and Howard Blitman, P.E., Scholarship To Promote Diversity In Engineering

WASHINGTON

S American Indian Endowed Scholarship

S First People's Scholarship

S Master's in Social Work Minority Scholarship

S Microsoft Scholarship Program

S Northwest Indian Housing Association Scholarship

A Seattle University Regents Award

S Washington Indian Gaming Association Scholarships

S Yakama Nation Tribal Scholarship

WASHINGTON DC

G AAUW Educational Foundation Career Development Grants

S ACS Scholars Program

S American Chemical Society (ACS) Scholars Program

P American Chemistry Society Scholars Program

S American Indian Scholarship

S American Indian Scholarships

S BIA Higher Education Grant

G Bureau of Indian Education Higher Education Grant Program

S Carmen E. Turner Scholarship

S Caroline E. Holt Nursing Scholarship

S Center for Native American Youth Scholarship

A Fulbright Occassional Lecturer Fund

F National Congress of American Indians Fellowships

I National Congress of American Indians Internships

F National Congress of American Indians Native Graduate Health Fellowship

S National Essay Contest for Native American High School Students

I Native American Political Leadership Program Ongoing Internship

S NIEA John C. Rouillard and Alice Tonemah Memorial Scholarship

S Project SEED Scholarships

F Robert D. Watkins Minority Graduate Research Fellowship

S SAA Arthur C. Parker Scholarship or NSF Scholarship for Archaeological Training

S SAA Native American Graduate Archaeology Scholarship

S SAA Native American Undergraduate Archaeology Scholarship

I Washington Internships for Native Students (WINS)

WISCONSIN

S Menominee Adult Vocational Training Scholarship

INSIGHTS

"It Opened up a Whole New World to Me"

"Going to college opened up a world for me. Before I'd been in high school, raised in East L.A., and then I joined the Army. When I left the Army, under the relatively new G.I. Bill, I was able to enroll in college and it opened up a whole new world to me. From that standpoint, because of teachers, family support, and the G.I. Bill I was able to achieve all the things I wanted to achieve in life. Today I've been a U.S. Ambassador, a Congressman, a State Commissioner, I have a number of honorary doctorate degrees, and I have a high school that is named after me. That's what college did for me."

Esteban Torres, *Member of Congress, reitred*

INDEXES

Overall Diverse Scholarships By State & Name

On the enclosed CD you will find detailed searchable profiles on each of the following awards (A), fellowships (F), grants (G), internships (I), programs (P), and scholarships (S).

Type & Name of the Scholarship

Arizona

- S BigSun Scholarships
- A Diversity Award
- I Morris K. Udall Foundation Internships
- S Morris K. Udall Scholarship

Arkansas

- S National Dental Association/Colgate Palmolive Dr. Bessie Elizabeth Delaney Scholarship
- S National Dental Association/Colgate Palmolive Dr. Clifton O. Dummett & Lois Doyle Dummett Scholarship
- S National Dental Association/Colgate Palmolive Pre-Doctoral Scholarship
- S National Dental Association/Colgate Palmolive Dr. Joseph L. Henry Scholarship
- S National Dental Association/Colgate Palmolive Memorial Scholarship

California

- S (AAHCPA) Scholarship Program
- F AAJA Fellowship Program
- A AAJA Lifetime Achievement Award
- A AAJA National Awards
- A AAJA Special Recognition Award
- F Academy Fellowships
- A Alana Leadership Merit Award
- S Anthem Essay Contest
- S Asian Pacific American Support Group Scholarship
- P Atlas Shrugged Essay Contest
- S Bay Area Minority Law Scholarship
- S Black Alumni Association / Ebonics Support Group
- P California State University, Chico (Talent Search)
- S CANFit Program Scholarship
- F Chancellor's Postdoctoral Fellowship Program for Academic Diversity
- A College Television Awards
- I CSRC Getty Undergraduate Summer Arts Internship
- I CSRC Getty Undergraduate Summer Arts Internship
- S CSU Minority Business Graduate Scholarship
- S CSU Minority Engineering Program Scholarship
- G CSU National Action Council for Minorities in Engineering (NACME) Grants
- S CSUF TELACU Scholarship Program
- S CTA Martin Luther King, Jr. Memorial Scholarship Fund
- P Edison Scholars Program
- P Extended Opportunity Programs & Services
- P Fellowship Program on Health and Environmental Health for California Ethnic Media Journalists
- S Ford/EEOC Endowed Scholarship Program
- P Fountainhead Essay Contest
- A HP Scholar Award
- S HSF / Marathon Petroleum Corporation College Scholarship Program
- S Imperial Valley College
- S Independent Colleges of Southern California (ICSC) Scholarships
- P Irvine Minority Scholar Program
- S James S. Bosco Minority Incentive Graduate Scholarship
- S Jesse Arias Scholarship Fund
- I Kaiser Media Internships in Urban Health Reporting
- S Leadership for Diversity Scholarship
- S Mary Moy Quon Ing Memorial Scholarship Award
- S Minority Media Scholarship
- P Minority Science Programs
- S Minoru Yasui Memorial Scholarship Award
- S Mister Rogers Memorial Scholarship
- S Nissan Scholarship Program
- A Pass-It-On Awards Program
- S Robert A. Hine Memorial Scholarship
- F Robert Toigo MBA Fellowship
- A SACNAS National Conference Travel & Lodging Awards
- S Shaw Industries Achievement Scholarship

Colorado

Connecticut

Delaware

Florida

Georgia

Hawaii

Idaho

- S Diversity Out-of-State Tuition Waiver
- S Diversity Scholarship Program
- S Minority Student Scholarships
- S National Cesar E. Chavez Blood Drive Challenge - Student Organizer Scholarship
- S State of Idaho Minority at Risk Scholarship

Illinois

- S Abbott and Fenner Scholarship Program
- F ABF Summer Research Fellowship in Law & Social Studies for Minorities
- S Academy of Nutrition and Dietetics Scholarships
- S ADHA Institute for Oral Health Dental Hygiene Scholarship Program
- S AHBAI Scholarships
- S ALA Scholarship Program
- S Albert W. Dent Graduate Student ScholarshipS
- S Alice S. Marriott Scholarship
- S American Art Therapy Association Student Scholarship
- P Bridge To Professional Leadership
- I Chicago Sun-Times Minority Scholarship & Internship Program
- S Colgate Bright Smiles, Bright Futures Minority Scholarship
- S DePaul University Minority Student Scholarship
- A Diversity Award
- S Doris Roethlisberger Scholarships
- A George A. Strait Minority Stipend
- S George M. Brooker Collegiate Scholarship for Minorities
- S GM Women's Retail Network Dealer Development Scholarship
- S Government Finance Officers Association Scholarship
- S Institute of Real Estate Management (IREM) Foundation
- S Johnetta Haley Scholarship
- A Living Faith Award
- S Mel Larson Scholarships
- S Minority Teachers of Illinois Scholarship Program
- S MLA Scholarship for Minority Students
- S Music Scholarships
- S Presidential Scholarship for Minority Students
- S Society of Actuaries Minority Student Scholarships
- A The Curt Tech Award
- A The Diane Hauser-Grell Award
- A The Marshall Award
- A The Ruth Kantzer Award
- S Underrepresented Minority Dental Student Scholarship

Indiana

- S Eagle Scout of the Year
- S Eight & Forty Lung and Respiratory Disease Nursing Scholarship
- S Eli Lilly and Company/BDPA Scholarship
- S The American Legion Baseball Scholarship

Iowa

- S Hy-Vee Foundation Scholarship
- S Principal Financial Group Scholarship Program

Kansas

- A Athletic, Forensic, Music, & Theater Awards
- S Board of Directors' Scholarship
- S Brown Foundation Scholarships
- S Cardinal John Henry Newman Scholarship
- S Community Leadership Scholarship
- S Kansas Ethnic Minority Scholarship
- G Leadership Grant
- G Leaven Grant For Minority Students
- S Monsignor McNeill Scholarship
- S National Merit Scholarship
- S Newman University Dean's Scholarship
- S Sacred Heart Scholarship
- G Trustee Grant
- A Wells Award

Kentucky

- A Minority Leadership Award
- S Minority Teacher Education Program Scholarship
- S Student Opportunity Scholarships for Ethnic Minority Groups

Louisiana

- A Graduate Tuition Awards

Maryland

- S Allison E. Fisher Scholarship
- S Center for Student Opportunity Scholarship
- P Minority Research Infrastructure Support Program
- S NABA National Scholarship Program

- **S** Berrien Fragos Thorn Arts Scholarship for Migrant Farmworkers
- **S** Bill Bernbach Diversity Scholarship
- **S** Breakthrough To Nursing Scholarships For Ethnic People of Color
- **S** Celia Cruz Foundation
- **S** Cultural Diversity Scholarships
- **A** Elmira College Key Award
- **S** Elmira College Minority Scholarships
- **I** Emma L. Bowen Foundation For Minority Interest in Media Internships
- **S** ESA Foundation Computer & Video Game Scholarship Program
- **F** Fellowships for Minority Doctoral Students
- **S** Frank Kazmierczak Memorial Migrant Scholarship
- **S** Friends of Senator Jack Perry Migrant Scholarship
- **F** Graduate Newspaper Fellowship & Apprenticeship for Minorities
- **S** Health Facility Planning & Design
- **S** Jackie Robinson Foundation Scholarship Program
- **A** Kodak Minority Academic Awards
- **S** Loyola Scholarships
- **F** Magnet/Humana Foundation Doctoral Fellowships
- **S** Mayor's Graduate Scholarship Program
- **S** Migrant Farmworker Baccalaureate Scholarship
- **S** Minority Graduate Accounting Scholarships
- **F** Minority Postdoctoral Fellowship Program
- **S** NACME Pre-Engineering Student Scholarships
- **F** National Urban Fellowship Award
- **A** New York State Higher Education Opportunity Award
- **I** Newhouse Newspaper Graduate Fellowship/Internship for Minorities
- **S** Newsday Scholarship In Communications
- **S** NSF Scholarship
- **S** Operation JumpStart
- **F** Rockefeller Brothers Fund Fellowship Program
- **S** Stephen D. Pisinski Memorial Scholarship
- **P** Time Inc. Summer Editorial Intern Program
- **S** Xerox Technical Minority Scholarship

North Carolina

- **P** Landmark Scholars Program
- **G** Minority Presence Grants (General Program II)

North Dakota

- **S** North Dakota Indian Scholarship

Ohio

- **S** AES Engineers Scholarship
- **S** AGC of Ohio Education Foundation Scholarships
- **S** Bexley Women's Club College/University Scholarship
- **S** Bexley Women's Club High School Scholarship
- **S** Colombus Rotary Phoenix Scholarship
- **S** CSOHIMSS Jane A. Blank Scholarship Program
- **S** Darwin T. Turner Scholarship
- **S** Denison University HLA Scholarship
- **S** Denison University Multicultural Achievement Scholarship
- **S** Gustavo A. Parajon Scholarship
- **S** HBCU Minority Student Scholarships
- **A** Incentive Award
- **A** King-Chavez-Parks Award
- **S** Nationwide Children's Hospital Scholarship
- **P** Templeton Scholars Program
- **S** The Columbus Chapter Scholarships
- **S** University of Toledo Student Achievement Scholarship

Oklahoma

- **S** Amoco Accounting Scholarships
- **S** Blackwell Scholarships
- **S** Langston's Non-Black Scholarship

Oregon

- **A** George Fox University Multi Ethnic Student Awards
- **S** Katu Thomas R. Dargan Scholarship

Pennsylvania

- **S** Big 33 Scholarships
- **S** Dr. Charles Richard Drew Scholarships
- **S** Edinboro University Diversity Scholarships
- **S** Indiana University of Pennsylvania Board of Governor's Scholarship
- **S** Minority Scholarship Fund
- **S** Racial-Ethnic Education Scholarship
- **S** The President's Council Scholarship

South Carolina

- **P** Coca-Cola Clemson Scholars Program
- **P** Multicultural Scholar Program

- **I** CSIS Minority Internship in International Affairs
- **S** David E. Lumley Young Scientist Scholarship
- **A** Diversity Leaders Award
- **S** Donna Jamison Lago Memorial Scholarship
- **S** Ed Bradley Scholarship
- **S** Ellen Masin Persina Scholarship
- **F** Feldman Fellowship for Graduate Studies in Journalism
- **F** Ford Foundation Dissertation Fellowships for Minorities
- **F** Ford Foundation Postdoctoral Fellowships for Minorities
- **F** Ford Foundation Predoctoral & Dissertation Fellowships for Minorities
- **F** Humanities Fellowship in Latino Cultural Research in a National Museum Context
- **P** Hyatt Hotels Fund for Minority Lodging Management Students
- **F** Jacque Minnotte Health Reporting Fellowship
- **S** Javits-Frasier Teacher Scholarship Fund for Diverse Talent Development
- **G** Kellogg Leadership Grant
- **F** Michele Clarke Fellowship
- **F** Minority Fellowship Program
- **F** N.S. Bienstock Fellowship
- **P** National Research Council Research Associateship Programs
- **F** NSF Graduate Research Fellowship Program (GRFP)
- **S** Persina Scholarship for Minorities in Journalism
- **S** René Matos Scholarship
- **F** Robert D. Watkins Minority Graduate Research Fellowship
- **S** RTNDA Scholarship
- **S** Scholarship for Journalism Diversity
- **P** Summer Medical and Dental Education Program
- **S** The Esperanza Scholarship for GED Holders
- **S** The Esperanza Scholarship for High School Seniors
- **S** The General Electric/LULAC Scholarship Program
- **S** The LULAC National Scholarship Fund
- **I** USDA Summer Internship Program

Wisconsin

- **S** Agriculture Scholarship
- **S** Ebbie and Peggy Neese Scholarship
- **G** Madison Minority Retention Grant
- **P** Something Good From the Hood
- **S** Tona Diebels Scholarship
- **S** Wisconsin Future Teachers Scholarship

Wyoming

- **S** Multicultural Pride Scholarship
- **S** University of Wyoming Chicano Studies Scholarship

Insights

"I Was Able to Repay the Tribe"

"Our tribe was not a rich tribe, but back in 1969 they received a land settlement and they put that in a trust fund for tribal members. I was one of a few tribal members that took advantage of that scholarship fund and that helped me go through college. I also got scholarships from other entities and put it all together I was able to go through four year of college and graduated with a degree in Urban & Regional Planning & Growth Management with a minor in Economics. The tribe supported me through college and I was able to repay the tribe by coming back and working for the tribe and developing the properties we have now."

Gary George, *CEO, Wildhorse Resort & Casino, Cayuse, Umatilla and Walla Walla Tribes of Pendleton, Oregon*

Section Eight
1,000's More Scholarships

- Please turn the page and you'll find a CD with 3,700 pages of helpful research and searchable scholarships.
- Further you can go to www.EmpoweringStudents.com where we're adding new scholarships every month.
- Finally, on our website you can sign up for our eNewsletter Empowering Students which is the best way to stay up-to-date on all of our information.

1,000s More Scholarships

Insights
"College Opens Doors"

"Going to college was the first time I left home. Even though it was only 2 hours away, I didn't have a car. It forced me to find independence at the age of 18. College opens doors. I went to the University of Arizona where the ethnic studies issue is so hot right now. It is very concerning because part of what opened my eyes were the Mexican American Studies, Chicano Studies and Latin American Studies classes that taught me my history here in the U.S., and my communities history in Latin America. What our contributions were in politics and the economy, what happened, it's all part of our history. This was all essential to my self esteem, values and self-worth—and to what I could become individually."

Delia de la Vara,
Vice President,
California Region, National Council of La Raza

WPR BOOKS

is dedicated to improving portrayals and expanding opportunities for Latinos in the USA

WPR BOOKS, formerly known as WPR Publishing, has been publishing books and directories since 1983. WPR Books has seven imprints: Comida, Helping Hands, Heroes, Latino Insights, Latin American Insights, Para los Niños, and Total Success.

Latino Print Network, WPR BOOKS sister organization, works with over 625 Hispanic newspapers and magazines. These publications have a combined circulation of 19 million in 180 markets nationwide.

Hispanic Marketing 101 is a twice-weekly enewsletter that provides a variety of helpful information. A subscription is free at www.HM101.com

We have these and other programs that may be of interest to you. For more information please go to www.WPRbooks.com or call us at 760-434-1223.

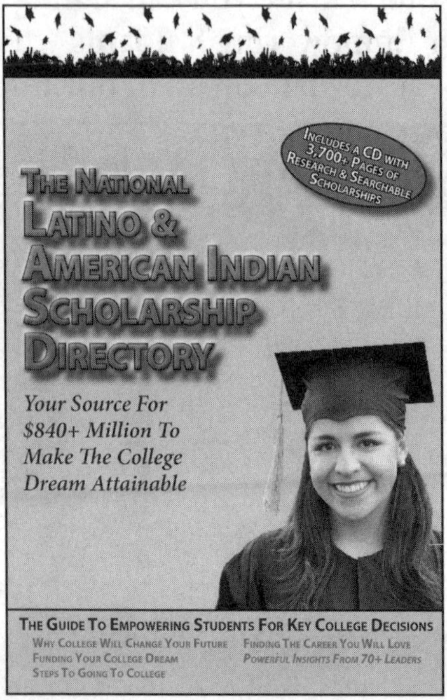